COMPLIMENTARY
COPY $ 500

D1259291

Foundations
of the
Calculus

SAUNDERS MATHEMATICS BOOKS

Consulting Editor
BERNARD R. GELBAUM, University of California

HENRY F. DeBAGGIS

ASSOCIATE PROFESSOR OF MATHEMATICS, FORDHAM UNIVERSITY

KENNETH S. MILLER

SENIOR STAFF SCIENTIST, COLUMBIA UNIVERSITY ELECTRONICS
RESEARCH LABORATORIES; ADJUNCT PROFESSOR
OF MATHEMATICS, FORDHAM UNIVERSITY

Foundations
of the
Calculus

W. B. SAUNDERS COMPANY · PHILADELPHIA · LONDON · 1966

W. B. Saunders Company: West Washington Square
Philadelphia, Pa. 19105

12 Dyott Street
London, W.C.1

Foundations of the Calculus

© 1966 by W. B. Saunders Company. Copyright under the International Copyright Union.
All rights reserved. This book is protected by copyright. No part of it may be duplicated or
reproduced in any manner without written permission from the publisher. Made in the United
States of America. Press of W. B. Saunders Company. Library of Congress catalog card
number 66–15619.

QA
303
.029

517
D 35

To

KARL MENGER

Preface

This book is addressed mainly to bright young college freshmen and sophomores, as well as to high school teachers and prospective high school teachers. The emphasis is directed towards achieving at an early stage an understanding of mathematics and is not primarily concerned with development of mere manipulative skills. We believe that the text is particularly suitable for In-Service and Pre-Service programs (such as those sponsored by the National Science Foundation for secondary school teachers), and as a terminal course for undergraduates who do not plan to major in mathematics. Preliminary versions of this book have been satisfactorily used in such courses by our colleagues and by one of the authors.

Much effort was devoted to the problem of deciding what material to cover, where to begin, and what to assume on the part of the reader—especially when it was desired to keep the text as compact and unified as possible. Many books take anywhere from three to three hundred pages to arrive at our Chapter 1. Our experience with the type of student for whom this book is intended led us to conclude that the field axioms are the most rewarding starting point. We assume the reader is already familiar, in part, with the real number system, has at least an intuitive notion of set, and is acquainted with such symbols as $\in$ (is an element of), $\cup$ (union), $\cap$ (intersection), $\subset$ (is contained in), and $\varnothing$ (the empty set). In the present age of mathematical sophistication, which reaches down to the primary grades, these assumptions do not appear unreasonable. Accordingly, we unify the student's past mathematical experience within a postulational framework. We introduce the complete ordered field by means of the least upper bound axiom. Some analytic geometry is developed via the complete ordered field axioms in conjunction with the axioms of synthetic geometry, even though geometry is not essential for the treatment of the calculus. (The between relation is introduced in terms of the distance axiom.)

In conformity with modern trends, the emphasis throughout the rest of the text is on the function concept. In developing this important idea we follow the lead of Karl Menger. However, we prefer to retain Menger's notation j for the identity function and his original notation f^* for the inverse function with respect to composition (rather than his more recent notation $j//f$). We use the conventional symbol $\circ$ to denote the operation of composition, and juxtaposition to denote multiplication. Throughout the text we make a careful distinction between the function f and its value $f(x)$ at a specified number x. To avoid confusion, in the case of the constant function, we write **k** for the function and k for its value.

Except for the least upper bound axiom, the only new concept the reader encounters is limit. We are careful and patient in developing this concept. We then proceed to show how the main results of the calculus may be deduced from the axioms and results obtained in the first four chapters. Many interesting corollaries and results are left as exercises, so that we get to the heart of the matter (the fundamental theorem) as directly and expeditiously as possible.

A short course will find a logical stopping point at the end of Chapter 6—where we prove the integrability of a continuous function and the fundamental theorem of the calculus. Chapter 7 goes on to consider the logarithmic function and its inverse (the exponential function) in some detail. The number $e = 2.718\cdots$ is analyzed at some length. We also find this chapter a convenient vehicle for introducing Taylor's Theorem (with the Lagrange remainder). We conclude with some applications to growth and decay problems. The final chapter (Chapter 8) is devoted to some formal techniques of integration: integration by parts, integration by substitution, and the method of partial fractions. It seems appropriate to introduce methods for finding approximations to definite integrals when explicit techniques are difficult or do not exist. Accordingly we include the Trapezoidal Rule and Simpson's Rule together with a derivation of their error formulas.

Although practical applications to science are not entirely neglected, the emphasis is mathematical. Whenever possible we give a geometric flavor to our treatment both for the sake of motivation and to make new concepts more concrete.

H. F. DeB.
K. S. M.

Acknowledgments

We wish to express our deep gratitude to Professor Karl Menger, whose work in algebra of functions inspired much of what is herein contained; to Professor Bernard Gelbaum, the editor of this series, for his constructive comments and suggestions; to our colleagues at Fordham University; and in particular to Professor Michael Aissen, who made helpful comments while using a preliminary version of this text in a Summer Institute course.

Thanks are also due to the staff of W. B. Saunders Company, especially Walter Zablocki and John Dwyer, for their cooperation and help, and Mr. Ashland Harlan, for his faithful execution of the illustrations.

H. F. DeB.
K. S. M.

Contents

1

THE REAL NUMBERS 1

   1. Fields 1
   2. Incompleteness 8
   3. Upper and lower bounds 9
   4. The real numbers 13
   5. Absolute values and inequalities 16

Exercises 17

2

ANALYTIC GEOMETRY 22

   1. Coordinates on a line 25
   2. Fundamental theorem of analytic geometry 28
   3. Equations of lines 37
   4. Some properties of lines 42
   5. The intersection of two lines 49

Appendix   The length of a circular arc 53

Exercises 59

3

FUNCTIONS 65

1. Some special functions 66
2. Graphs of functions 67
3. The algebra of functions 71
4. Addition and multiplication 73
5. Composition 75
6. Further properties of functions 79

Exercises 81

4

LIMITS AND CONTINUITY.................... 83

1. Limits 84
2. Limits of compound functions 91
3. Limits of composite functions 97
4. Limits of some special functions 98
5. Continuous functions 100
6. Continuity on an interval 103

Exercises 106

5

DERIVATIVES 109

1. Definition of the derivative 113
2. Derivatives of some special functions 117
3. Some general rules of differentiation 121
4. Maxima and minima, Rolle's theorem, and consequences.................................... 127
5. The generalized law of the mean and l'Hospital's
   rule 135
6. Some elementary applications................. 136

Exercises 141

6

THE DEFINITE INTEGRAL 148

    1. The definite integral 153
    2. Integrability of a continuous function 160
    3. The fundamental theorem of the calculus 165
    4. Some applications 167
Exercises 172

7

THE LOGARITHMIC FUNCTION AND ITS INVERSE 176

    1. The logarithmic function 177
    2. The inverse logarithmic function 179
    3. The number e 182
    4. Applications to decay problems 187
Exercises 189

8

TECHNIQUES FOR FINDING ANTIDERIVATIVES 193

    1. Antiderivatives by parts 195
    2. Antiderivatives by substitution 196
    3. Partial fractions 202
    4. Concluding remarks 206
Exercises 213

REFERENCES 216

SOME HINTS AND ANSWERS 217

INDEX 229

1

THE REAL NUMBERS

The three important concepts on which rest the foundations of the calculus are the concept of number, the concept of function, and the concept of limit. The reader is already familiar with the first two and, perhaps, even has some familiarity with the third. In what follows we shall formalize whatever previous knowledge the reader may have about these concepts and show how the results of the calculus may be derived on the basis of a set of axioms and some definitions concerning these concepts.

1. FIELDS

The reader is familiar with the natural numbers, or positive integers, $1, 2, 3, \cdots$; and with addition and multiplication of these numbers. Subtraction and division may be performed with pairs of natural numbers, and under certain conditions will yield other natural numbers. Thus $b - a$ is a natural number if and only if b is greater than a. Or, to put it in another way, the equation $a + x = b$ has a solution if and only if b is greater than a. If we work in the extended domain of all integers (positive integers, negative integers, and zero) then $a + x = b$ has a (unique) solution no matter how b is related to a.

Similarly, in the domain of integers, the equation $ax = b$, $(a \neq 0)$, has a solution if and only if b is an integral multiple of a. In the domain of rational numbers (fractions with nonzero denominators) $ax = b$, $(a \neq 0)$, always has the (unique) solution $x = b/a$. We may view the fractions as containing the set of integers; and the operations among fractions obey the well-known rules called field axioms. We

1

shall formalize these axioms below. Remembering our intuitive grasp of arithmetic, but relying upon this intuition only to *suggest* formal reasoning and no more, we proceed as follows.

Definition.   *A set $\mathscr{F}$ is called a* **field** *if there are two binary operations, $+$ and $\cdot$, such that the elements of $\mathscr{F}$ and these operations satisfy Axioms $\mathbf{F}_1$ to $\mathbf{F}_{11}$ below.*

$\mathbf{F}_1$ If a and b belong to the set $\mathscr{F}$, then $a + b$ is defined and is an element of $\mathscr{F}$.

$\mathbf{F}_2$ If a and b belong to $\mathscr{F}$, then $a + b = b + a$.

$\mathbf{F}_3$ If a, b, and c belong to $\mathscr{F}$, then $a + (b + c) = (a + b) + c$.

$\mathbf{F}_4$ There exists a unique element 0 (read: zero) in $\mathscr{F}$ such that $a + 0 = a$ for all a in $\mathscr{F}$.

$\mathbf{F}_5$ For each a in $\mathscr{F}$ there is a unique element $-a$ (read: minus a) in $\mathscr{F}$ such that $a + (-a) = 0$.

$\mathbf{F}_6$ If a and b are in $\mathscr{F}$, then $a \cdot b$ is defined and is an element of $\mathscr{F}$.

$\mathbf{F}_7$ If a and b are in $\mathscr{F}$, then $a \cdot b = b \cdot a$.

$\mathbf{F}_8$ If a, b, and c are in $\mathscr{F}$, then $a \cdot (b \cdot c) = (a \cdot b) \cdot c$.

$\mathbf{F}_9$ There exists a unique element 1 (read: one) in $\mathscr{F}$ such that $a \cdot 1 = a$ for all a in $\mathscr{F}$.

$\mathbf{F}_{10}$ For each $a \neq 0$ in $\mathscr{F}$ there is a unique element a^{-1} (read: a inverse) in $\mathscr{F}$ such that $a \cdot a^{-1} = 1$.

$\mathbf{F}_{11}$ If a, b, and c are in $\mathscr{F}$, then $a \cdot (b + c) = a \cdot b + a \cdot c$.

The informal or intuitive system of rational numbers with the usual notations of $+$ (addition) and $\cdot$ (multiplication) constitutes a field. In Axioms $\mathbf{F}_1$–$\mathbf{F}_9$ and $\mathbf{F}_{11}$ the reader will recognize the familiar properties associated with the set of all integers. Axiom $\mathbf{F}_{10}$, of course, is not satisfied by the set of all integers. For example, if $n = 2$, say, there is no integer n^{-1} such that $2 \cdot n^{-1} = 1$. It is Axiom $\mathbf{F}_{10}$, therefore, that distinguishes the set of all integers from the set of rational numbers.

Using the $\mathbf{F}$ axioms we may derive all the familiar properties, of the (intuitive) system of rational numbers, that involve equality. Here we shall derive some of the most important relationships; others will be left as exercises.

Theorem 1.   *If a is an element of a field $\mathscr{F}$, and 0 is the zero element of $\mathscr{F}$, then:*

$$a \cdot 0 = 0 \cdot a = 0.$$

PROOF.   By Axioms $\mathbf{F}_9$, $\mathbf{F}_{11}$, and $\mathbf{F}_4$,

$$a + a \cdot 0 = a \cdot 1 + a \cdot 0 = a \cdot (1 + 0) = a \cdot 1 = a.$$

But Axiom $\mathbf{F}_4$ also states that there is only one zero element in $\mathscr{F}$ such that $a + 0 = a$. Therefore $a \cdot 0 = 0$. Commutativity, Axiom $\mathbf{F}_7$, now states that $a \cdot 0 = 0 \cdot a$.

Theorem 2. *If a is an element of a field $\mathscr{F}$, and if 1 is the unique one in $\mathscr{F}$, then:*

$$a \cdot (-1) = (-1) \cdot a = -a.$$

PROOF. By Axioms $\mathbf{F}_9$, $\mathbf{F}_{11}$, $\mathbf{F}_5$, and Theorem 1,

$$a + a \cdot (-1) = a \cdot 1 + a \cdot (-1) = a \cdot [1 + (-1)] = a \cdot 0 = 0.$$

But Axiom $\mathbf{F}_5$ also implies that there is a unique element $-a$ in $\mathscr{F}$ such that $a + (-a) = 0$. Thus

$$-a = a \cdot (-1).$$

Commutativity, Axiom $\mathbf{F}_7$, then establishes $a \cdot (-1) = (-1) \cdot a$.

Corollary. $0 = -0$.

PROOF. Let $a = 0$ in Theorem 2 and apply Theorem 1.

Theorem 3. *If a and b are elements of a field $\mathscr{F}$, then*

$$b \cdot (-a) = (-a) \cdot b = -(a \cdot b) = -(b \cdot a).$$

PROOF. By Axioms $\mathbf{F}_{11}$, $\mathbf{F}_5$, and Theorem 1,

$$b \cdot a + b \cdot (-a) = b \cdot [a + (-a)] = b \cdot 0 = 0.$$

Another application of Axiom $\mathbf{F}_5$ and commutativity (Axiom $\mathbf{F}_7$) completes the proof.

Theorem 4. *If a and b are elements of a field $\mathscr{F}$, then*

$$(-a) \cdot (-b) = a \cdot b.$$

PROOF. By Theorem 3, Axioms $\mathbf{F}_{11}$, $\mathbf{F}_5$, and Theorem 1,

$$(-a) \cdot (-b) + [-(a \cdot b)] = (-a) \cdot (-b) + (-a) \cdot b$$
$$= (-a) \cdot (-b + b) = (-a) \cdot 0 = 0.$$

Axiom $\mathbf{F}_5$ completes the proof.

For convenience we shall denote $a \cdot a$ by a^2.

Corollary. *If $a \in \mathscr{F}$, then*

$$(-a) \cdot (-a) = a \cdot a = a^2.$$

We shall leave as an exercise for the reader the proof of the statement

$$-(-a) = a$$

for any a in a field $\mathscr{F}$.

In all the above theorems, no use was ever made of Axiom $\mathbf{F}_{10}$. (See the comments following the definition of a field.) We shall make use of this axiom in the next three theorems. Also, to simplify the notation we shall write ab in place of the more precise $a \cdot b$ (where $a, b \in \mathscr{F}$). This is a standard convention.

Theorem 5. *If a and b are elements of a field $\mathscr{F}$, and $a \neq 0 \neq b$, then*

$$(ab)^{-1} = a^{-1}b^{-1}.$$

PROOF. By Axioms $\mathbf{F_7}$, $\mathbf{F_8}$, $\mathbf{F_{10}}$, $\mathbf{F_9}$, $\mathbf{F_{10}}$,

$$(ab)(a^{-1}b^{-1}) = (ba)(a^{-1}b^{-1}) = b(aa^{-1})b^{-1} = b \cdot 1 \cdot b^{-1} = bb^{-1} = 1.$$

But again, by Axiom $\mathbf{F_{10}}$, there is only one element $(ab)^{-1}$ such that $(ab)(ab)^{-1} = 1$. Hence our proof is complete.

Theorem 6. *If a, b, c, d are elements of a field $\mathscr{F}$, and if $b \neq 0 \neq d$, then*

$$ab^{-1} + cd^{-1} = (ad + cb)(bd)^{-1}.$$

PROOF. By Axioms $\mathbf{F_{10}}$, $\mathbf{F_9}$, $\mathbf{F_7}$, $\mathbf{F_8}$, $\mathbf{F_7}$, $\mathbf{F_{11}}$, and Theorem 5,

$$
\begin{aligned}
ab^{-1} + cd^{-1} &= (ab^{-1})(dd^{-1}) + (cd^{-1})(bb^{-1}) \\
&= a(b^{-1}d)d^{-1} + c(d^{-1}b)b^{-1} \\
&= a(db^{-1})d^{-1} + c(bd^{-1})b^{-1} \\
&= (ad)(b^{-1}d^{-1}) + (cb)(d^{-1}b^{-1}) \\
&= (ad)(b^{-1}d^{-1}) + (cb)(b^{-1}d^{-1}) \\
&= (ad + cb)(b^{-1}d^{-1}) \\
&= (ad + cb)(bd)^{-1}.
\end{aligned}
$$

The above formula is nothing more than the familiar result

$$\frac{a}{b} + \frac{c}{d} = \frac{ad + cb}{bd}$$

where we have set pq^{-1}, $(q \neq 0)$, equal to p/q.

In the (intuitive) system of rational numbers we know that a fraction may have more than one representation. For example,

$$\frac{1}{2} = \frac{2}{4} = \frac{3}{6} = \frac{-5}{-10}, \text{ etc.}$$

The following theorem tells us that this is a general property in arbitrary fields.

Theorem 7. *If a, b, c, d are in $\mathscr{F}$, and if $b \neq 0 \neq d$, then $ab^{-1} = cd^{-1}$ if and only if $ad = cb$.*

PROOF. First we shall show that $ab^{-1} = cd^{-1}$ implies $ad = cb$. Using our field axioms, we see that

$$a = a(b^{-1}b) = (ab^{-1})b = (cd^{-1})b = (cb)d^{-1}.$$

Hence

$$ad = [(cb)d^{-1}]d = cb.$$

Now we show that $ad = cb$ implies $ab^{-1} = cd^{-1}$. Again using our field axioms we find

$$a = a(dd^{-1}) = (ad)d^{-1} = (cb)d^{-1} = (cd^{-1})b.$$

Hence

$$ab^{-1} = [(cd^{-1})b]b^{-1} = cd^{-1}.$$

There are sets other than the (intuitive) system of rational numbers that satisfy the **F** axioms. An example of one such set is $\mathscr{F}_3 = \{0, 1, 2\}$ with addition and multiplication defined according to the following tables:

	0	1	2
0	0	1	2
1	1	2	0
2	2	0	1

Addition

	0	1	2
0	0	0	0
1	0	1	2
2	0	2	1

Multiplication

(If in the above arrays we denote the elements of the left-hand column by a_i and those of the top row by a_j, then $a_i + a_j$ and $a_i \cdot a_j$ are found in the ith row and jth column of the corresponding array.) The reader may easily verify that all the **F** axioms are satisfied by the set $\mathscr{F}_3$ with addition and multiplication so defined. Sets of this type are called *finite fields*. (For other examples of fields see Miller [6].)

The familiar *order relation* < (less than) associated with the intuitive system of rational numbers motivates the following *order relation axioms*. The order relation axioms also guarantee that any field satisfying these additional axioms must be at least as large as the (intuitive) system of rational numbers.

There is an *order relation*: < (read: less than) defined among the elements of $\mathscr{F}$ such that:

O$_1$ (*Trichotomy law*.) If a and b are in $\mathscr{F}$, then exactly one of the following holds:

    (i) $a < b$
    (ii) $b < a$
    (iii) $a = b$.

O$_2$ If a, b, and c are in $\mathscr{F}$ with $a < b$ and $b < c$, then $a < c$.

O$_3$ If 0 is the zero element of $\mathscr{F}$ and a, b, and c are in $\mathscr{F}$ with $0 < c$ and $a < b$, then $ac < bc$.

O$_4$ If a, b, and c are in $\mathscr{F}$ and $a < b$, then $a + c < b + c$.

We define $a > b$ (a greater than b) by the statement: a is greater than b if and only if $b < a$. Equivalently we say: $a > b$ implies and is implied by $b < a$.

Sets with two binary operations satisfying Axioms **F**$_1$–**F**$_{11}$ and Axioms **O**$_1$–**O**$_4$ are called *ordered fields*. Let us now turn to the proof of certain inequality theorems that are true in such fields. The reader will recall these results as familiar inequality properties of the (intuitive) system of rational numbers.

Theorem 8.   *Let a and b be elements of an ordered field. Let $a < b$. Then*

$$-b < -a.$$

PROOF.   By Axiom $\mathbf{O}_4$

$$a + [-b + (-a)] < b + [-b + (-a)]$$

and by Axioms $\mathbf{F}_2$, $\mathbf{F}_3$,

$$[a + (-a)] - b < [b + (-b)] - a.$$

Axiom $\mathbf{F}_5$ now implies $0 - b < 0 - a$ and Axiom $\mathbf{F}_4$ completes the proof.

Corollary.   *If a and b are elements in an ordered field, and if $-b < -a$; then $a < b$.*

Theorem 9.   *If a is an element of an ordered field and $a \neq 0$; then*

$$a^2 > 0.$$

PROOF.   By Axiom $\mathbf{O}_1$ the statement $a \neq 0$ implies

(i) $0 < a$ or   (ii) $a < 0$.

Case (i).   If $0 < a$, Axiom $\mathbf{O}_3$ implies

$$0 = 0 \cdot a < a \cdot a = a^2.$$

Case (ii).   If $a < 0$, then by Theorem 8 we have

$$0 < -a.$$

By Axiom $\mathbf{O}_3$

$$0(-a) < (-a)(-a)$$

and by Theorem 1 and the Corollary to Theorem 4,

$$0 < a^2.$$

Corollary.   *In an ordered field*

$$1 > 0 \quad and \quad -1 < 0.$$

PROOF.   From Axiom $\mathbf{F}_9$ and Theorem 1 we conclude that $1 \neq 0$, and from Axiom $\mathbf{F}_9$ and Theorem 9,

$$1 = 1 \cdot 1 > 0.$$

To show that $-1 < 0$ we use Theorem 8 and the Corollary to Theorem 2.

Theorem 10.   *If a is an element of an ordered field, and if $a > 0$, then $a^{-1} > 0$.*

PROOF. First we note that $a^{-1} \neq 0$. For if it were zero, then by Axiom $\mathbf{F}_{10}$ and Theorem 1,

$$1 = aa^{-1} = a \cdot 0 = 0$$

which contradicts the Corollary to Theorem 9.

Now suppose $a^{-1} < 0$. Then by Axiom $\mathbf{O}_3$,

$$1 = a^{-1}a < 0 \cdot a = 0$$

—a contradiction. Thus by Axiom $\mathbf{O}_1$ we must have $a^{-1} > 0$.

Earlier we mentioned (without proof) that the order relation axioms assure us of a number system at least as large as the (intuitive) system of rational numbers. There are many types of finite fields, but their behavior, as far as ordering is concerned, is essentially the same as that of $\mathscr{F}_3 = \{0, 1, 2\}$. From our definition of addition and multiplication for $\mathscr{F}_3$, the elements 0 and 1 behave as the "zero" element and the "one" element, respectively, of the field. Accordingly, from the Corollary to Theorem 9, we see that the only possible ordering for $\mathscr{F}_3$ is $0 < 1 < 2$. But by Axiom $\mathbf{O}_4$, $1 = 0 + 1 < 2 + 1 = 0$, which contradicts the statement $0 < 1$. Thus $\mathscr{F}_3$ is not an ordered field.

We now give an example of a *nonfinite* field (containing the rational numbers) that cannot be ordered. Consider the set $\{a + ib\}$ where a and b belong to the (intuitive) system of rational numbers and $i^2 = -1$. In this set (of rational complex numbers) $c_1 = a_1 + ib_1$ and $c_2 = a_2 + ib_2$ are equal if and only if $a_1 = a_2$ and $b_1 = b_2$. Also $0 = 0 + i0$, $c_1 + c_2 = (a_1 + a_2) + i(b_1 + b_2)$, and $c_1c_2 = (a_1a_2 - b_1b_2) + i(a_1b_2 + a_2b_1)$. This set satisfies the field axioms $\mathbf{F}_1$–$\mathbf{F}_{11}$. But if $c = 0 + i$, then $c^2 = -1$, which contradicts Theorem 9. Thus the field of rational complex numbers is not an ordered field.

Additional properties of ordered fields will be left as exercises at the end of the chapter. Here we shall single out one well-known property of the (intuitive) system of rational numbers, viz.: for every two rational numbers a and b with $a < b$ there is a third rational number c with the property that $a < c < b$. (We say c is *between* a and b.) Clearly, $c = \frac{1}{2}(a + b)$ has this property. Repeating this argument we obtain rational numbers d and e satisfying $a < d < c < e < b$, etc. We conclude that there is a dense crowding of the rational numbers, and yet, as we shall see below, there are "gaps" in the (intuitive) system of rational numbers. This fact leads us to a final axiom about ordered fields—a completeness axiom that rules out gaps. The (intuitive) system of rational numbers fails to satisfy the completeness axiom. However, we shall discover how to relate the rational number system to an ordered field that satisfies the completeness axiom.

2. INCOMPLETENESS

We begin by observing that no (intuitive) rational number has a square equal to 2. The proof of this fact proceeds as follows.

Suppose a rational number x exists with the property that $x^2 = 2$. Then $x = p/q$ where p and q, ($q \neq 0$), are integers. We may assume without loss of generality that p and q have no common factors. From $x^2 = 2$ and $x = p/q$ we conclude

$$x^2 = \frac{p^2}{q^2} = 2$$

or

$$p^2 = 2q^2.$$

Since p^2 is twice the integer q^2, we see that p^2 is an even integer. We also conclude that p is even. (If p were odd, say, $p = 2n + 1$, where n is some integer, then $p^2 = 2(2n^2 + 2n) + 1$, which is odd.) Thus $p = 2m$, m an integer, $p^2 = 4m^2 = 2q^2$ and $q^2 = 2m^2$. Hence q^2 is even. This implies (as for p) that q is even and contradicts our assumption that p and q have no common factor.

An important formulation of the above phenomenon is: In the (intuitive) system of rational numbers, the set $\mathscr{S}$ of all rational numbers x such that $x^2 \leq 2$ has no greatest element. In other words, for each x such that $x^2 \leq 2$, there is a $y > x$ such that $y^2 \leq 2$.

To see why the above statement is true we note that if $x^2 \leq 2$ and $x \leq 1$, then we may let $y = 1.4$. Whereupon, $y > x$ and $y^2 = 1.96 \leq 2$. If $x^2 \leq 2$ and $x > 1$, then, of course, $x^2 < 2$ since we know x^2 cannot be 2. Certainly $x < 2$ since $2^2 = 4 > 2$. Hence we may assume $1 < x < 2$. If we let $d = 2 - x^2$, then $0 < d < 1$. We shall show that there is a positive rational number t such that $(x + td)^2 < 2$. (The rational number $x + td$, which is greater than x, will then be our y.) Indeed

$$(x + td)^2 = x^2 + 2xtd + t^2d^2 = 2 - d + 2xtd + t^2d^2$$
$$< 2 - d + 4td + t^2d^2 = 2 - d(1 - 4t - t^2d).$$

Now if $t = 1/5$, then $4t = 4/5$, $t^2d = d/25 < 1/25$ and

$$1 - 4t - t^2d = 1 - \frac{4}{5} - \frac{d}{25} > 0.$$

Hence

$$(x + td)^2 < 2 - d(1 - 4t - t^2d) < 2.$$

Since the set $\mathscr{S}$ is bounded above by 2 (that is, for each x in $\mathscr{S}$ we have $x \leq 2$), we see that in the (intuitive) system of rational numbers there is a set $\mathscr{S}$, bounded above and having no greatest element. But we seek a system of numbers wherein such a "gapiness" does not occur. To this end we add to our list of axioms the *least upper bound* axiom as described below.

3. UPPER AND LOWER BOUNDS

A set of numbers $\mathscr{B}$ has an *upper bound* M if every number of $\mathscr{B}$ is less than or equal to M. For example, the (intuitive) set $\mathscr{C} = \{1, 1/2, 1/3, \cdots, 1/n, \cdots\}$ has an upper bound. We may take $M = 1$. Of course, if M is an upper bound, then any number greater than M is also an upper bound. Similarly, a set $\mathscr{B}$ has a *lower bound* m if every member of $\mathscr{B}$ is greater than or equal to m. In the example given above we see that 0 is a lower bound for $\mathscr{C}$. If m is a lower bound, then any number less than m is also a lower bound. A set that has both an upper bound and a lower bound will be called a *bounded set*.

A number L is called a *least upper bound* (l.u.b.) of a set $\mathscr{B}$ if L is an upper bound for $\mathscr{B}$ and there is no upper bound M for $\mathscr{B}$ such that $M < L$. The *greatest lower bound* (g.l.b.) for $\mathscr{B}$ is defined analogously. Thus, a number ℓ is called a greatest lower bound of $\mathscr{B}$ if ℓ is a lower bound for $\mathscr{B}$ and there is no lower bound m for $\mathscr{B}$ such that $\ell < m$. For the set $\mathscr{C} = \{1, 1/2, 1/3, \cdots, 1/n, \cdots\}$ introduced above we see that $1 = \text{l.u.b.} \, \mathscr{C}$ and $0 = \text{g.l.b.} \, \mathscr{C}$. Note that if a set has a greatest lower bound, this g.l.b. need not belong to the set. Similarly, a least upper bound of a set may or may not be a member of the set. For example, if $\mathscr{C} = \{1, 1/2, 1/3, \cdots, 1/n, \cdots\}$ again, then $1 \in \mathscr{C}$, but $0 \notin \mathscr{C}$. That is, the l.u.b. of $\mathscr{C}$ is *in* $\mathscr{C}$, but the g.l.b. of $\mathscr{C}$ is *not* in $\mathscr{C}$. As a matter of fact, it is also *not* necessarily true that in an ordered field $\mathscr{F}$ every nonempty set having an upper bound has a least upper bound in the field $\mathscr{F}$. (Similar remarks, of course, apply to the greatest lower bound.)

We saw above that in the (intuitive) system of rational numbers, the set, (say $\mathscr{S}$), of rational numbers x such that $x^2 \leq 2$ has an upper bound (2, say), but no greatest element. We now show that $\mathscr{S}$ has no least upper bound. Indeed, such a least upper bound L, if it exists, would have to be less than $3/2$ since $x^2 \leq 2$ implies $x < 3/2$. We know $L^2 \neq 2$, and our earlier argument shows that L^2 cannot be less than 2. Thus we must have $L^2 > 2$.

To complete our proof we must show the existence of a positive Y less than L such that $Y^2 > 2$. Towards this end let $D = L^2 - 2$. Then since $L < 3/2$ we have $0 < D < 1$. We shall show that there is a positive rational number r such that $(L - rD)^2 > 2$. (The rational number $L - rD$, which is less than L, will then be our Y.)

This time we note that

$$(L - rD)^2 = L^2 - 2rLD + r^2D^2 = 2 + D - 2rLD + r^2D^2$$
$$> 2 + D(1 - 3r + r^2D)$$

since $L < 3/2$. We now see that if $r = 1/4$, then $1 - 3r + r^2D = 1 - 3/4 + D/16 > 1/4$. Hence

$$(L - rD)^2 > 2.$$

This example shows that even though a nonempty subset of a set satisfying the axioms of an ordered field may have an upper bound, it need not have a least upper bound. In this sense the (intuitive) system of rational numbers is incomplete. To secure a complete ordered field we shall add the following *completeness axiom*:

C If a nonempty set of an ordered field has an upper bound, then it has a least upper bound.

Any set of elements satisfying the axioms of an ordered field and Axiom **C** is called a *complete ordered field*. Although we *postulate* the *existence* of such a field, its existence may be derived from more primitive sets of axioms (say, those from set theory, or the famous Peano axioms for the natural numbers, positive integers, etc.). However we arrive at a complete ordered field, the final object R (the real numbers) is unique in the sense that if R and R' are two complete ordered fields, then there is a one–one correspondence between the elements of R and those of R' and this correspondence preserves the algebraic and order relation in the two fields. (That is, R and R' are algebraically, and also with respect to order, indistinguishable.)

Before giving a formal definition of the integers (positive and negative) and the rational numbers, we recall (see the Corollary to Theorem 9) that if 0 is the "zero" element and 1 the "one" element of an ordered field R, then $1 > 0$. If now we let $2 = 1 + 1, 3 = 2 + 1$, etc., then

$$0 < 1 < 2 < \cdots < n < \cdots$$

and

$$0 > -1 > -2 > \cdots > -n > \cdots.$$

The following definition formalizes all this and produces the positive integers.

Definition. *Let $\mathscr{S}$ be a subset of an ordered field R. Then $\mathscr{S}$ is called an* **inductive set** *if:*

(1) *$\mathscr{S}$ contains 1*

and

(2) *$\mathscr{S}$ contains $x + 1$ whenever it contains x.*

We may now define the set of positive integers N to be the intersection of all inductive sets. The set of integers I is now defined as the set $N \cup (-N) \cup \{0\}$, that is, the set of all positive integers, their additive inverses (negatives), and zero. The set Q of rational numbers is the set of quotients a/b where a and b are elements of I and $b \neq 0$. All other elements of R not in Q are called *irrational* numbers.

Inductive sets lead to many important consequences. One such consequence is the following:

Theorem 11. *Any nonempty set of positive integers contains a least or smallest number.*

PROOF.   To see this, let S be the given set. Let P be the set of positive integers satisfying $p \leq s$ for each $s \in S$ and $p \in P$. The integer 1 is certainly in P. Now if $s \in S$, then $s + 1 > s$ and $s + 1$ is not in P. So we have $P \neq N$. Hence there is a $p' \in P$ such that $p' + 1$ does not belong to P. We claim that p' is the least member of S: for if $p' < s$ for each $s \in S$, then $p' + 1 \leq s$. This contradicts the fact that $p' + 1$ is not in P.

Later it will be convenient to denote $a \cdot a \cdots a$ (n factors, $n \in N$) by a^n. Therefore we make the following recursive definition:

$$a^1 = a, \qquad a^{n+1} = a^n \cdot a.$$

Accordingly, once a^n is known, a^{n+1} also is known.

Our next task is to explore R and its relation to N, Q, and I. In doing so we shall rely only on the axioms and definitions we have laid down, and the rules we have derived therefrom.

Theorem 12. *If a is any real number, then there is an integer n such that $n > a$.*

PROOF.   Suppose there is no such integer n. Then $n \leq a$ for all integers n. Thus the set of integers has an upper bound, and by Axiom **C**, a least upper bound. Call this least upper bound L. Then by definition of least upper bound, $L - 1$ is *not* a least upper bound. Therefore there is an integer m such that $m > L - 1$. But $m + 1$ is also an integer, and $m + 1 > (L - 1) + 1 = L$, which is a contradiction.

Corollary 1 (*The Archimedean property of real numbers*).   *If a and b are any positive real numbers, then there is a positive integer n such that $nb > a$.*

PROOF.   By hypothesis, $a \neq 0 \neq b$. Therefore by Theorem 10 and Axiom $\mathbf{O}_3$, a/b is a (positive) real number. By Theorem 12 there is an integer n such that $n > a/b$, and the corollary follows.

Corollary 2. *For any number $e > 0$ there is a positive integer n such that $1/n < e$.*

PROOF.   Suppose there is no such n. Then $1/n \geq e$ or $n \leq 1/e$ for all positive integers n. This contradicts Theorem 12.

Using Axiom **C** and Corollary 2 we now prove:

Theorem 13. *The set of rational numbers whose square is less than 2 has a least upper bound, say d, and $d^2 = 2$.*

PROOF.   Let S be the set of rational numbers r such that $r^2 < 2$. This set is not empty since $1 \in S$, and furthermore S is bounded from above (for example, by 2). Therefore the set S has a positive least upper bound, say d (which must be less than 2). To show that $d^2 = 2$ we must rule out the possibilities that $d^2 > 2$ or $d^2 < 2$.

Case 1. Assume $d^2 > 2$. Then $d^2 - 2 > 0$. Let $e = d^2 - 2$. Then, by Corollary 2 to Theorem 12, there exists a positive integer n such that $1/n < e/4$. Consider now

$$\left(d - \frac{1}{n}\right)^2 = d^2 - \frac{2d}{n} + \frac{1}{n^2} > d^2 - \frac{4}{n} + \frac{1}{n^2}.$$

(If $2d < 4$ then $2d/n < 4/n$.) Thus, since $4/n < e$,

$$\left(d - \frac{1}{n}\right)^2 > d^2 - e + \frac{1}{n^2} = 2 + \frac{1}{n^2} > 2.$$

We therefore have found a number, namely $d - 1/n$, that is less than d, but whose square exceeds 2. Thus d cannot be the least upper bound of S.

Case 2. Assume $d^2 < 2$ and let $2 - d^2 = e > 0$. Again, by Corollary 2 to Theorem 12 there exists a positive integer n greater than 1 such that $1/n < e/10$. Consider now the identity

$$\left(d + \frac{1}{n}\right)^2 = d^2 + \frac{2d}{n} + \frac{1}{n^2}. \tag{1}$$

Without loss of generality we may assume $d > 1$. Then since $d^2 < 2$ we have $d < 2$ and hence

$$\frac{2d}{n} < \frac{4}{n}.$$

Also

$$\frac{1}{n^2} < \frac{1}{n}$$

since $n > 1$. Therefore, from (1),

$$d^2 < \left(d + \frac{1}{n}\right)^2 < d^2 + \frac{4}{n} + \frac{1}{n} = d^2 + \frac{5}{n} < d^2 + \frac{e}{2} < 2.$$

Thus we have found a number, namely $d + 1/n$, that is greater than d, but whose square is less than 2. This contradicts the assumption that d is a least upper bound for S.

We conclude, therefore, that the least upper bound d for the set S must be such that $d^2 = 2$.

Thus we see that the irrational number $\sqrt{2}$ may be expressed as the least upper bound of a certain set of rational numbers. We assert that *all* real numbers have this property. That is, if *r* is any real number, then the set $\mathscr{E}$ of rational numbers less than or equal to *r* has *r* for its least upper bound.

First we prove the preliminary result that between any two distinct real numbers *a* and *b* there is a rational number. (We have already shown this in the case when both *a* and *b* are rational.) If $a < 0$ and $b > 0$, then 0 is a rational number with the property that $a < 0 < b$. Now suppose $0 < a < b$. Then by the Archimedean property (Corollary 1 to Theorem 12) there exists a positive integer *n* such that $n(b - a) > 1$. By Theorem 11 the set of integers greater than or equal to *nb* has a least member, say $B + 1$. Thus *B* is the greatest integer less than *nb*. Now we see that

$$nb \leqq B + 1$$

and

$$B + 1 - na > 1$$

or

$$B - na > 0.$$

Finally we have

$$na < B < nb.$$

Hence there is at least one rational number, namely B/n, that lies between *a* and *b*. If $a < b < 0$, a similar argument may be used.

Now let *r* be any real number and $\mathscr{E}$ the set of all rational numbers *s* less than or equal to *r*. Then *r* is an upper bound for $\mathscr{E}$. We claim *r* is also the least upper bound for $\mathscr{E}$. Otherwise, there would be a real number r' less than *r* such that for each $s \in \mathscr{E}$ we would have $s \leqq r' < r$. But, as proved above, there is a rational number s' between r' and *r*. That is, $r' < s' < r$. Hence $s' \in \mathscr{E}$ and r' cannot be a least upper bound of $\mathscr{E}$.

4. THE REAL NUMBERS

We stated above that a one–one correspondence may be established between two complete ordered fields so that they are algebraically and with respect to order *isomorphic* or indistinguishable. In what follows we shall establish the truth of this claim.

First of all we explain briefly the idea of a one–one correspondence. Suppose *S* and S' are two given sets. Suppose further that with each element $s \in S$ we can pair or match a unique element $s' \in S'$ and conversely. Then we say we have set up a one–one correspondence between *S* and S'. If the sets are finite and contain the same number of

elements the one–oneness is easily established. For example, consider
$\mathscr{F}_3 = \{0, 1, 2\}$ and $\mathscr{S} = \{a, b, c\}$. The correspondence

$$0 \leftrightarrow a$$
$$1 \leftrightarrow b$$
$$2 \leftrightarrow c$$

is clearly one–one. If, moreover, $\mathscr{S}$ satisfies the field axioms for the
operations $\oplus$ and $\odot$ with the "addition" and "multiplication"
tables:

$\oplus$	a	b	c
a	a	b	c
b	b	c	a
c	c	a	b

$\odot$	a	b	c
a	a	a	a
b	a	b	c
c	a	c	b

then the two sets $\mathscr{F}_3$ and $\mathscr{S}$ are algebraically indistinguishable.

Nonfinite sets present more interesting problems. For instance, a
one–one correspondence may be established between the set of positive
integers and the set of even integers (see the exercises at the end of the
chapter). Even more interesting is the fact that a one–one correspondence may be set up between the set of *all* rational numbers or
fractions and the positive integers.

To see this, we shall arrange the fractions into disjoint sets in a
certain manner. The first set will contain only zero. The second set
will contain only the integer 1. The nth set, $n = 3, 4, 5, \cdots$, will contain the integer $n - 1$ and all fractions of the form a/b where a and b
are positive integers and $a + b = n$—except those fractions where a
and b have a common factor. For example, the eighth set contains

$$7, \tfrac{1}{7}, \tfrac{3}{5}, \tfrac{5}{3}.$$

The set consisting of all such sets contains all the nonnegative fractions
and each fraction will be contained in exactly one of the sets. We now
augment each of the n sets, $n \neq 1$, so as to include as the immediate
successor of each fraction of each set, its negative. The one–one
correspondence is now easily established:

$$0, 1, -1, 2, -2, \tfrac{1}{2}, -\tfrac{1}{2}, 3, -3, \tfrac{1}{3}, -\tfrac{1}{3}, 4, -4, \tfrac{1}{4}, -\tfrac{1}{4}, \tfrac{2}{3}, -\tfrac{2}{3}, \tfrac{3}{2}, -\tfrac{3}{2}, 5, \cdots$$
$$\updownarrow\,\updownarrow \quad \updownarrow\,\updownarrow \quad \updownarrow\,\updownarrow \quad \updownarrow\,\updownarrow \quad \updownarrow\,\updownarrow \quad \updownarrow\,\updownarrow \quad \updownarrow\,\updownarrow \quad \updownarrow\,\updownarrow \quad \updownarrow\,\updownarrow \quad \updownarrow\,\updownarrow$$
$$1\;2 \quad 3\;4 \quad 5\;6 \quad 7\;8 \quad 9\;10 \quad 11\;12 \quad 13\;14 \quad 15\;16 \quad 17\;18 \quad 19\;20\cdots$$

In the preceding section we saw that all real numbers may be
defined as the least upper bounds of certain sets of rational numbers.
If the defining set is finite, then the least upper bound is itself a
member of the set and therefore is a rational number. If the defining
set is nonfinite, the least upper bound may be a rational number or an
irrational number. Suppose $t = $ l.u.b. S and $t' = $ l.u.b. S' where S
and S' are both sets of rational numbers. Then t and t' are real

numbers. We claim that $t + t' = $ l.u.b. $(S + S')$ where by $S + S'$ we mean the set of all rational numbers $s + s'$ where $s \in S$ and $s' \in S'$.

First we note that $t + t'$ is *an* upper bound for $S + S'$ since for each $s \in S$ and $s' \in S'$ we have $t \geqq s$ and $t' \geqq s'$; and hence $t + t' \geqq s + s'$. Now suppose $\tau = $ l.u.b. $(S + S')$. Then if $\tau < t + t'$, set $t + t' - \tau = \varepsilon > 0$. Since t and t' are least upper bounds of S and S' respectively, there exists an s in S and an s' in S' such that $t - \frac{1}{2}\varepsilon < s$ and $t' - \frac{1}{2}\varepsilon < s'$. Then $\tau + \varepsilon = t + t' < s + s' + \varepsilon$. We conclude that $\tau < s + s'$. Thus the assumption that $\tau < t + t'$ has led to a contradiction and we must conclude that $t + t' = $ l.u.b. $(S + S')$. Using similar arguments the reader may prove (see the exercises at the end of the chapter) that $tt' = $ l.u.b. SS' (where S and S' are sets of positive rational numbers with $t = $ l.u.b. S, $t' = $ l.u.b. S', and SS' is the set of all rational numbers ss' with $s \in S$ and $s' \in S'$). Finally, $t > t'$ implies that there is an $s^* \in S$ such that $s^* > s'$ for all $s' \in S'$.

We now proceed to set up an isomorphism between two complete ordered fields R and R'. To this end we must show that to each $x \in R$ there corresponds a unique $x' \in R'$ and if $a \leftrightarrow a'$, $b \leftrightarrow b'$, and $a < b$; then $a + b \leftrightarrow a' + b'$, $ab \leftrightarrow a'b'$, and $a' < b'$.

Denote the zero and one of R by 0 and 1 respectively, and those of R' by $0'$ and $1'$. As for R, the ordered field axioms imply for R' that

$$0' < 1' < 2' < \cdots < n' < \cdots$$

and

$$0' > -1' > -2' > \cdots > -n' > \cdots.$$

For R' we now define the "prime" rationals Q' as in R and make the correspondence $0 \leftrightarrow 0'$, $1 \leftrightarrow 1'$, and in general $n \leftrightarrow n'$ where n is an integer of R and n' the "prime" integer obtained by adding $1'$ to itself n times. Accordingly, for the rational numbers the correspondence

$$\frac{p}{q} \leftrightarrow \frac{p'}{q'}$$

is one–one [where p, q, $(q \neq 0)$, are integers in R and p', q' are the corresponding "prime" integers of R']. Moreover, the same rules for "addition" and "multiplication" are derivable for R'. Thus $a \leftrightarrow a'$, $b \leftrightarrow b'$ imply $a + b \leftrightarrow a' + b'$, $ab \leftrightarrow a'b'$, and $a < b$ implies $a' < b'$.

There remains only the problem of extending the one–one correspondence to the irrationals of R and R'. If $t \in R$ is an irrational number it is the least upper bound of a set, say $\mathscr{S}$, of rational numbers in R. But the rational numbers may be put into a one–one correspondence with the positive integers. Consequently, for each $s_i \in \mathscr{S}$ there is an $s_i' \in \mathscr{S}' \subset R'$. According to Axiom **C**, $\mathscr{S}'$ also has a least upper bound, say t', which leads us to the correspondence

$$t \leftrightarrow t'.$$

We show that the above correspondence between the irrational numbers is one–one, by assuming that there is another set $\mathscr{S}_1 \subset Q$ that also has t for its least upper bound and proving that the corresponding set $\mathscr{S}'_1 \subset Q'$ also has t' for its least upper bound. Accordingly, let t'_1 ($t'_1 \neq t'$) be the least upper bound of $\mathscr{S}'_1$. Without loss of generality we may assume $t' < t'_1$. But $t' < t'_1$ implies there is an $s'_{1i} \in \mathscr{S}'_1$ satisfying $t' < s'_{1i} \leq t'_1$ so that s'_{1i} is greater than all $s'_i \in \mathscr{S}'$. Now corresponding to the "prime" rational s'_{1i}, there is an $s_{1i} \in \mathscr{S}_1$ and s_{1i} is greater than all $s_i \in \mathscr{S}$. Therefore $s_{1i} \geq t$ (the least upper bound of $\mathscr{S}$) and also $s_{1i} \leq t$ (the least upper bound of $\mathscr{S}_1$). Hence $t = s_{1i}$ and t is rational. This contradicts the hypothesis that t is irrational. We must therefore conclude that t' is also the least upper bound of $\mathscr{S}'_1$.

Thus the correspondence $t \leftrightarrow t'$, where $t = $ l.u.b. $\mathscr{S}$ and t' is the least upper bound of the corresponding set of "prime" rationals $\mathscr{S}'$, gives us a one–one correspondence between the members of R and those of R'; and further, if $t_1 \leftrightarrow t'_1$, $t_2 \leftrightarrow t'_2$, and $t_1 < t_2$; then $t_1 + t_2 \leftrightarrow t'_1 + t'_2$, $t_1 t_2 \leftrightarrow t'_1 t'_2$, and $t'_1 < t'_2$.

5. ABSOLUTE VALUES AND INEQUALITIES

In discussing the concept of limit (cf. Chapter 4) we shall need some properties of *absolute values* and *absolute inequalities*. We shall therefore briefly mention a few results that will prove useful later on.

The *absolute value* of a real number a is written $|a|$. It is defined as a if $a \geq 0$ and is defined as $-a$ if $a < 0$. Thus, for example, $|2| = 2$, $|0| = 0$, $|-5| = -(-5) = 5$. From the definition it follows that $|a|$ is always nonnegative and

$$|a| \geq a. \tag{1}$$

We may also conclude that

$$|a| = |-a|. \tag{2}$$

For if $a > 0$, $|a| = a = -(-a) = |-a|$ and, by symmetry, (2) holds if $a < 0$. If $a = 0$, the result is trivial. Another elementary property is

$$|ab| = |a| \cdot |b|. \tag{3}$$

For if a and b are nonnegative, $|a| = a$, $|b| = b$, and $|a|\,|b| = ab = |ab|$. If a and b are both negative, then $|a| = -a$, $|b| = -b$, and $|a|\,|b| = (-a)(-b) = ab = |ab|$ (see Theorem 4). If $a < 0$ and $b \geq 0$, then $|a|\,|b| = -ab = |ab|$ (see Theorem 3). The proof is similar if $a \geq 0$ and $b < 0$.

One of the most important and useful results is the *triangle inequality* expressed in (4) below:

$$|a + b| \leq |a| + |b|. \tag{4}$$

To prove (4) we note that $|a + b|$ equals $(a + b)$ or $-(a + b)$; and hence we always have

$$|a + b|^2 = (a + b)^2 = a^2 + 2ab + b^2 = |a|^2 + 2ab + |b|^2.$$

By (1) and (3)

$$2ab \leqq 2|ab| = 2|a|\,|b|.$$

Thus

$$|a + b|^2 \leqq |a|^2 + 2|a|\,|b| + |b|^2 = (|a| + |b|)^2.$$

To complete the proof we must now show that if $x \geqq 0$, $y \geqq 0$, and $x^2 \geqq y^2$; then $x \geqq y$. Clearly the result is trivial if any of the equality signs in the hypotheses hold. We may therefore restrict ourselves to proving that if $x > 0$, $y > 0$ and $x^2 > y^2$, then $x > y$. This fact is easily demonstrated. If $x^2 > y^2$, then $x^2 - y^2 > 0$ and $(x + y)(x - y) > 0$. But $x > 0$ and $y > 0$ mean that $x + y > 0$, and consequently $x - y > 0$—which implies $x > y$.

Two final simple results are

$$|a| - |b| \leqq |a - b| \tag{5}$$

and

$$|\,|a| - |b|\,| \leqq |a - b|. \tag{6}$$

To prove (5) we write $a = (a - b) + b$ and invoke (4) to obtain $|a| \leqq |a - b| + |b|$ or

$$|a| - |b| \leqq |a - b|$$

—which is (5). Interchanging the roles of a and b in (5) leads to

$$|b| - |a| \leqq |b - a|.$$

But by (2), $|b - a| = |a - b|$. Thus the above equation may be written as

$$|b| - |a| \leqq |a - b|. \tag{7}$$

Combining (5) and (7), we establish the truth of (6).

EXERCISES

1. Prove that the set Q of rational numbers satisfies Axioms $\mathbf{F}_1$–$\mathbf{F}_{11}$. That is, prove that Q is indeed a field.

2. If a, b, c, d are integers with $b \neq 0$ and $d \neq 0$, and if Q is the field of rational numbers, prove that

$$\left(\frac{a}{b}\right)\left(\frac{c}{d}\right) = \frac{ac}{bd}.$$

3.   For elements a, b, c, d in a field prove that $(a + b)(c + d) = ac + bc + ad + bd$.

4.   If $\mathscr{F}$ is a field and a is any element in $\mathscr{F}$, prove that $-(-a) = a$.

5.   In an arbitrary field prove that $ab = 0$ implies a or b (or both) are the zero element.

6.   In a field $\mathscr{F}$ prove that if a, b, c are in $\mathscr{F}$ and $a \neq 0$, then $ab = ac$ implies $b = c$.

7.   In a field $\mathscr{F}$ we have defined a^2 as $a \cdot a$ (where $a \in \mathscr{F}$). Prove that if $a^2 = b^2$, then either $a = b$ or $a = -b$.

8.   If a is an element of a field, prove that $(-a)^n = (-1)^n a^n$ where n is a positive integer. [*Hint:* Recall the definition of a^n.]

9.   If a is any element in a field $\mathscr{F}$ and $a \neq 0$, prove that $(a^{-1})^{-1} = a$.

10.   If a and b are elements of a field $\mathscr{F}$ and if $a \neq 0$, find an element $x \in \mathscr{F}$ such that $ax + b = 0$. Show that this element x is unique. (The element x is called the *solution* of the equation $ax + b = 0$.)

11.   Find the rational numbers that are solutions of the following equations:

(i) $x^2 - 9 = 0$	(v) $x^2 + 7x + 12 = 0$
(ii) $x^2 + 2x = 0$	(vi) $3x^2 + 5x + 2 = 0$
(iii) $x^2 + 5x = -6$	(vii) $x^3 - x^2 - x + 1 = 0$.
(iv) $4x^2 + 9x + 5 = 0$	

12.   Let $\mathscr{F}_5 = \{0, 1, 2, 3, 4\}$. Define an addition and multiplication table similar to those for $\mathscr{F}_3$. Does the set $\mathscr{F}_5$ with addition and multiplication so defined constitute a field?

13.   Is it possible to define an addition and multiplication for $\mathscr{F}_4 = \{0, 1, 2, 3\}$ so that the result yields a field? If not, why not?

14.   Let $\mathscr{F}_p = \{0, 1, 2, \cdots, p - 1\}$ where p is a prime number (that is, the only integral divisors of p are ± 1 and $\pm p$). It is possible to define addition and multiplication for $\mathscr{F}_p$ so that the result will be a field. Show that such a field cannot be ordered. [*Hint:* Recall the Corollary to Theorem 9.]

15.   Let S be the set of integers $\{0, 2, 4, 6, 8\}$. Define "addition" in S as ordinary addition followed by the casting out of multiples of 10. (That is, we add "modulo ten.") Define "multiplication" in S as ordinary multiplication followed by the casting out of multiples of 10. (That is, we multiply "modulo ten.") Show that S satisfies all the **F** axioms except Axiom $\mathbf{F}_{10}$. What is the "one" in S?

16.   Prove the following statements if a, b, c, d are elements of an ordered field:

(i) $a < b$ and $c < d$ imply $a + c < b + d$.
(ii) $a < b$ and $c < 0$ imply $bc < ac$.
(iii) $a < 0$ and $b < 0$ imply $0 < ab$.
(iv) $a > 0$, $b > 0$, and $a < b$ imply $b^{-1} < a^{-1}$.

  (v) $a < 0$, $b < 0$, and $a < b$ imply $b^{-1} < a^{-1}$.

  (vi) $a > 0$, $b > 0$, and $a^2 > b^2$ imply $a > b$.

  (vii) $a > 0$, $b > 0$, and $a > b$ imply $a^2 > b^2$.

  (viii) $ab < 0$ implies $a < 0$ or $b < 0$.

17. Find the set of rational numbers x such that each of the following inequalities holds:

  (i) $5x - 3 > 0$ (iv) $x^2 + 5x + 6 > 0$

  (ii) $3x + 2 > 2x - 5$ (v) $2x^2 - 3x + 1 < 0$

  (iii) $3x - 7 > 5x - 2$ (vi) $x^2 - 3x - 18 > 0$.

18. Prove that $\sqrt{3}$, $\sqrt{6}$, $\sqrt{7}$, $\sqrt{8}$ are not rational numbers.

19. Let p be a prime number. Prove that the least upper bound of the set of positive rational numbers such that $r^2 < p$ does not belong to the field Q of rational numbers.

20. (i) Give an example of a set having both a least upper bound M and a greatest lower bound m, but such that *neither* M nor m is an element of the set.

    (ii) Give an example of a set such that *both* M and m are elements of the set.

    (iii) Give an example of a set where M is *not* an element and m *is* an element of the set.

21. Show that the least upper bound (if it exists) of a set is unique.

22. Prove that if a nonempty set of a complete ordered field has a lower bound, then it has a greatest lower bound.

23. If $a, b \in I$, and $b \neq 0$, then $a/b \in Q$. Prove that if a/b is *not* an integer (element of I), then neither is $(a/b)^2$.

24. If n is a positive integer, prove that $\sqrt{n}$ is either an integer or an irrational number. [*Hint:* Cf. Exercise 23.]

25. Let the least upper bound t of a subset S of an ordered field $\mathscr{F}$ exist. Let S' be the set of all elements $a \in \mathscr{F}$ with the property that $-a \in S$. Prove that

$$-t = \text{g.l.b. } S'.$$

26. The principle of mathematical induction may be stated in terms of the concept of inductive sets as follows: If

  (*a*) The integer 1 is in $\mathscr{P}$,

  (*b*) $\mathscr{P}$ is an inductive set,

then $\mathscr{P}$ contains all positive integers.

For an example of the application of this principle, let $\mathscr{P}$ be the set of integers for which it is true that

$$1 + 2 + 3 + \cdots + p = \frac{p(p + 1)}{2}.$$

We shall prove that the set of integers—for which it is true that the sum of the first p integers is one half the product of the last integer in the sum by its successor—is the set of all positive integers. We note first that $1 \in \mathscr{P}$ since

$$1 = \frac{1 \cdot (1 + 1)}{2}.$$

To show that $\mathscr{P}$ is inductive we must show that if $p \in \mathscr{P}$, then $p + 1$ also belongs to $\mathscr{P}$. We proceed on the assumption that $p \in \mathscr{P}$. Then

$$[1 + 2 + 3 + \cdots + p] + (p + 1) = \frac{p(p + 1)}{2} + (p + 1)$$

$$= (p + 1)\left[\frac{p}{2} + 1\right]$$

$$= \frac{(p + 1)(p + 2)}{2}.$$

Thus we see that $p + 1 \in \mathscr{P}$ and therefore $\mathscr{P}$ is inductive. But according to the principle of mathematical induction, it follows that $\mathscr{P}$ contains all the positive integers. Therefore the formula is true for all positive integers.

Prove the principle of mathematical induction. [*Hint:* Assume that $\mathscr{P}$ does not contain all the positive integers and use Theorem 11 to arrive at a contradiction.]

27. Prove that the set $\mathscr{P}$ for which

(i) $1^2 + 2^2 + 3^2 + \cdots + p^2 = \dfrac{p(p + 1)(2p + 1)}{6}$

(ii) $1^3 + 2^3 + 3^3 + \cdots + p^3 = \left[\dfrac{p(p + 1)}{2}\right]^2$

(iii) $1 + 3 + 5 + \cdots + (2p - 1) = p^2$

(iv) $\dfrac{1}{1\cdot 2} + \dfrac{1}{2\cdot 3} + \dfrac{1}{3\cdot 4} + \cdots + \dfrac{1}{p(p + 1)} = \dfrac{p}{p + 1}$ is the set of positive integers.

(v) Find $1^2 + 3^2 + 5^2 + \cdots + (2p - 1)^2$. [*Hint:* Use part (i).]

28. Prove that the set of positive integers $\{p\}$ for which $5^{2p} - 1$ is divisible by 24 is the set of all positive integers.

29. Prove that for $p \geq 4$,

$$2^p < p!$$

(where $p! = 1\cdot 2\cdot 3\cdot \;\cdots\; \cdot(p - 1)\cdot p$. We read $p!$ as "p factorial.")

30.   Prove by mathematical induction that if a and b are elements of a field, then

$$(ab)^p = a^p b^p$$

for all positive integers p.

31.   Prove that there is a real number d such that $d^2 = 3$.

32.   Prove that there is no smallest positive real number.

33.   Prove that I (the set of integers) may be put into one–one correspondence with the set of positive integers.

34.   Prove that the set of positive even integers may be put into one–one correspondence with N (the set of positive integers).

35.   Let S and S' be sets of positive rational numbers in the real field R. Define SS' as the set of all products ss' where $s \in S$ and $s' \in S'$. If $t = $ l.u.b. S and $t' = $ l.u.b. S', prove that $tt' = $ l.u.b. SS'.

36.   Show that $|x| < a$ implies $-a < x < a$.

37.   Find the set of real numbers x such that the following inequalities hold:

(i) $|x| < 6$

(ii) $|x + 5| < 7$

(iii) $|x + 6| < 3x - 2$

(iv) $|x - 9| < -2x + 3$

(v) $|x^2 - 9| < 3x + 9$

(vi) $|x^2 - 9| > 3x + 9$.

2

ANALYTIC GEOMETRY

Synthetic geometry deals with two classes of undefined elements: *points* and *lines*, and some undefined relations concerning these two classes such as: *on*—a relation concerning points and lines, *between*—a relation concerning a point and a pair of points, *congruent*—a relation about pairs of points, and *congruent angles*. Some assumptions then are made about these undefined elements and relations. The system of statements that can be derived from these assumptions or postulates by purely logical reasoning is called *synthetic geometry*. The type of geometric system one thus obtains will vary according to the postulates one chooses. For example, in familiar *Euclidean geometry*, ordinary plane geometry, one has the *Euclidean parallel postulate* which states that "through a point P not on a given line ℓ there is exactly one line ℓ' not intersecting ℓ." If we replace this "parallel postulate" by: "through P there are at least two lines not intersecting ℓ," one obtains what we call *Bolyai-Lobachefskian* (or *hyperbolic*) *geometry*. Clearly these postulates are contradictory, yet at the turn of the century Hilbert gave proofs for the *consistency* of *both* geometries. Thus from the standpoint of logic, both Euclidean and Lobachefskian geometries are valid.

Which of these geometries is "true" in the sense that it actually describes real space can be settled only by way of experimentation. But Euclidean space is in some sense the limiting case of hyperbolic geometry. Hence we are not able to distinguish (on the basis of the approximate measurements we obtain by way of experiments) a very close approximation from the limiting case.

Analytic geometry makes a connection between postulational or synthetic geometry and the real numbers. Sometimes it is treated as a part of synthetic geometry in which properties of the plane are studied by setting up a one–one correspondence between the points on the plane and ordered pairs of real numbers. It is not our purpose here to develop completely synthetic Euclidean geometry. However, we shall attempt to point out how—following the lead of Birkhoff and Beatley [2] and more recently of MacLane [3]—one can build up the traditional system of geometry more quickly than did Euclid, and at the same time introduce coordinates in a "natural way." Traditionally, synthetic geometry is developed by introducing the *between relation* as an undefined concept and laying down several postulates concerning this relation. The axioms for betweenness are quite subtle. An equivalent approach—which we shall follow here—is to introduce the *distance relation* as a primitive concept and lay down two simple axioms regarding this relation. The between relation will then be defined in terms of the distance relation. However, to proceed in this manner we must assume the postulates for the real number system—and we have already done this in Chapter 1.

Accordingly, we find it convenient to introduce as primitive concepts the elements *point* and *line* and the relations *on, distance, angle measure.* The "on axioms," sometimes called the "postulates for incidence," are:

L₁ Each line contains more than one point.
L₂ Two distinct points determine one and only one line.
L₃ There are three points not all on the same line.

The "postulates on distance" are the following two axioms:

D₁ With every pair of points A, B there is associated a nonnegative number $d(A, B)$ $[= d(B, A)]$, and $d(A, B) = 0$ if and only if $A = B$.
D₂ If A, B, C are points, then $d(A, B) + d(B, C) \geq d(C, A)$.

From our intuitive notions of geometry the above axioms are not bizarre. Let us now make the definition of *betweenness*.

Definition. *The point B is said to lie **between** the points A and C (written $\langle A, B, C \rangle$) if all three points are distinct and $d(A, B) + d(B, C) = d(A, C)$. If $A \neq C$, the **interval** AC [written $I(A, C)$] is the set of all points P such that $\langle A, P, C \rangle$.*

From the above definition of betweenness we are led to lay down the additional "on" axiom:

L₄ Three distinct points lie on a line if and only if one is between the other two.

The "geometric space" (see Figure 2.1) consisting of the five points P_1, P_2, P_3, P_4, P_5 and the five lines $\ell_1, \ell_2, \ell_3, \ell_4, \ell_5$—$\ell_5$ containing four points and the other four lines containing precisely two points—

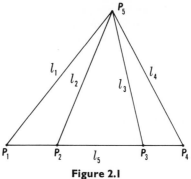

Figure 2.1

satisfies all the **L** and **D** axioms. Consequently, to obtain a geometric space that will be rich in theorems we must enlarge our set of postulates. To this end we shall introduce first the concept of *ray*.

If we have two fixed points, say O and P, then $\langle O, A, P \rangle$ is illustrated

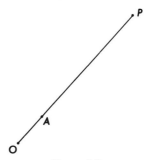

Figure 2.2

in Figure 2.2 above. However, we should like to have as well some terminology to describe the situation illustrated in Figure 2.3 below when O and P are given. We achieve this by defining *ray*.

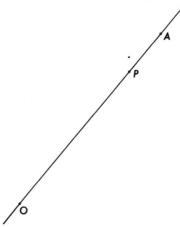

Figure 2.3

Definition. *If $O \neq A$, then* Ray OA *is the set of all points P with $P \neq O$ and $d(A, P) = |d(O, A) - d(O, P)|$.*

This definition is equivalent to saying that P is on the Ray OA if $A = P$, or $\langle O, A, P \rangle$ or $\langle O, P, A \rangle$. Ray OA is called the ray from O through A. We are thus led to lay down the following axioms:

R$_1$ On each ray from a point O and for every positive real number b there is exactly one point B with the property that $d(O, B) = b$.

R$_2$ If $B \in$ Ray OA, then Ray $OA =$ Ray OB.

An immediate consequence of Axiom **R$_2$** is that any two rays from a fixed point are either equal or disjoint.

To illustrate the above axioms and definitions we shall prove the following statement: If $\langle O, B, A \rangle$, then $I(O, B) \subset I(O, A)$.

PROOF. Let $P \in I(O, B)$. Then $d(O, B) = d(O, P) + d(P, B)$. Also $\langle O, B, A \rangle$ implies $d(O, A) = d(O, B) + d(B, A)$. These two equalities lead to

$$\begin{aligned}
d(O, A) &= [d(O, P) + d(P, B)] + d(B, A) \\
&= d(O, P) + [d(P, B) + d(B, A)].
\end{aligned} \tag{1}$$

But by Axiom **D$_2$**, $d(P, B) + d(B, A) \geq d(P, A)$ and (1) becomes

$$d(O, A) \geq d(O, P) + d(P, A).$$

But again from Axiom **D$_2$**, $d(O, A) \leq d(O, P) + d(P, A)$. These last two inequalities imply

$$d(O, A) = d(O, P) + d(P, A)$$

which in turn implies $\langle O, P, A \rangle$. Therefore $P \in I(O, A)$. Since P was an arbitrary point in $I(O, B)$ and every point P is in $I(O, A)$, we infer that $I(O, B) \subset I(O, A)$.

I. COORDINATES ON A LINE

The following theorem (cf. Figure 2.4) will enable us to define coordinates on a line λ.

Theorem 1. *If O is any point on the line λ, then λ contains exactly two distinct rays emanating from O; and every point $B \neq O$ on λ is on one of these rays.*

PROOF. From Axiom **L$_1$** it follows that there is a point $A \neq O$ on λ. By Axiom **R$_1$** there is a point A' on Ray AO such that $d(A, A') = 2d(O, A)$. Since $A' \in$ Ray AO, either $\langle A, A', O \rangle$ or $\langle A, O, A' \rangle$. But $d(A, A') = 2d(O, A)$ rules out $\langle A, A', O \rangle$. Hence we have $\langle A, O, A' \rangle$ and there are at least two rays, namely Ray OA and Ray OA' on λ.

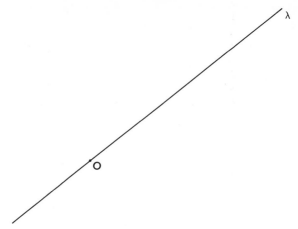

Figure 2.4

Let $a = d(O, A)$ and $d(A, A') = 2a$. Now let B be any point on λ distinct from O, A, and A'. If $B \notin$ Ray OA, then by Axiom $\mathbf{L}_4$ and the definition of a ray we must have $\langle A, O, B \rangle$ and $d(A, B) = a + d(O, B)$. If in addition $B \notin$ Ray OA', then $\langle A', O, B \rangle$ and $d(A', B) = a + d(O, B)$. But A, A', and B are collinear and distinct. Therefore, from the definition of betweenness and Axiom $\mathbf{L}_4$, one of the three numbers $a + d(O, B)$, $a + d(O, B)$, and $2a$ must be the sum of the other two. But this is impossible. Therefore either $B \in$ Ray OA or $B \in$ Ray OA'; but not both, since by Axiom $\mathbf{R}_2$, Ray OA and Ray OA' have no points in common.

Therefore, any ray from O and contained in λ must have a point on Ray OA or Ray OA', and so by Axiom $\mathbf{R}_2$, it must be either Ray OA or Ray OA'. We call Ray OA' the ray *opposite* Ray OA and denote them by r^+ and r^- respectively.

We now proceed to define coordinates on a line λ. If O is on λ, we choose one of the two rays on λ emanating from O and call it r^+ (the positive ray). Similarly, we call r^- (the negative ray) the other ray from O on λ. For every point P belonging to λ we associate a real number $x(P)$ in the following manner: $x(O) = 0$, $x(P) = d(O, P)$ if $P \in r^+$, and $x(P) = -d(O, P)$ if $P \in r^-$. From the definition of absolute value of a real number it follows that $d(O, P) = |x(P)|$. We shall call the mapping x of the points of λ on the real numbers a *coordinate function*. We may then prove:

Theorem 2. *Each coordinate function x on the line λ is a one–one mapping of λ on the set of real numbers; furthermore $d(P, Q) = |x(P) - x(Q)|$ for all P and Q on λ.*

PROOF. If $P = O \neq Q$ or $P \neq O = Q$, then $d(P, Q) = d(O, Q) = |x(Q)|$ or $d(P, Q) = d(P, O) = |x(P)|$. Correspondingly we also have

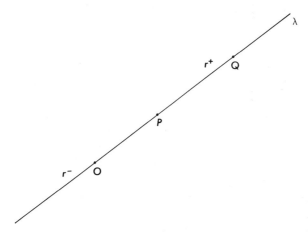

Figure 2.5

$|x(P) - x(Q)| = |0 - x(Q)| = |-x(Q)| = |x(Q)|$ or $|x(P) - x(Q)| = |x(P) - 0| = |x(P)|$ and the theorem is proved. If $P = Q \neq O$, the proof is similar.

Now consider the case $O \neq P \neq Q \neq O$. Then either P and Q are on r^+ or P and Q are on r^-, or $P \in r^+$ and $Q \in r^-$, or $P \in r^-$ and $Q \in r^+$. Suppose first that P and Q are on r^+ (cf. Figure 2.5 above). Then either $\langle O, P, Q \rangle$ or $\langle O, Q, P \rangle$ and $d(P, Q) = |d(O, P) - d(O, Q)|$. That is, $d(P, Q) = \pm [x(P) - x(Q)]$—whichever is positive. Hence $d(P, Q) = |x(P) - x(Q)|$. If P and Q are on r^-, the proof is similar.

Now suppose $P \in r^-$ and $Q \in r^+$. Then $\langle P, O, Q \rangle$, cf. Figure 2.6, and $d(O, P) + d(O, Q) = d(P, Q) = \pm [-x(P) + x(Q)]$—whichever is positive. So again $d(P, Q) = |x(P) - x(Q)|$. The final case, $P \in r^+$, $Q \in r^-$ is treated in the same manner.

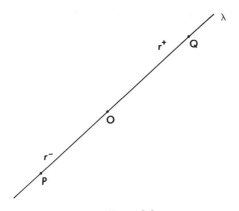

Figure 2.6

2. FUNDAMENTAL THEOREM OF ANALYTIC GEOMETRY

For the moment we shall appeal to the reader's previous knowledge (intuitive or formal) of geometry. We consider a circle of radius r and center at a point O, say. Let A be a point on the circumference of the circle. Now suppose we rotate the Ray OA about the point O in a counterclockwise (positive) direction, cf. Figure 2.7 (a clockwise direction will be called negative). Its initial position OA and terminal position OA' determine a geometric figure called an angle. If the portion of the circumference of the circle (the circular arc $\widehat{AA'}$) swept out by the Ray OA is equal in length to the radius of the circle we say the measure of the angle is one radian (1 rad.) and if it is $1/360$ of the circumference of the circle its measure is given as one degree ($1°$). (See the appendix to this chapter for a rigorous discussion of the length of a circular arc.) Since the circumference of the circle is $2\pi r$ (π equals one-half the circumference of a circle of unit radius) the Ray OA—while making one complete counterclockwise revolution—will sweep out an angle whose measure is 2π rad. Thus an angle whose measure is $360°$ is the same as an angle whose measure is 2π rad. And angles of measure $180°$, $90°$, $45°$ are the same as angles of measure π, $\pi/2$, $\pi/4$ rad., respectively. In general, if $O \leq c \leq 2\pi$, an angle of measure c rad. will indicate that the Ray OA has swept out a circular arc on the circumference equal in length to c times the radius of the circle. Thus an angle of measure c rad. is the same as an angle of measure $\left(\dfrac{360}{2\pi} c\right)°$.

If a ray makes more than one complete revolution, the measure of the angle is given by $(c + n2\pi)$ rad., see Figure 2.8, where $n \in I$ and $0 \leq c < 2\pi$. Thus the measure of an angle may be any (real) number of radians. Consequently, the same geometric figure may be represented by different real numbers of radians or degrees—the difference being an integral multiple of 2π or an integral multiple of 360. This

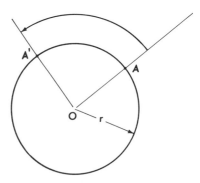

Figure 2.7

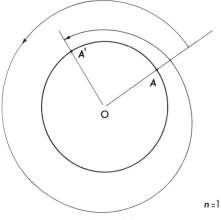

$n = 1$

Figure 2.8

may be stated succinctly as: the measure of an angle is a real number modulo 2π.

Simply because it will be more convenient later on, we shall henceforth speak only of *radian measure* for angles.

We now formalize these ideas (cf. Figure 2.9).

Definition.   *An* **angle** *is an ordered triple consisting of a point and two rays from that point. If* $s = $ Ray OA *and* $t = $ Ray OB, *we write the angle as* $[AOB]$ *or* $[Ost]$. *We denote the* **measure** *of the angle by* $\angle AOB$ *or* $\angle st$.

We now introduce the following axioms for angles.

A_1   If s and t are two rays from the same point, then $\angle st$ is a real number modulo 2π.

A_2   If s is a ray from O and C is a real number, then there is a ray t from O such that $\angle st = c$ (radians) with $0 \leqq c < 2\pi$ and c differing from C by an integral multiple of 2π.

A_3   If s, t, v are three rays from the same point, then $\angle st + \angle tv = \angle sv$.

A_4   If $A \neq O \neq B$, then $0 \neq \angle AOB = \angle BOA$ if and only if $d(A, B) = d(A, O) + d(O, B)$.

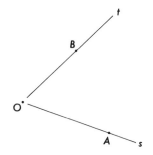

Figure 2.9

One may now introduce either the parallel axiom or the *similarity axiom* for triangles, and the *continuity axiom* to complete the set of axioms needed to develop the entire system of Euclidean geometry. We recall the definition of *triangle* and *similarity*.

Definition. *By a* **triangle** *we mean the figure* $\triangle ABC$ *formed by three distinct (noncollinear) points A, B, and C.*

Definition. *Two triangles* $\triangle ABC$ *and* $\triangle A'B'C'$ *are* **similar** *if there is a number $k > 0$ and a number $e = \pm 1$ such that* $\angle ABC = e \angle A'B'C'$, $\angle BCA = e \angle B'C'A'$, $\angle CAB = e \angle C'A'B'$; *and* $d(A', B') = kd(A, B)$, $d(A', C') = kd(A, C)$, *and* $d(B', C') = kd(B, C)$.

(If the above definition holds with $k = 1$, then we say $\triangle ABC$ and $\triangle A'B'C'$ are *congruent*.) We are thus led to lay down the following *similarity axiom*:

S If two triangles $\triangle ABC$ and $\triangle A'B'C'$ have $\angle ABC = e \angle A'B'C'$ and $d(A, B) = kd(A', B')$ and $d(B, C) = kd(B', C')$ for $e = \pm 1$ and $k > 0$; then they are similar.

Before stating the continuity axiom we make the following definitions. If $0 \leq \angle st < \pi$, we call $[Ost]$ a *proper angle*. If $\pi < \angle st < 2\pi$ we call $[Ost]$ an *improper angle*. If $\angle st = \pi$, we call $[Ost]$ a *straight angle*. If $0 < \angle st \leq \pi$, the *supplement* of $[Ost]$ is an angle whose measure is $\pi - \angle st$. Clearly the supplement of a proper angle is proper, and the (additive) inverse of a proper angle is improper. If $\angle st = \pm \pi/2$, we call $[Ost]$ a *right angle* and the lines containing the rays s and t are said to be *perpendicular*.

The continuity axiom may now be stated (cf. Figure 2.10).

CA Let $[AOB]$ be a proper angle. If D is between A and B, then $0 < \angle AOD < \angle AOB$. Conversely, if $0 < \angle AOC < \angle AOB$, then Ray OC meets $I(A, B)$.

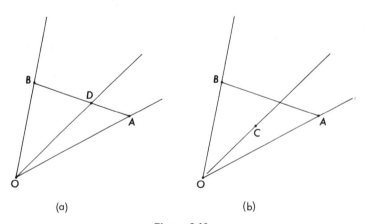

(a) (b)

Figure 2.10

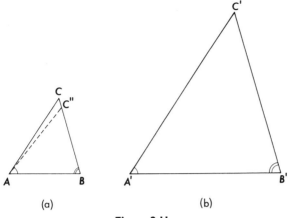

Figure 2.11

Armed with all the above axioms one may now prove the theorems of Euclidean geometry. We shall limit ourselves to proving four important theorems. Two theorems concern similarity, one the sum of the angles of a triangle. The fourth is the *classical Pythagorean theorem.*

It will be convenient in the next four theorems and corollaries to assume that the measures of all angles in all triangles considered lie between $-\pi$ and $+\pi$. This involves no loss of generality.

Theorem 3.   *Two triangles $\triangle ABC$ and $\triangle A'B'C'$ are similar if the absolute values of the measures of two angles of $\triangle ABC$ are equal to the absolute values of the measures of two angles of $\triangle A'B'C'$.*

PROOF.   Referring to Figure 2.11, we may assume without loss of generality that $\angle BAC = e \angle B'A'C'$ and $\angle ABC = e \angle A'B'C'$ and $d(A, B) = kd(A', B')$ where $e = \pm 1$ and $k > 0$.

By Axiom $\mathbf{R}_1$ there is a point C'' on Ray BC such that $d(B, C'') = kd(B', C')$. By Axiom $\mathbf{S}$, $\triangle ABC''$ and $\triangle A'B'C'$ are similar. Therefore $\angle B'A'C' = e \angle BAC''$. But $\angle B'A'C' = e \angle BAC$, so that $\angle BAC'' = e \angle BAC$. Now Axiom $\mathbf{CA}$ tells us that the point C'' is also on Ray AC as well as on Ray BC. Therefore, by Axiom $\mathbf{L}_2$, $C = C''$ and hence $\triangle ABC''$ and $\triangle ABC$ are identical. But we have shown that $\triangle ABC''$ and $\triangle A'B'C'$ are similar. Thus $\triangle ABC$ and $\triangle A'B'C'$ are similar.

Corollary 1.   *If two sides of a triangle are equal, the measure of the angles opposite them are equal up to a factor of ± 1, and conversely.*

PROOF.   Consider the triangle from two points of view, viz.: as $\triangle ABC$ and $\triangle BCA$. Then $d(A, C) = 1 \cdot d(B, C)$ and $\angle ACB = -\angle BCA$. Axiom $\mathbf{S}$ completes the proof.

To prove the converse, use Theorem 3.

Corollary 2.   *If $\triangle ACB$ and $\triangle AC'B$ are such that $d(A, C) = d(A, C')$ and $d(C, B) = d(C', B)$, then $\angle ACB = e \angle AC'B$ where $e = \pm 1$.*

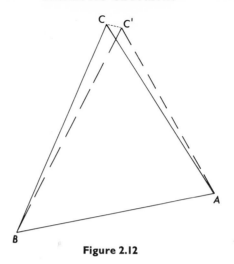

Figure 2.12

PROOF. In Figure 2.12, connect C and C'. Then by Corollary 1, $\angle C'CB = e \angle CC'B$ and $\angle C'CA = e \angle CC'A$. Theorem 3 completes the proof.

Corollary 3. *If* $\triangle ABC$ *and* $\triangle A'B'C'$ *are such that* $\angle BAC = e \angle B'A'C'$, $(e = \pm 1)$, $d(A, B) = d(A, C)$ *and* $d(A', B') = d(A', C')$, *then the triangles are similar.*

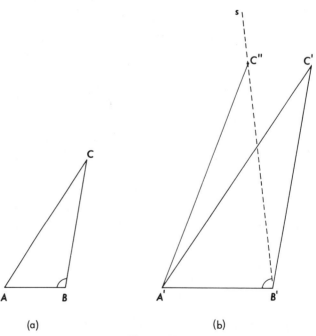

(a)   (b)

Figure 2.13

We leave the proof as an exercise for the reader.

Theorem 4. *If △ABC and △A'B'C' satisfy the conditions $d(C, A) = kd(C', A'), d(A, B) = kd(A', B')$ and $d(B, C) = kd(B', C')$ where $k > 0$, then they are similar.*

PROOF. By Axiom $\mathbf{A}_1$ there is a Ray s from B' which makes an angle with Ray $B'A'$ equal in measure to $e \angle ABC$ (see Figure 2.13). If s coincides with Ray $B'C'$ we are finished, (Axiom **S**). Otherwise, choose a point C'' on s such that $d(B', C'') = d(B', C') = kd(B, C)$. Again by Axiom **S**, $\triangle A'C''B'$ and $\triangle ACB$ are similar. Therefore $d(A, C) = kd(A', C'')$ and by Corollary 2, $\angle A'C''B' = e \angle A'C'B'$. This implies $\angle ACB = e \angle A'C'B'$. Thus $\triangle ABC$ and $\triangle A'B'C'$ are similar.

Theorem 5. *The sum of the absolute values of the measures of the three angles of a triangle is equal to the measure of a straight angle (or π rad.).*

PROOF. Consider the triangle $\triangle ABC$ of Figure 2.14. Choose A', B', C' on $I(A, C), I(A, B)$, and $I(C, B)$ respectively such that $d(A, A') = \frac{1}{2}d(A, C), d(B, B') = \frac{1}{2}d(B, A)$, and $d(C, C') = \frac{1}{2}d(C, B)$. Such points A', B', C' exist by Axiom $\mathbf{R}_1$. Now $\angle CBA = \angle C'BB'$. Thus by Axiom **S**, $\triangle ABC$ and $\triangle B'BC'$ are similar. Thus $d(B', C') = \frac{1}{2}d(A, C)$, and

$$|\angle BAC| = |\angle BB'C'|. \tag{1}$$

In the same manner we can show that $\triangle AB'A'$ is similar to $\triangle ABC$ and hence

$$|\angle CBA| = |\angle A'B'A|. \tag{2}$$

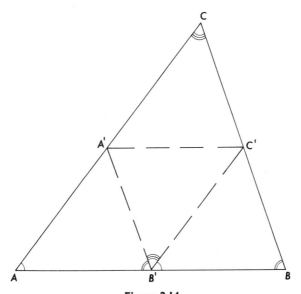

Figure 2.14

Furthermore, since $\triangle A'C'C$ is also similar to $\triangle ABC$ we see that $\triangle A'B'C'$ and $\triangle ABC$ are also similar. Thus

$$|\angle ACB| = |\angle C'B'A'|. \tag{3}$$

Adding equations (1), (2), and (3) we obtain the desired result.

Corollary 1. *Given $\triangle ABC$. Let D be a point on the Ray AC such that $\langle A, C, D \rangle$. Then $|\angle DCB| > |\angle CBA|$ and $|\angle DCB| > |\angle CAB|$.*

The proof is left to the reader.

Corollary 2. *Given $\triangle ABC$. If $d(A, B) > d(A, C)$, then $|\angle ACB| > |\angle ABC|$. (That is, the angle opposite the larger side has a larger measure than the angle opposite the smaller side.)*

PROOF. [*Hint:* Let D be a point on Ray AC such that $d(A, D) = d(A, B)$. Then $\langle A, C, D \rangle$. Why? Now use Corollary 1 of Theorem 3, Axiom **CA** and Corollary 1 above.]

Corollary 3. *Given $\triangle ABC$. If $|\angle ABC| < |\angle ACB|$, then $d(A, C) < d(A, B)$.*

PROOF. [*Hint:* Show that $d(A, C) = d(A, B)$ and $d(A, B) < d(A, C)$ are impossible. Use Corollary 1 of Theorem 3 and Corollary 2 above.]

Corollary 4. *Given $\triangle AOB$ and $d(O, A) = d(O, B)$. Let A' and B' be points on Ray OA and Ray OB such that $\langle O, A, A' \rangle$ and $\langle O, B, B' \rangle$. Then $d(A', B') > d(A, B)$.*

PROOF. Let $d(O, A') < d(O, B')$. Let P be a point on Ray BB' such that $d(B, P) = d(A, A')$. Corollary 3 of Theorem 3 in conjunction with the hypothesis $\langle O, A, A' \rangle$, $\langle O, B, B' \rangle$ yields

$$\frac{d(A', P)}{d(A, B)} = \frac{d(O, A')}{d(O, A)} > 1.$$

Hence $d(A', P) > d(A, B)$. Now, since $|\angle OA'P| = |\angle OPA'|$, we see that $|\angle OPA'| < \pi/2$. Therefore $|\angle A'PB'| > \pi/2$ and $|\angle A'BP| < \pi/2$. Therefore by Corollary 3 above, $d(A', B') > d(A', P) > d(A, B)$.

Theorem 6 (*Pythagorean Theorem*). *Let $\triangle ABC$ be a right triangle (that is, one angle, say $[ACB]$, has measure $\pm\pi/2$). Let $d(A, C) = b$, $d(C, B) = a$, $d(A, B) = c$. Then $c^2 = a^2 + b^2$.*

PROOF. In Figure 2.15 let A' be a point on Ray CA such that $d(C, A') = b^2$ and C' a point on Ray AC such that $d(C, C') = a^2$. On Ray CB let B' be a point such that $d(C, B') = ab$. The points A', B', C' exist by Axiom **R₁**.

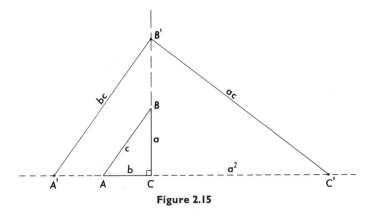

Figure 2.15

Now in the triangles $\triangle ACB$ and $\triangle A'CB'$, $d(C, A') = bd(C, A)$, $d(C, B') = bd(C, B)$ and $\angle BCA = e\angle B'CA$. Therefore the triangles are similar, (Axiom **S**). Hence $d(A', B') = bd(A, B)$. Also, $\triangle ACB$ and $\triangle C'CB$ are similar since $\angle C'CB' = e\angle BCA$, $d(C, C') = ad(C, B)$, $d(C, B') = ad(A, C)$. Hence $d(C', B') = ad(B, A)$.

From Theorem 5 we now infer that $[A'B'C']$ is a right angle and so its measure equals $e\angle BCA$. Since $d(A', B') = bc$ and $d(B', C') = ac$ we infer from Axiom **S** that $d(A', C') = c \cdot c = c^2$. But $d(A', C') = a^2 + b^2$ (see Figure 2.15). Hence our theorem is proved.

Corollary. *Let a, b, c be the sides of $\triangle ABC$. If $a^2 + b^2 = c^2$, then $\triangle ABC$ is a right triangle.*

PROOF. On a line ℓ (see Figure 2.16) choose a point C'. From C' there is, by Axiom $\mathbf{R}_1$, a point A' such that $d(C', A') = b$. By Axiom $\mathbf{A}_2$, there is a ray, Ray $C'P$, such that $\angle A'C'P = -\pi/2$. On Ray $C'P$ there is, by Axiom $\mathbf{R}_1$, a point B' such that $d(C', B') = a$.

In view of Theorem 6, for $\triangle A'B'C'$ we have $[d(A', B')]^2 = a^2 + b^2$. But Theorem 4 implies $\triangle A'B'C'$ is congruent to $\triangle ABC$ (see Figure 2.15). Therefore the corresponding angles have equal measure up to a factor of $e = \pm 1$ (Theorem 4 and Axiom **S**) and the corollary is proved.

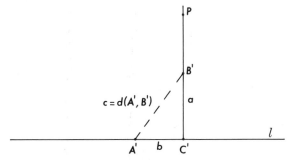

Figure 2.16

We now turn to the problem of setting up a one–one mapping between ordered pairs of real numbers and the points of the Euclidean plane. This can be done as follows:

Choose two distinct points O and P on a line ℓ_x and call $d(O, P)$ the unit distance. We call O the *origin* and P the unit point on ℓ_x. Let Q be any point on the line ℓ_x. Denote by q the ratio $d(O, Q)/d(O, P)$ and assign to Q the coordinates $x(Q) = q$ if $Q \in \text{Ray } OP = r^+$ and $x(Q) = -q$ if $Q \notin \text{Ray } OP$. From Theorem 2 this procedure establishes a one–one mapping of the points of ℓ_x *onto* the real numbers.

Now consider a line ℓ_y through O and *perpendicular* to ℓ_x. In the same way, for some point $S \neq O$ on the line ℓ_y we call the number $d(O, S)$ the unit distance. To the point T on ℓ_y we assign the coordinate $y(T) = t$ [where $t = d(O, T)/d(O, S)$] if $T \in \text{Ray } OS = r^+$ and $y(T) = -t$ if $T \notin \text{Ray } OS$. In conformity with longstanding convention we call r^+ the ray on ℓ_x to the right of the line ℓ_y and call r^- the ray to the left. On ℓ_y we call r^+ the ray above the line ℓ_x, and r^- the ray below ℓ_x.

If Q and Q' are any two points on the line ℓ_x, then by Theorem 2, $d(Q, Q') = |x(Q) - x(Q')|$. Similarly, if T and T' are points on the line ℓ_y, then Theorem 2 also implies $d(T, T') = |y(T) - y(T')|$.

It is not necessary that the unit distances $d(O, P)$ and $d(O, S)$ on lines ℓ_x and ℓ_y be equal. However, for convenience, and with no real loss of generality, we shall assume throughout the remainder of this book that the unit distances *are* equal.

We are now in a position to prove the *fundamental theorem of analytic geometry*. In the proof we shall adopt the convention (which we shall also use throughout the Calculus) of identifying the points on ℓ_x and ℓ_y with the coordinates associated with these points. Since we have already established a one–one correspondence between the points of a line and the real numbers no confusion will arise if we use the coordinate to name the point.

Theorem 7 (*Fundamental Theorem of Analytic Geometry*). *There is a one–one correspondence between all ordered pairs of real numbers and all points of the Euclidean plane.*

PROOF.   Consider any point P belonging to the Euclidean plane. Through P there are lines ℓ_1 and ℓ_2 parallel to the lines ℓ_y and ℓ_x respectively. (See Exercises 8 and 9 at the end of the chapter.) The lines ℓ_1 and ℓ_2 intersect ℓ_x and ℓ_y at the points $x(P)$ and $y(P)$ respectively, see Figure 2.17. So with the point P we shall associate the *ordered pair* of numbers $(x(P), y(P))$ and refer to this ordered pair as the *point P*.

Conversely, if we begin with an ordered pair of numbers $(x(P), y(P))$ and construct from the point $x(P)$ a line parallel to ℓ_y, and through

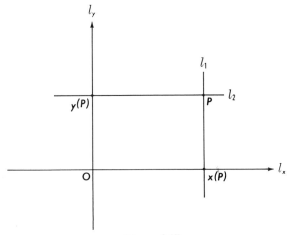

Figure 2.17

the point $y(P)$ a line parallel to ℓ_x—then the lines will intersect at exactly one point in the plane.

If we denote the points P on ℓ_x by $(x(P), 0)$ and those on ℓ_y by $(0, y(P))$, we shall have set up a one–one mapping of all ordered pairs of real numbers onto the points of the Euclidean plane—and our theorem is proved.

3. EQUATIONS OF LINES

Let ℓ_1 be a line parallel to the line ℓ_x (cf. Figure 2.18). It intersects the line ℓ_y on the point $(0, y(P))$. Since, through each of its points, ℓ_1 is the unique parallel to ℓ_x; each point $Q = (x(Q), y(Q))$ on ℓ_1 is such that $y(Q) = y(P)$. Thus $Q = (x(Q), y(P))$ for all points Q on ℓ_1.

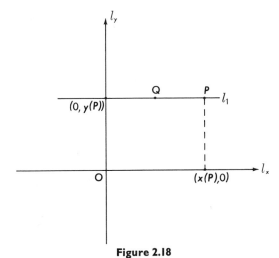

Figure 2.18

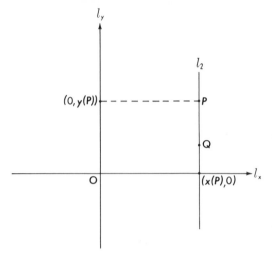

Figure 2.19

Now consider the equation $0x + y = y(P)$. All points $Q = (x(Q), y(P))$ satisfy this equation when x is replaced by $x(Q)$ and y by $y(P)$; that is, all ordered pairs $(x(Q), y(P))$ satisfy this equation. Conversely, every ordered pair $(x(S), y(S))$ which satisfies this equation must have $y(S) = y(P)$.

Thus, any line parallel to ℓ_x and having second coordinate equal to $y(P)$ may be characterized by the equation $0x + 1 \cdot y = y(P)$ [or $y = y(P)$]. We denote such a line by $\lambda(0, 1, y(P))$ (where 0 is the coefficient of x and 1 is the coefficient of y).

Similarly, the points on a line ℓ_2 parallel to ℓ_y (cf. Figure 2.19) and passing through the point $P = (x(P), y(P))$ can be characterized by the equation $1 \cdot x + 0y = x(P)$ [or $x = x(P)$], and such a line will be denoted by $\lambda(1, 0, x(P))$ (where 1 is the coefficient of x and 0 is the coefficient of y).

We now consider a line ℓ that is neither parallel to the line ℓ_y nor the line ℓ_x. Thus if P and Q are distinct points on such a line, $|x(P) - x(Q)|$ and $|y(P) - y(Q)|$ are both different from zero (cf. Figure 2.20). Thus the quantity

$$m = \frac{y(P) - y(Q)}{x(P) - x(Q)} \tag{1}$$

is defined and different from zero. We call the number m the *slope* of ℓ. Clearly m may be greater or less than zero.

Our present task is to show that for the line ℓ the number m is unique. That is to say, if R is a point of ℓ different from the points P and Q, then

$$\frac{y(P) - y(R)}{x(P) - x(R)} = m.$$

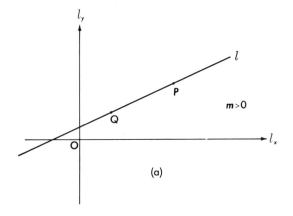

(a)

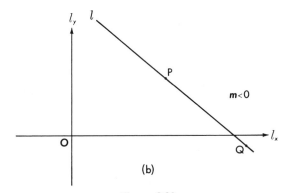

(b)

Figure 2.20

From the Euclidean theorem on similar triangles (cf. Figure 2.21) we have that

$$\frac{|y(P) - y(R)|}{|x(P) - x(R)|} = \frac{|y(P) - y(Q)|}{|x(P) - x(R)|} = |m|.$$

Thus

$$\frac{y(P) - y(R)}{x(P) - x(R)} = \pm m.$$

To prove uniqueness of m, let us assume that

$$\frac{y(P) - y(R)}{x(P) - x(R)} = -m. \tag{2}$$

By the same reasoning as above we note that

$$\frac{y(Q) - y(R)}{x(Q) - x(R)} = \pm m. \tag{3}$$

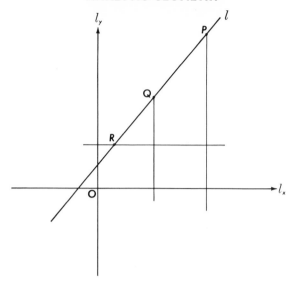

Figure 2.21

We shall prove that by virtue of (1) and both alternatives of (3), that (2) leads to a contradiction.

Case 1.   Assume that in (3) we have $-m$. Then (1), (2), and (3) yield the following equations:

$$y(P) - y(Q) = m[x(P) - x(Q)] \tag{4a}$$

$$y(P) - y(R) = -m[x(P) - x(R)] \tag{4b}$$

$$y(Q) - y(R) = -m[x(Q) - x(R)]. \tag{4c}$$

Subtracting (4c) from (4b) we obtain

$$y(P) - y(Q) = -m[x(P) - x(Q)]$$

—which contradicts (4a).

Case 2.   Assume that in (3) we have m. Then (4c) becomes

$$y(Q) - y(R) = m[x(Q) - x(R)]. \tag{4c'}$$

Adding (4a) and (4c') we obtain

$$y(P) - y(R) = m[x(P) - x(R)]$$

—which contradicts (4b). Thus (2) is false and the assertion that the slope is unique has been proved.

Let us turn our attention to finding the *equation* of a line ℓ which is neither vertical nor horizontal. Let ℓ be a line with nonzero slope m

which passes through a given point P. From the fact that the slope is unique we have

$$\frac{y(P) - y(R)}{x(P) - x(R)} = m \tag{5}$$

for each point R ($\neq P$) on ℓ. Now (5) implies

$$mx(P) - mx(R) = y(P) - y(R)$$

or

$$-mx(R) + y(R) = y(P) - mx(P). \tag{6}$$

Let b be any nonzero number, and let $a = -mb$ and $c = b[y(P) - mx(P)]$. Then we see that $(x(R), y(R))$ must satisfy the equation

$$ax + by = c. \tag{7}$$

[Note that any point that satisfies (7) also satisfies

$$kax + kby = kc \tag{8}$$

for any number k. If $k \neq 0$, then (7) and (8) are the same line.] Conversely, any point R' which is not on ℓ does not satisfy (7). For if R' is not on ℓ, then

$$\frac{y(P) - y(R')}{x(P) - x(R')} = m' \neq m.$$

To prove this last statement we note that the angle which the line through P and R' makes with $\lambda(0, 1, y(P))$ is different from the angle that the line through P and R makes with $\lambda(0, 1, y(P))$ (see Figure 2.22). Hence the triangles defined by the points $(x(P), y(P))$;

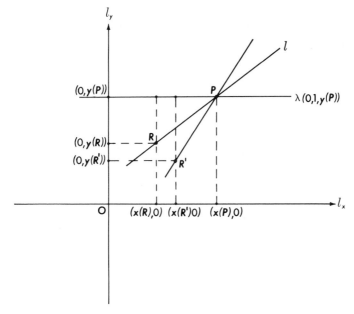

Figure 2.22

$(x(R),y(P))$; $(x(R),y(R))$ and $(x(P),y(P))$; $(x(R'),y(P))$; $(x(R'),y(R'))$ are not similar and

$$\frac{y(P) - y(R)}{x(P) - x(R)} \neq \frac{y(P) - y(R')}{x(P) - x(R')}.$$

Consequently, the coordinates $(x(R'), y(R'))$ cannot satisfy (7).

Our discussion leads to the following conclusion: The line with slope $m \neq 0$ passing through the point P is characterized by the equation $ax + by = c$ where $-m = a/b$ and $c = b[y(P) - mx(P)]$. We denote such a line by $\lambda(a, b, c)$. In view of this and our conclusions regarding lines parallel to the lines ℓ_x and ℓ_y we can say that equations of the form $ax + by = c$ are equations of lines provided not both a and b are zero. Hence the line $\lambda(a, b, c)$ is well-defined if not both a and b are zero.

4. SOME PROPERTIES OF LINES

In this section we shall consider some of the elementary formulas expressing well known properties of lines and points. We first mention the *distance formula* which states that if P and Q are any two points in the plane, then

$$d(P, Q) = \sqrt{[x(P) - x(Q)]^2 + [y(P) - y(Q)]^2}. \qquad (1)$$

(Cf. Theorem 6 and Figure 2.23.) For example, the distance between the two points $P = (-2, 3)$ and $Q = (-5, -4)$ (cf. Figure 2.24) is

$$d(P, Q) = \sqrt{[-2 - (-5)]^2 + [3 - (-4)]^2}$$
$$= \sqrt{3^2 + 7^2} = \sqrt{58} = 7.62.$$

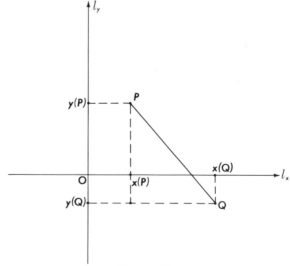

Figure 2.23

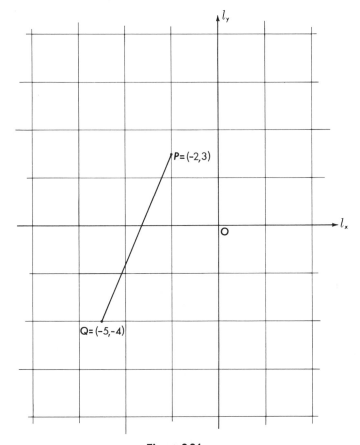

Figure 2.24

The first important result we shall derive is the relation between the *slopes of perpendicular lines.*

Theorem 8.   *Two lines, neither of which is parallel to ℓ_y, are perpendicular if and only if the product of their slopes is -1; that is, one slope is the negative reciprocal of the other.*

(This theorem may be proved by finding the equation of the perpendicular bisector of a given line segment and then comparing the slope of the perpendicular bisector with the slope of the given line. We shall prove the theorem by another more direct method.)

PROOF.   Let $\lambda(m, -1, c)$ and $\lambda(m', -1, c')$ be two mutually perpendicular lines and denote their point of intersection by $P = (x(P), y(P))$. Since P is on both lines we see that (cf. Figure 2.25)

$$c = mx(P) - y(P) \qquad (2)$$

and

$$c' = m'x(P) - y(P). \qquad (3)$$

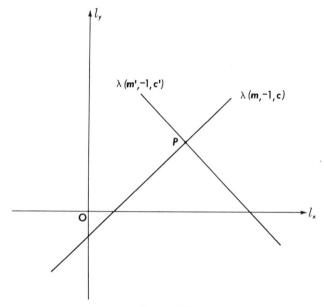

Figure 2.25

Substituting (2) and (3) into the equations of the lines $mx - y = c$ and $m'x - y = c'$ respectively, we obtain

$$mx - y = mx(P) - y(P) \tag{4}$$

and

$$m'x - y = m'x(P) - y(P) \tag{5}$$

Thus it is easily seen from (4) that the point

$$R = (x(P) + 1, y(P) + m)$$

is on $\lambda(m, -1, c)$ and from (5) that the point

$$Q = (x(P) + 1, y(P) + m')$$

is on $\lambda(m', -1, c')$. Since the lines are perpendicular, the Pythagorean Theorem yields

$$d^2(R, Q) = d^2(R, P) + d^2(P, Q) \tag{6}$$

or

$$(m - m')^2 = (1 + m^2) + (1 + m'^2).$$

Simplifying this last expression we obtain $m^2 - 2mm' + m'^2 = 2 + m^2 + m'^2$ or

$$mm' = -1 \tag{7}$$

—as we desired to prove.

The converse can readily be established by starting with the last equality, (7), and working back to the first, (6), which by the Corollary to the Pythagorean Theorem yields the perpendicularity of the two lines.

Our next result will be a formula for calculating the *distance from a point to a line*. We recall that the distance from a point P to a line ℓ is defined as the distance from P to Q where Q is the point of intersection of the perpendicular from P to ℓ. (If ℓ is parallel to ℓ_x or ℓ_y the problem is trivial.) A natural way of doing this is to find the equation of the perpendicular from P to ℓ, then to find the point of intersection, Q, of the two lines, and finally to compute $d(P, Q)$ by using the distance formula (1). This is a tedious process at best. We shall develop, therefore, a formula that yields the desired result more readily.

Let P be a point not on the line $\ell = \lambda(a, b, c)$ (where ℓ is not parallel to x or y) and let Q be the intersection of the perpendicular from P with ℓ (cf. Figure 2.26). Now set

$$s = x(P) - x(Q) \tag{8}$$

and

$$t = y(P) - y(Q). \tag{9}$$

Substituting $x(Q)$ and $y(Q)$ from (8) and (9) into the equation of the line $\ell = \lambda(a, b, c)$ [which is $ax + by = c$] we obtain

$$a[x(P) - s] + b[y(P) - t] - c = 0$$

or

$$as + bt = ax(P) + by(P) - c. \tag{10}$$

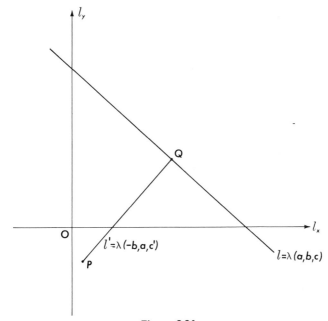

Figure 2.26

The line ℓ' through Q and P is of course perpendicular to ℓ. Hence we may represent it by $\ell' = \lambda(-b, a, c')$ (see Theorem 8). Thus $-bx + ay = c'$ is the equation of ℓ'. Since Q is on ℓ',

$$c' = a\left[y(Q) - \frac{b}{a}x(P)\right] = ay(Q) - bx(Q).$$

Thus, from the equation of ℓ',

$$-bx(P) + ay(P) = -bx(Q) + ay(Q),$$

since P is also on ℓ'. This last equation implies

$$b[x(P) - x(Q)] = a[y(P) - y(Q)]$$

or [cf. (8) and (9)]

$$bs - at = 0. \tag{11}$$

Now square both sides of (10) and (11) and add. We obtain

$$(a^2 + b^2)(s^2 + t^2) = [ax(P) + by(P) - c]^2,$$

or

$$s^2 + t^2 = \frac{[ax(P) + by(P) - c]^2}{a^2 + b^2}.$$

If we recall the definitions of s and t we have

$$[x(P) - x(Q)]^2 + [y(P) + y(Q)]^2 = \frac{[ax(P) + by(P) - c]^2}{a^2 + b^2},$$

and the distance from P to ℓ is

$$d(P, Q) = \frac{|ax(P) + by(P) - c|}{\sqrt{a^2 + b^2}}. \tag{12}$$

For our final result, we derive the formula for computing the *area of a triangle* with given vertices. Consider, then, the triangle $\mathcal{T}$ whose vertices are $P = (x(P), y(P))$, $Q = (x(Q), y(Q))$, $R = (x(R), y(R))$, cf. Figure 2.27. Let us call $I(R, Q)$ the base of $\mathcal{T}$. Then the altitude is given by the distance from P to the line passing through R and Q.

Let the equation of the line passing through Q and R be

$$ax + by = c$$

where we may take

$$a = y(R) - y(Q)$$

$$b = -[x(R) - x(Q)]$$

$$c = -[x(R) - x(Q)]\left[y(Q) - \frac{y(R) - y(Q)}{x(R) - x(Q)}x(Q)\right].$$

(Without loss of generality we may assume that $I(R, Q)$ is neither perpendicular nor parallel to ℓ_x. Why?) Thus by (12) the altitude h, of $\mathscr{T}$ is

$$h = \frac{[y(R) - y(Q)]x(P) - [x(R) - x(Q)]y(P) + [x(R) - x(Q)]y(Q) - [y(R) - y(Q)]x(Q)}{\sqrt{a^2 + b^2}}$$

and by (1) the base, β, of $\mathscr{T}$ is $\sqrt{a^2 + b^2}$. Thus $\mathscr{A}(\mathscr{T})$, the area of $\mathscr{T}$, is given by

$$\begin{aligned}
\mathscr{A}(\mathscr{T}) &= \tfrac{1}{2}\beta h \\
&= \tfrac{1}{2}|[y(R) - y(Q)]x(P) - [x(R) - x(Q)]y(P) \\
&\qquad + [x(R)y(Q) - y(R)x(Q)]|.
\end{aligned} \tag{13}$$

If we recall the definition of *determinant*, we may write $\mathscr{A}(\mathscr{T})$ in a more compact (and easily remembered) form. The square array

$$\delta = \begin{vmatrix} a & b \\ c & d \end{vmatrix}$$

of the four real numbers a, b, c, d is called a two-by-two determinant. Its value is defined to be $ad - bc$. We shall not find it necessary to distinguish between a determinant and the value of a determinant. Thus we shall write

$$\delta = ad - bc.$$

The array

$$\Delta = \begin{vmatrix} a_1 & a_2 & a_3 \\ b_1 & b_2 & b_3 \\ c_1 & c_2 & c_3 \end{vmatrix}$$

is called a three-by-three determinant and its value is defined as

$$\Delta = a_1 \begin{vmatrix} b_2 & b_3 \\ c_2 & c_3 \end{vmatrix} - a_2 \begin{vmatrix} b_1 & b_3 \\ c_1 & c_3 \end{vmatrix} + a_3 \begin{vmatrix} b_1 & b_2 \\ c_1 & c_2 \end{vmatrix}. \tag{14}$$

Each of the three two-by-two determinants that appear in (14) may be further expanded as was δ. Thus

$$\Delta = a_1(b_2c_3 - b_3c_2) - a_2(b_1c_3 - b_3c_1) + a_3(b_1c_2 - b_2c_1).$$

(Inductively one may define *n*-by-*n* determinants. That is, an *n*-by-*n* determinant is a certain sum of n, $(n - 1)$-by-$(n - 1)$ determinants. However we shall have no occasion to use any but two-by-two and three-by-three determinants.)

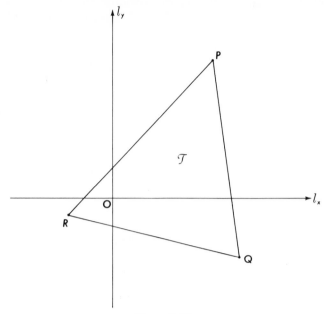

Figure 2.27

Returning to (13) we see that in determinantal notation, the area of triangle $\mathcal{T}$ of Figure 2.27 is precisely one-half the absolute value of the determinant

$$\begin{vmatrix} x(P) & y(P) & 1 \\ x(Q) & y(Q) & 1 \\ x(R) & y(R) & 1 \end{vmatrix}. \tag{15}$$

For an illustration of this formula consider the triangle $\mathcal{T}$ whose vertices are given by $P = (1, 2)$, $Q = (5, 6)$, and $R = (3, 1)$ (see Figure 2.28). Then the area $\mathcal{A}(\mathcal{T})$ of $\mathcal{T}$ is given by

$$\mathcal{A}(\mathcal{T}) = \tfrac{1}{2} \text{ abs. val. of } \begin{vmatrix} 1 & 2 & 1 \\ 5 & 6 & 1 \\ 3 & 1 & 1 \end{vmatrix}$$

$$= \tfrac{1}{2} \text{ abs. val. of } \left[\begin{vmatrix} 6 & 1 \\ 1 & 1 \end{vmatrix} - 2 \begin{vmatrix} 5 & 1 \\ 3 & 1 \end{vmatrix} + \begin{vmatrix} 5 & 6 \\ 3 & 1 \end{vmatrix} \right]$$

$$= \tfrac{1}{2} |(6 - 1) - 2(5 - 3) + (5 - 18)| = \tfrac{1}{2} |-12|$$

$$= \tfrac{12}{2} = 6.$$

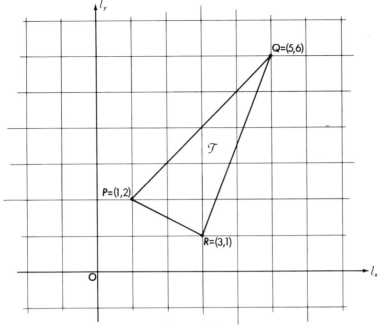

Figure 2.28

5. THE INTERSECTION OF TWO LINES

We now consider the important problem of determining the intersection of two lines. Let $\lambda(a_1, b_1, c_1)$ and $\lambda(a_2, b_2, c_2)$ be two lines whose equations, of course, are

$$a_1x + b_1y = c_1$$

and

$$a_2x + b_2y = c_2$$

respectively. If they intersect at a point P, both equations must be satisfied when x and y are replaced by $x(P)$ and $y(P)$ respectively; that is,

$$a_1x(P) + b_1y(P) = c_1 \tag{1}$$

$$a_2x(P) + b_2y(P) = c_2. \tag{2}$$

Solving these equations in the usual manner for $x(P)$ and $y(P)$ we obtain

$$x(P) = \frac{\begin{vmatrix} c_1 & b_1 \\ c_2 & b_2 \end{vmatrix}}{\begin{vmatrix} a_1 & b_1 \\ a_2 & b_2 \end{vmatrix}} = \frac{c_1b_2 - b_1c_2}{a_1b_2 - a_2b_1} \tag{3}$$

and

$$y(P) = \frac{\begin{vmatrix} a_1 & c_1 \\ a_2 & c_2 \\ a_1 & b_1 \\ a_2 & b_2 \end{vmatrix}} = \frac{c_2 a_1 - c_1 a_2}{a_1 b_2 - a_2 b_1}. \tag{4}$$

We see that if $a_1 b_2 - a_2 b_1 \neq 0$, then (1) and (2) have a common solution and the point P is on both lines. Moreover, it may be shown that (1) and (2) have a unique solution if and only if $a_1 b_2 - a_2 b_1 \neq 0$. Thus we may say: *Two distinct lines intersect if and only if $a_1 b_2 - a_2 b_1 \neq 0$ and their point of intersection $P = (x(P), y(P))$ is given by (3) and (4).*

For example, we find the point of intersection of the lines $\lambda(1, 2, 3)$ and $\lambda(5, -4, 1)$, see Figure 2.29. From (3) and (4)

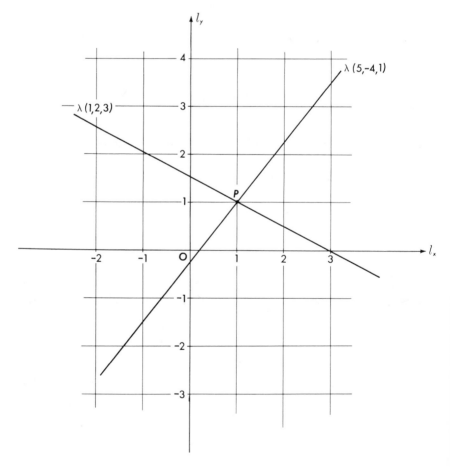

Figure 2.29

$$x(P) = \frac{\begin{vmatrix} 3 & 2 \\ 1 & -4 \end{vmatrix}}{\begin{vmatrix} 1 & 2 \\ 5 & -4 \end{vmatrix}} = \frac{-12 - 2}{-4 - 10} = 1,$$

$$y(P) = \frac{\begin{vmatrix} 1 & 3 \\ 5 & 1 \end{vmatrix}}{-14} = \frac{1 - 15}{-14} = 1.$$

Thus the point

$$P = (1, 1)$$

is on both lines.

It should be recalled that if the number k is unequal to zero and

$$\begin{aligned} a_1 &= ka_2 \\ b_1 &= kb_2 \\ c_1 &= kc_2, \end{aligned} \tag{5}$$

then the lines $\lambda(a_1, b_1, c_1)$ and $\lambda(a_2, b_2, c_2)$ are identical. For if Q is on one of the lines its coordinates will satisfy the equation of the other line. Thus two lines are distinct if and only if at least one of the equalities of (5) does not hold.

In the above analysis and example we assumed $a_1 b_2 - a_2 b_1 \neq 0$. We shall now consider the case where $a_1 b_2 - a_2 b_1$ *is* zero. If $a_1 b_2 - a_2 b_1 = 0$, then we may write

$$\frac{a_1}{b_1} = \frac{a_2}{b_2},$$

if $b_1 \neq 0 \neq b_2$ and thus the two lines $\lambda(a_1, b_1, c_1)$ and $\lambda(a_2, b_2, c_2)$ have the same slope. If $b_1 = 0 = b_2$, then the lines are parallel to the line ℓ_y. The cases $b_1 = 0$ and $b_2 \neq 0$ or $b_1 \neq 0$ and $b_2 = 0$ are impossible. (For if $b_1 = 0$, the equation $a_1 b_2 - a_2 b_1 = 0$ would imply $b_2 = 0$ or $a_1 = 0$. Now if $a_1 = 0$, we would have both a_1 and b_1 equal to zero. That is, the equation of $\lambda(a_1, b_1, c_1)$ would not involve either x or y.)

Now in either of the cases $b_1 \neq 0 \neq b_2$ or $b_1 = 0 = b_2$ we may write

$$\begin{aligned} a_1 &= ka_2 \\ b_1 &= kb_2 \end{aligned} \tag{6}$$

for some $k \neq 0$. (If $c_1 \neq kc_2$, then the two lines $\lambda(a_1, b_1, c_1)$ and $\lambda(a_2, b_2, c_2)$ are distinct and have no point in common.) Thus we conclude that two lines $\lambda(a_1, b_1, c_1)$ and $\lambda(a_2, b_2, c_2)$ are parallel if and only if there is a number k such that (6) holds.

Therefore, to obtain a line through a point P parallel to the line

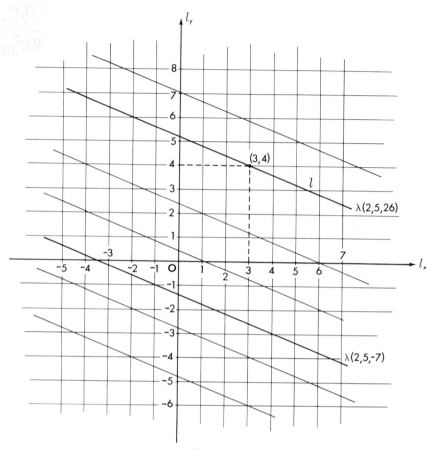

Figure 2.30

$\lambda(a, b, c)$ we need only replace c by $ax(P) + by(P)$ since $\lambda(a, b, ax(P) + by(P))$ is parallel to $\lambda(a, b, c)$.

To illustrate this last comment let us find the equation of the line through the point $(3, 4)$ and parallel to the line $\lambda(2, 5, -7)$, see Figure 2.30. The line we seek belongs to the family of parallel lines $\lambda(2, 5, c)$ where c is an arbitrary real number. Out of this class we pick the line through the point $(3, 4)$ by setting $2(3) + 5(4)$ equal to c. (That is, $ax(P) + by(P) = 2(3) + 5(4) = 26$.) Thus the line ℓ we want is $\lambda(2, 5, 26)$ and its equation is

$$2x + 5y = 26.$$

Appendix

THE LENGTH OF A CIRCULAR ARC

We know what is meant by the length of an interval, say $I(A, B)$. It is simply $d(A, B)$. But what is meant by the length of an arc of a circle? In fact, does such a statement have meaning? The answer is yes. We shall see that with the aid of the completeness axiom, Axiom **C**, we may make a meaningful definition of arc length.

Consider then the points $A = (1, 0)$ and $P = (0, 1)$. These points are on the unit circle C defined by the equation

$$x^2 + y^2 = 1. \tag{1}$$

We define the arc on C from A to P (written $\widehat{AP}$) to be the set of points $\{(x, y)\}$ that satisfy (1) and $0 \leq x \leq 1$. Thus the point $B = (x_n, y_n)$ is on $\widehat{AP}$ if (x_n, y_n) satisfies (1) and $0 \leq x_n \leq 1$. (See Figure 2.31.) If $0 < x_n < 1$, the set $\{(x, y)\}$ that satisfies (1) and $x_n \leq x \leq 1$ is $\widehat{AB}$. Let the sequence of points $A = A_0, A_1 = (x_1, y_1), A_2 = (x_2, y_2), \cdots,$ $A_n = (x_n, y_n) = B$ be on $\widehat{AB}$. We call such a set an *ordered* sequence if $x_0 = 1 > x_1 > x_2 > \cdots > x_n$. If $\{A_i\}$ is an ordered sequence, the union of all the intervals $I(A_{i-1}, A_i)$ and the points A_i, $i = 1, 2, \cdots, n$ is called an open inscribed polygon in $\widehat{AB}$ and its length is given by

$$\rho_n = \sum_{i=1}^{n} d(A_{i-1}, A_i) = d(A_0, A_1) + d(A_1, A_2) + \cdots + d(A_{n-1}, A_n).$$

Let $\mathscr{S} = \{\rho_n\}$ be the set of all real numbers that are lengths of inscribed polygons in $\widehat{AB}$. We define the length of $\widehat{AB}$ to be

$$\rho = \text{l.u.b. } \mathscr{S}.$$

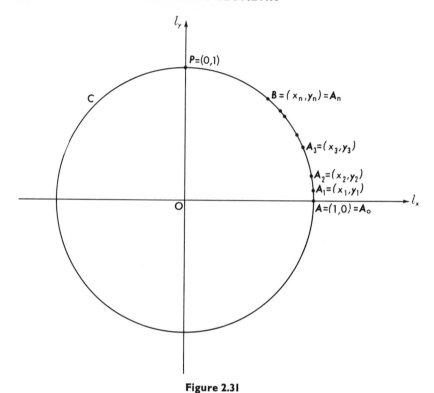

Figure 2.31

This definition will have meaning if we can show that $\mathscr{S}$ has an upper bound. Then, by Axiom **C**, we can conclude that ρ exists.

To this end let ℓ be the perpendicular to the x-axis at the point A and let $\{A_i\}$, $i = 0, 1, \cdots, n$ be an ordered sequence on $\widehat{AB}$. (See Figure 2.32.) Call A_i' the point of intersection of the Ray OA_i [where $O = (0, 0)$] with ℓ. Then $\langle O, A_i, A_i' \rangle$. (Why?) Hence by Axiom **CA**, $\angle OAA_i < \angle OAA_i'$ and by Corollary 3 of Theorem 5, $d(A, A_i) < d(A, A_i')$. From Corollary 4 of Theorem 5 we see that $d(A_i, A_{i+1}) < d(A_i', A_{i+1}')$, $i = 1, 2, \cdots, n - 1$. But on ℓ, $\langle A_{i-1}', A_i', A_{i+1}' \rangle$, $i = 1, 2, \cdots, n - 1$, (why?). Hence

$$d(A, A_i') + \sum_{i=1}^{n-1} d(A_i', A_{i+1}') = d(A, A_n')$$

is an upper bound for $\mathscr{S}$ and we conclude that the set $\mathscr{S} = \{\rho_n\}$ is bounded. Hence $\mathscr{S}$ has a least upper bound, ρ.

In the same way we may show that $\widehat{BP}$ also has length. Now let ℓ' be the perpendicular to the y-axis at P and call Q' the intersection of ℓ and ℓ'. (See Figure 2.33.) It is easily shown that $d(A, Q') + d(Q', P)$ is an upper bound for the open inscribed polygon obtained from any

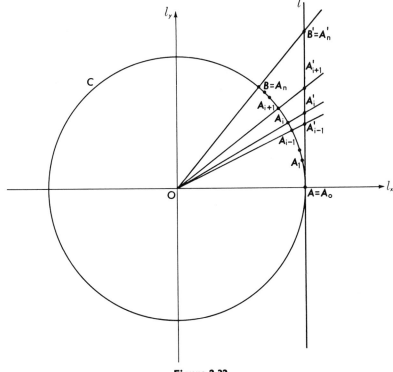

Figure 2.32

ordered sequence $A = A_0, A_1, \cdots, A_n = P$ on $\widehat{AP}$. Thus $\widehat{AP}$ has length and we call it $\rho = \pi/2$.

Next we shall show that if B is on $\widehat{AP}$ and ρ_1 is the length of $\widehat{AB}$ and ρ_2 is the length of $\widehat{BP}$, then

$$\rho = \rho_1 + \rho_2.$$

To see this we shall show first that $\rho > \rho_1 + \rho_2$ is impossible.

Let $A = A_0, A_1, A_2, \cdots, A_n = P$ be an ordered sequence on $\widehat{AP}$. (See Figure 2.34.) If for some k, $0 < k < n$ we have $A_k = B$ then $A = A_0, A_1, \cdots, A_k$ is an ordered sequence on $\widehat{AB}$ and $A_k, A_{k+1}, \cdots, A_n = P$ is an ordered sequence on $\widehat{BP}$. Hence

$$\sum_{i=1}^{n} d(A_{i-1}, A_i) = \sum_{i=1}^{k} d(A_{i-1}, A_i) + \sum_{i=k+1}^{n} d(A_{i-1}, A_i) \leqq \rho_1 + \rho_2.$$

If no such k exists, then B is on some $\widehat{A_{k-1}A_k}$—and the ordered sequence $A = A_0, A_1, \cdots, A_{k-1}, B$ is on $\widehat{AB}$ while the ordered sequence

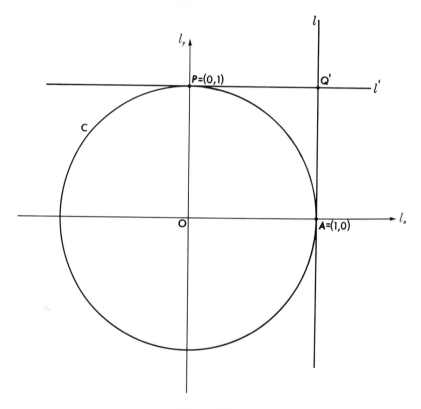

Figure 2.33

$B, A_k, A_{k+1}, \cdots, A_n = P$ is on $\widehat{AP}$. Thus since $d(A_{k-1}, A_k) \leq d(A_{k-1}, B) + d(A_k, B)$,

$$\sum_{i=1}^{n} d(A_{i-1}, A_i) \leq \sum_{i=1}^{k-1} d(A_{i-1}, A_i) + d(A_{k-1}, B) + d(B, A_k) + \sum_{i=k+1}^{n} d(A_{i-1}, A_i)$$

$$\leq \rho_1 + \rho_2.$$

In either case, then, $\sum_{i=1}^{n} d(A_{i-1}, A_i) \leq \rho_1 + \rho_2$ and $\rho_1 + \rho_2$ is an upper bound for the lengths of the open inscribed polygons in $\widehat{AP}$. We conclude that ρ, the length of $\widehat{AP}$, is less than or equal to $\rho_1 + \rho_2$.

We now show that $\rho = \rho_1 + \rho_2$, by assuming $\rho < \rho_1 + \rho_2$ and deriving a contradiction. Accordingly, we set $\rho_1 + \rho_2 - \rho = \varepsilon$ where $\varepsilon > 0$. Let $A = A_0, A_1, \cdots, A_k$ be an ordered sequence on $\widehat{AB}$ such that

$$\sum_{i=1}^{k} d(A_{i-1}, A_i) > \rho_1 - \frac{\varepsilon}{2}. \tag{2}$$

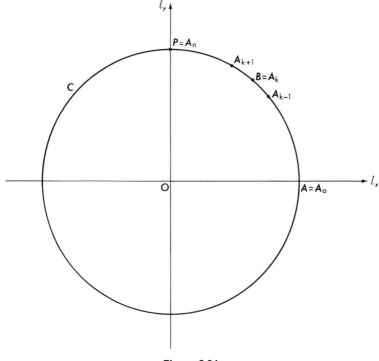

Figure 2.34

Such a sequence exists since ρ_1 is the least upper bound of the lengths of all open inscribed polygons in $\widehat{AB}$. Similarly, let $B = A_k, A_{k+1}, \cdots,$ $A_n = P$ be an ordered sequence on $\widehat{BP}$ such that

$$\sum_{i=k+1}^{n} d(A_{i-1}, A_i) > \rho_2 - \frac{\varepsilon}{2}. \tag{3}$$

We add (2) and (3) and get

$$\sum_{i=1}^{k} d(A_{i-1}, A_i) + \sum_{i=k+1}^{n} d(A_{i-1}, A_i) > \rho_1 + \rho_2 - \varepsilon = \rho. \tag{4}$$

But the left-hand side of (4) is an open inscribed polygon in $\widehat{AP}$. This contradicts the fact that ρ is the least upper bound of all such polygons. Therefore we conclude that

$$\rho = \rho_1 + \rho_2.$$

We note that for each point (x, y) that satisfies (1) and $0 \leq x \leq 1$ there is a corresponding point $(-x, y)$ that also satisfies (1). Thus for

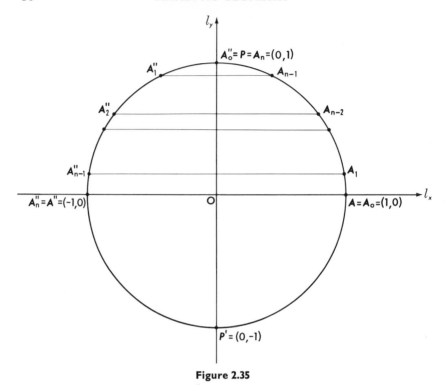

Figure 2.35

each ordered sequence $P = A_0'', A_1'', \cdots, A_n'' = A'' = (-1, 0)$ there is a corresponding sequence $A = A_0, A_1, \cdots, A_n = P$ where if $A_k'' = (-x_k, y_k)$ we have $A_{n-k} = (x_k, y_k)$. (See Figure 2.35.) Thus

$$\sum_{i=1}^{n} d(A_{i-1}'', A_i'') = \sum_{i=1}^{n} d(A_{i-1}, A_i)$$

and the reader may readily obtain that the length of $\widehat{PA''} = \pi/2 =$ the length of $\widehat{AP}$. Analogously $\widehat{A''P'}$ (with $P' = (0, -1)$) and $\widehat{P'A}$ also have length $\pi/2$. Thus the circumference of the unit circle—the union of the four arcs $\widehat{AP}$, $\widehat{PA''}$, $\widehat{A''P'}$, and $\widehat{P'A}$ has length 2π.

We recapitulate by relating angular measure and arc length.

One can show that there is a simple method for assigning to an angle $[AOB]$ a measure $\angle AOB$, where $0 \le \angle AOB < 2\pi$, such that the Axioms $\mathbf{A}_1 - \mathbf{A}_4$ are satisfied (where addition is performed modulo 2π). Indeed:

Let $A = (x(A), y(A))$ and $B = (x(B), y(B))$ be two points on the unit circle with center at $O = (0, 0)$. A and B may be in any one of $8 \times 8 = 64$ relative positions (A on the positive x-axis, positive y-axis, negative x-axis, negative y-axis, first, second, third, or fourth quadrant, B on the positive x-axis, positive y-axis, negative x-axis, negative y-axis, first, second, third, or fourth quadrant).

For each of the 64 relative positions of A and B we may now define an arc $\widehat{AB}$ on the unit circle with center at $O = (0, 0)$ that corresponds to the intuitive notion of "counterclockwise rotation from A to B." For example, if A is in the third quadrant and B is on the positive y-axis, the arc in question is

$$\widehat{AB} = \{(x, y) \,|\, x^2 + y^2 = 1, x(A) \leq x \leq 1, y \leq 0\}$$
$$\cup \{(x, y) \,|\, x^2 + y^2 = 1, 0 \leq x \leq 1, y \geq 0\}.$$

The measure of $[AOB]$ may now be shown to be

$$\angle AOB = \text{length of } \widehat{AB}.$$

The proof depends on the additive properties of arc length (e.g., $\rho = \rho_1 + \rho_2$).

In conclusion we note that the number π is defined to be twice the length of the arc $\{(x, y) \,|\, x^2 + y^2 = 1, 0 \leq x, y \leq 1\}$.

EXERCISES

1. Prove that $\langle A, B, C \rangle$ implies $\langle C, B, A \rangle$.

2. Prove that $\langle A, B, C \rangle$ implies not $\langle A, C, B \rangle$ and not $\langle C, A, B \rangle$.

3. In the proof of Theorem 1 we make the following statement, "$\cdots$ one of the three numbers $a + d(O, B)$, $a + d(O, B)$ and $2a$ must be the sum of the other two." Justify this statement.

4. Let $\triangle ABC$ be a right triangle with $\angle ACB = \pi/2$ and $\angle ABC = \pi/3$. Prove that $d(B, C) = \frac{1}{2}d(B, A)$. [*Hint:* On Ray BC choose a point D such that $d(B, D) = 2d(B, C)$ and then show that $d(A, D) = d(B, A)$.]

5. Let $\triangle ABC$ be as above. Determine $d(A, C)/d(B, A)$.

6. If $\triangle ABC$ is a right triangle with $\angle ACB = \pi/2$ and $\angle ABC = \pi/4$, prove that $d(A, C) = d(B, C) = d(B, A)/\sqrt{2}$.

7. Prove that through a point P not on a line ℓ, there is exactly one perpendicular from P to ℓ.

8. Prove that through a point P not on a line ℓ, there is at least one line ℓ' not intersecting ℓ.

9. Prove that through a point P not on a line ℓ, there is at most one line not intersecting ℓ.

10. We define a *circle* with center P to be a set of points equidistant from P. If $r = d(P, R)$ where $R = (x, y)$ is any point on some circle, prove that the points on the circle must satisfy the equation

$$(x - x(P))^2 + (y - y(P))^2 = r^2.$$

11. A *parabola* is defined as a set of points each of which is equidistant from a fixed line (the *directrix*) and a fixed point (the *focus*) not on the directrix. If the fixed line is $\lambda(1, 0, -p)$ and the fixed point is $(p, 0)$, show that the points of the parabola must satisfy the equation

$$y^2 = 4px.$$

12. An *ellipse* is defined as a set of points such that the sum of the distances of each point of the set from two fixed points (the *foci*) is the same. If the two fixed points are $(-c, 0)$ and $(c, 0)$, show that each point of the ellipse satisfies the equation

$$\frac{x^2}{a^2} + \frac{y^2}{b^2} = 1$$

where $2a$ is the sum of the distances mentioned in the definition and $b^2 = a^2 - c^2$.

13. A *hyperbola* is a set of points such that the absolute value of the difference between the distances of each point of the set from two fixed points (the *foci*) is the same. If the foci are $(-c, 0)$ and $(c, 0)$, show that each point on the hyperbola satisfies the equation

$$\frac{x^2}{a^2} - \frac{y^2}{b^2} = 1$$

where $2a$ is the absolute value of the differences mentioned in the definition and $b^2 = c^2 - a^2$.

14. Find the slopes and write the equations of the lines passing through the following pairs of points:

    (i) $(-2, 6)$, $(-2, -3)$
    (ii) $(6, -2)$, $(-3, -2)$
   (iii) $(3, -1)$, $(4, 2)$
   (iv) $(2, -6)$, $(5, 8)$
    (v) $(-5, 2)$, $(7, 1)$.

15. Find the distance between the pairs of points given in Exercise 14.

16. Find the line through P which is perpendicular to the line ℓ for each of the following cases:

    (i) $P = (3, 4)$, $\ell = \lambda(3, 1, 6)$
    (ii) $P = (-5, 6)$, $\ell = \lambda(-5, 8, 1)$
   (iii) $P = (7, 8)$, $\ell = \lambda(1, 2, 3)$
   (iv) $P = (2, 3)$, $\ell = \lambda(-2, -4, 6)$
    (v) $P = (2, 2)$, $\ell = \lambda(1, 1, 4)$.

17. In Exercise 16, find the line through P which is parallel to the line ℓ.

18. Find the points of intersection of the following pairs of lines:

    (i) $\lambda(1, 2, 3)$ and $\lambda(5, 6, 7)$
    (ii) $\lambda(5, -2, 1)$ and $\lambda(2, 5, 6)$

(iii) $\lambda(-3, 6, 8)$ and $\lambda(4, 1, 5)$
(iv) $\lambda(-2, 3, 1)$ and $\lambda(4, -6, -2)$
(v) $\lambda(1, 2, -3)$ and $\lambda(2, 4, -7)$.

19. Do the points of Exercise 16 (i), (ii), (iii) define a triangle? If so:

(i) Find the area of the triangle.
(ii) Find the lengths of the sides of the triangle.
(iii) Find the equation of the perpendicular bisector of each side.
(iv) Show that the perpendicular bisectors intersect on a common point.
(v) What is the common point of intersection of the medians of the sides of the triangle?

20. Show that the two lines $\lambda(a_1, b_1, c_1)$ and $\lambda(a_2, b_2, c_2)$ intersect on a unique point if and only if $a_1 b_2 - a_2 b_1 \neq 0$.
21. Find the points of intersection of the line $\lambda(a, 1, 0)$ and the circle whose equation is $x^2 + y^2 = 1$.
22. For what values of k will $\lambda(1, -1, k)$ be tangent to the circle whose equation is $x^2 + y^2 = 1$?
23. Sometimes an equation may be simplified by translating from

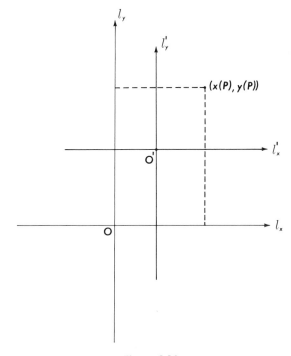

Figure 2.36

one set of coordinate axes to another. Consider a line ℓ'_y parallel to ℓ_y and a line ℓ'_x parallel to ℓ_x (see Figure 2.36). Call $O' = (h, k)$ their point of intersection. Now if we label the points on ℓ'_x and ℓ'_y as $(x(P)', 0')$ and $(0', y(P)')$ respectively and set $O' = (h, k) = (0', 0')$, then any point $(x(P), y(P))$ may be renamed relative to the ℓ'_x, ℓ'_y axes as follows:

$$x(P) = x(P)' + h \qquad x(P)' = x(P) - h$$

or

$$y(P) = y(P)' + k \qquad y(P)' = y(P) - k.$$

For an example consider the equation

$$x^2 + y^2 + 4x + 6y = 0.$$

If we let $O' = (-2, -3)$, (the intersection of ℓ'_x and ℓ'_y), then setting $x = x' - 2$ and $y = y' - 3$ we obtain

$$(x' - 2)^2 + (y' - 3)^2 + 4(x' - 2) + 6(y' - 3) = 0,$$

whereupon

$$x'^2 + y'^2 = 13.$$

Thus we see that $x^2 + y^2 + 4x + 6y = 0$ is the equation of a circle with radius $\sqrt{13}$ and center at $(-2, -3)$.

For the following equations find h and k so that the substitution $x' = x - h$ and $y' = y - k$ will reduce the equation to the form

$$\frac{x'^2}{a^2} \pm \frac{y'^2}{b^2} = 1.$$

(i) $x^2 + y^2 - 4x - 4y - 1 = 0$
(ii) $16x^2 + 81y^2 - 48x + 72y - 72 = 0$
(iii) $2x^2 - 2y^2 + 4x - 8y = 20$
(iv) $5x^2 - 10y^2 - 5y = 75$
(v) $7x^2 + 7y^2 - 14x = 0.$

24. The equation of the circle with center at (h, k) and radius r is given by

$$(x - h)^2 + (y - k)^2 = r^2.$$

Expanding this equation we obtain

$$x^2 + y^2 - 2hx - 2ky + h^2 + k^2 - r^2 = 0,$$

and multiplying by $A \neq 0$, it becomes

$$Ax^2 + Ay^2 + 2Bx + 2Cy + D = 0$$

where

$$h = -B/A$$
$$k = -C/A$$
$$h^2 + k^2 - r^2 = D/A.$$

Show that this last equation is either the equation of a circle, or that it is satisfied by only one point. [*Hint:* $r^2 = (B^2 + C^2 - AD)/A^2.$] What are the implications of $r^2 < 0$?

25.   Find the equation of the line with negative slope through the point $(5, 0)$ that is tangent to the circle having its center at $(0, 0)$ and radius equal to 2.

26.   Find the equation of a circle that is tangent to ℓ_x and ℓ_y and whose center is on the line $\lambda(3, -5, -16)$.

27.   The line containing the focus of a parabola and perpendicular to the directrix is called the *axis* of the parabola.

  (i) Find the equation of the parabola whose focus is at $(0, 0)$ and whose axis is ℓ_x.
 (ii) Find the equation of the parabola whose focus is $(0, 0)$ and whose axis is ℓ_y.

28.   The vertex of a conic section is the point on the conic "nearest" the directrix, (nearest in the sense of smallest distance). If the vertex of a parabola is $(2, 3)$ and its focus is $(2, 5)$, find its equation.

29.   The ellipse, parabola and hyperbola have the common characteristic of being the set of all points such that the distance from a fixed point (the focus) is a constant (the *eccentricity*) times the distance from a fixed line (the directrix). If the directrix is perpendicular to ℓ_x and the focus is on ℓ_x show that:

  (i) If the eccentricity $e = 1$, the equation is that of a parabola.
 (ii) If $e < 1$, the equation is that of an ellipse.
(iii) If $e > 1$, the equation is that of an hyperbola.

30.   (i) Show that if the circle whose equation is $(x - h)^2 + (y - k)^2 = r^2$ is to be tangent to the line $\lambda(a, b, c)$ then h, k, and r must satisfy the equation

$$\frac{ah + bk - c}{\sqrt{a^2 + b^2}} = \pm r.$$

(ii) Find the radius of the circle with center at $(1, 3)$ and tangent to the line $\lambda(4, 3, -2)$.

(iii) What condition must be satisfied by h and k if the center of the circle given in (i) is to lie on line $\lambda(\alpha, \beta, \gamma)$?

3

FUNCTIONS

One of the most important concepts in mathematics is that of "function." When a correspondence is defined between the elements of a set A and those of a set B so that to each element of A there corresponds a unique element of B, then we say a *function* is defined from A to B. This *correspondence* or *mapping* of A into B yields a collection or class of ordered pairs $\{(a, b)\}$ with $a \in A$ and $b \in B$. To avoid ambiguity we insist that to each element of A one and only one element of B is paired.

The concept of function has important applications in many fields other than mathematics and physics. Economists, for example, speak of a "demand function" that sets up a correspondence between the prices of a commodity and the collective demand for the same. Thus, if the collective demand for a commodity C is 100 units or less, the entrepreneur sets a price of, say $5 per unit, for C. If the demand is between 100 and 200 units he will ask $4 per unit; and if the demand is for more than 200 units, the asking price is $3 per unit. The entrepreneur has set up a correspondence between the set $A = N$ (units) and the set $B = \{5, 4, 3\}$ (dollars).

Since, in this book we shall be concerned only with functions where A and B are sets of real numbers, we make the following definition:

Definition. *A* **function** *is a set of ordered pairs of real numbers such that no two distinct pairs have equal first members. The set of first numbers is called the* **domain** *of the function, the set of second numbers is called the* **range** *or* **image** *of the function.*

Thus the set of ordered pairs $f = \{(1, 3), (4, 6), (7, 8), (9, 11)\}$ is a function. Its domain, Dom f, is the set $\{1, 4, 7, 9\}$ while its range,

Ran f, is $\{3, 6, 8, 11\}$. The set $\{(1, 3), (4, 6), (7, 8), (9, 11), (7, 9)\}$ is *not* a function since the distinct pairs $(7, 8)$ and $(7, 9)$ have the same first number.

When the function contains infinitely many ordered pairs, we cannot list them as in the above example. In this case we give a rule of correspondence. We say, for example, that f is a function whose rule of correspondence is (say) $f(x) = x^2 - 2x$, for all x such that $0 \leq x \leq 1$. By this we mean

$$f = \{(x, f(x)\}$$

or, more explicitly,

$$f = \{(x, x^2 - 2x)\}$$

and Dom f is the set of all numbers greater than or equal to zero and less than or equal to 1. If the rule of correspondence is given without specifying the domain, it is tacitly understood that the domain is the set of all real numbers for which $f(x)$ is also a real number. Thus, if the rule of correspondence $f(x) = \sqrt{x^2 - 1}$ is given, we understand that the domain is the set of all real numbers x such that $|x| \geq 1$. If the rule of correspondence

$$g(x) = \frac{x^2 - 1}{x + 1}$$

is given, we understand that the domain of g is the set of all real numbers x such that $x \neq -1$.

I. SOME SPECIAL FUNCTIONS

Here we shall define some special functions, which because of their frequent occurrence in mathematics, have been given special names.

(1) The *absolute value function*, denoted by $|\ \ |$, is the function whose rule of correspondence is

$$|x| = \begin{cases} x & \text{if } x \geq 0 \\ -x & \text{if } x < 0. \end{cases}$$

The domain of $|\ \ |$ is the set of all real numbers.

(2) The *square root function*, denoted by $\sqrt{\ \ }$ or $(\ )^{1/2}$, is the function whose domain is the set of all nonnegative real numbers and whose rule of correspondence is

$$\sqrt{x} = \text{the nonnegative real number whose square is } x.$$

(3) The *greatest integer function*, denoted by $[\ \ ]$, is the function whose domain is the set of all real numbers and whose rule of correspondence is

$$[x] = \text{the greatest integer not greater than } x.$$

For example, $[3] = 3, [3.2] = 3, [3.6] = 3, [-2.6] = -3, [\sqrt{5}] = 2.$

(4) Oddly enough, as Menger has pointed out, in spite of its importance in mathematics, the *identity function*, that is, the function that associates with each real number x the number x, has no traditional symbol. For the sake of clarity, we shall in this book, denote this function by the symbol j. Thus the identity function j has for its domain the set of all real numbers and the rule of correspondence is

$$j(x) = x.$$

The nth *power function* which associates with each real number x the number x^n (where n is a positive integer, that is $n \in N$) will be denoted by j^n. Thus

$$j^n(x) = x^n.$$

(5) The *constant function*, herein denoted by the symbol **k**, is the function that associates with each real number the number k. Thus

$$\mathbf{k} = \{(x, k)\} \tag{1}$$

for all real numbers x. To distinguish between the different constant *functions* we shall use bold face letters as above. Thus, for example,

$$\mathbf{1} = \{(x, 1)\}, \quad \text{for all } x,$$
$$\mathbf{2} = \{(x, 2)\}, \quad \text{for all } x,$$

and in general we have equation (1) for each real number k. The zero function, that is $\{(x, 0)\}$, will be denoted by **0**.

(6) The *signum function*, denoted by sgn, is the function whose domain is the set of all real numbers and whose rule of correspondence is

$$\operatorname{sgn} x = +1 \quad \text{for} \quad x > 0$$
$$\operatorname{sgn} x = 0 \quad \text{for} \quad x = 0$$
$$\operatorname{sgn} x = -1 \quad \text{for} \quad x < 0.$$

The range of sgn consists of the three distinct numbers $+1, 0, -1$.

2. GRAPHS OF FUNCTIONS

Having defined functions in terms of ordered pairs of real numbers and having previously proved (Theorem 7 of Chapter 2) that there is a one–one correspondence between all ordered pairs of real numbers and the points of the Euclidean plane, we infer that functions may also be regarded as *sets of points*. We define the graph of a function as follows:

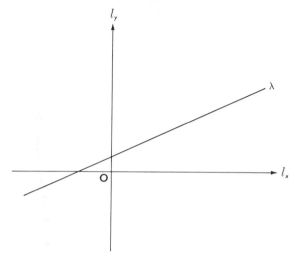

Figure 3.1

Definition. *The* **graph** *of a function f is the set of ordered pairs of f considered as points in the Euclidean plane.*

A *nonvertical line* $\lambda(a, b, c)$ may be considered as the graph of the function

$$f = \left\{ \left(x, \frac{c - ax}{b} \right) \right\},$$

(see Figure 3.1). A *parabola* whose equation is $y = 4px^2$ is the graph of the function

$$g = \{(x, 4px^2)\}$$

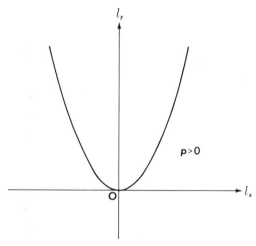

Figure 3.2

(see Figure 3.2). (The domains of f and g are both the set of all real numbers x; the range of f is again the set of all real numbers; but the range of g is only the set of nonnegative numbers.)

A *circle*, on the other hand, is not the graph of a function since if the point $(x(P), y(P))$ is on the circle, then so is the point $(x(P), -y(P))$, and if $y(P) \neq 0$, then $y(P) \neq -y(P)$. We may, however, consider a circle as the union of the graphs of the two functions

$$f = \{(x, \sqrt{r^2 - (x - x_1)^2} + y_1)\}$$

and

$$g = \{(x, -\sqrt{r^2 - (x - x_1)^2} + y_1)\}$$

(see Figure 3.3). The domain of f and g is all real numbers x such that $r^2 - (x - x_1)^2 \geq 0$. The center of the circle is the point (x_1, y_1) and its radius is r (see Figure 3.3).

We leave the analysis of the ellipse and hyperbola as exercises for the reader.

In the above brief list of special functions the trigonometric, exponential and logarithmic functions were conspicuous by their absence. The logarithmic and exponential functions will be treated in great detail in Chapter 7. Here we shall define the trigonometric functions.

Consider the graph of the circle with center at $O = (0, 0)$ and radius 1 (see Figure 3.4). The equation of this circle is $x^2 + y^2 = 1$ (cf. Exercise 10 of Chapter 2). We see that the points $P = (1, 0)$, $Q = (0, 1)$, $R = (-1, 0)$ and $S = (0, -1)$ are all on the circle. Let T be any other point on the circle. Then $\angle POT = \theta$ (rad.), say, with $0 \leq \theta < 2\pi$. On the other hand for any real number θ, $0 \leq \theta < 2\pi$, there is a ray, say Ray OU, such that $\angle POU = \theta$ (rad.) and Ray OU

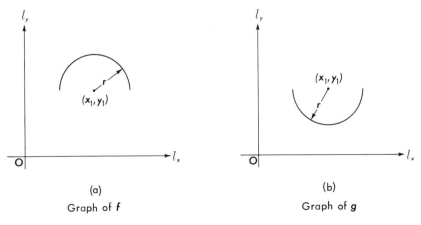

(a)

Graph of **f**

(b)

Graph of **g**

Figure 3.3

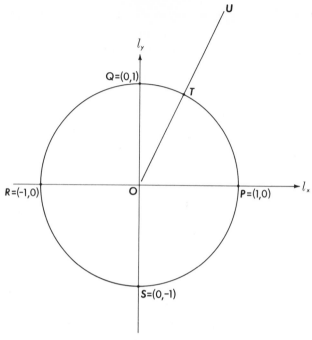

Figure 3.4

will intersect the circle on a unique point T. Thus we can set up a correspondence between the points T on the circle and the real numbers θ, $0 \leq \theta < 2\pi$. We may therefore define the functions cosine (cos) and sine (sin) as follows:

$$\cos = \{(\theta, \cos\theta \equiv x(T))\}$$

and

$$\sin = \{(\theta, \sin\theta \equiv y(T))\}$$

where tentatively Dom sin and Dom cos are all θ such that $0 \leq \theta < 2\pi$ and Ran sin, Ran cos is the interval between -1 and $+1$ inclusive.

From these definitions we see that

$$\sin 0 = 0, \qquad \cos 0 = 1$$

$$\sin \frac{\pi}{2} = 1, \qquad \cos \frac{\pi}{2} = 0$$

$$\sin \pi = 0, \qquad \cos \pi = -1$$

$$\sin \frac{3\pi}{2} = -1, \qquad \cos \frac{3\pi}{2} = 0.$$

Recalling Axiom $\mathbf{A}_2$, we see that to any real number Θ there corresponds a ray, say Ray OW, such that $\angle POW = \theta$ (rad.), $0 \leq \theta < 2\pi$, and $\Theta = \theta + 2n\pi$, $n \in I$. Thus any real number Θ will define the same point T (the intersection of Ray OW with the unit circle) as $\theta = \angle POW = \Theta - 2n\pi$. In view of this fact we *extend* the domain of the functions cos and sin so as to include all the real numbers. Consequently,

$$\cos \Theta = \cos (\theta + 2n\pi) = \cos \theta$$

and

$$\sin \Theta = \sin (\theta + 2n\pi) = \sin \theta$$

where $\Theta \in R$, $\theta = \Theta - 2n\pi$, $0 \leq \theta < 2\pi$, and $n \in I$.

We define the remaining four trigonometric functions tangent (tan), cotangent (cot), secant (sec), and cosecant (csc) in terms of cos and sin. To wit:

$$\tan = \frac{\sin}{\cos}, \quad \sec = \frac{1}{\cos}, \quad \theta \in R \text{ and } \theta \neq \frac{(2n + 1)\pi}{2}, \quad n \in I$$

while

$$\cot = \frac{\cos}{\sin}, \quad \csc = \frac{1}{\sin}, \quad \theta \in R \text{ and } \theta \neq n\pi, \quad n \in I.$$

The following identities result from the definitions:

$$(\sin \theta)^2 + (\cos \theta)^2 = 1, \quad \theta \in R$$

$$(\tan \theta)^2 + 1 = (\sec \theta)^2, \quad \theta \in R \text{ and } \theta \neq \frac{(2n + 1)\pi}{2}, \quad n \in I.$$

Other identities involving the trigonometric functions will be left as exercises for the reader.

3. THE ALGEBRA OF FUNCTIONS

We define operations on functions just as we do on numbers. There are, however, three basic operations for functions: addition, multiplication, and composition or substitution. For this reason the algebra of functions has been called by Menger a *tri-operational algebra*, [4, 5].

Before defining these operations we must say when two functions are equal. One might be tempted to say that two functions are equal if they have the same domain and the same range. Giving a little thought to the matter, one readily sees that this is not a satisfactory definition. For example, both the sine and cosine functions have the same domain—the set of all real numbers—and the same range—the set of all real numbers between -1 and $+1$ inclusive. Yet no one would say that the sine and cosine are the same function. Similarly, all non-vertical and nonhorizontal lines have the same domain and the same range—in each case, the set of all real numbers.

We shall say that two functions f and g are *equal* if $\text{Dom} f = \text{Dom} g$ and if for each x belonging to their common domain $f(x) = g(x)$. It may happen, and it often does, that f and g do not have the same domain, but that $f(x) = g(x)$ for $x \in (\text{Dom} f) \cap (\text{Dom} g)$. In this case we shall say $f = g$ on $(\text{Dom} f) \cap (\text{Dom} g)$. It may also happen that $\text{Dom} f = \text{Dom} g$ and that $f(x) = g(x)$ on a restricted set S belonging to these domains. In this case we shall say $f = g$ on $S \subset \text{Dom} f (= \text{Dom} g)$. To illustrate, consider the following examples:

Example 1. *Let*

$$f = \begin{cases} 1 & \text{for} \quad -1 \le x \le 1 \\ j & \text{for} \quad 1 < x \end{cases}$$

and let

$$g = j \quad \text{for} \quad x \ge 1$$

(see Figure 3.5). *Then* $f = g$ *on* $(\text{Dom} f) \cap (\text{Dom} g)$, *that is for all* $x \ge 1$.

Example 2. *Let*

$$f = 1 \quad \text{for} \quad -1 \le x \le 1$$

and let

$$g = \begin{cases} 1 & \text{for} \quad -1 \le x < 0 \\ 2 & \text{for} \quad 0 \le x \le 1 \end{cases}$$

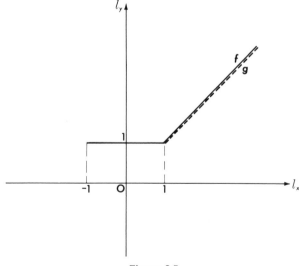

Figure 3.5

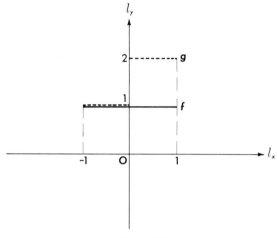

Figure 3.6

(see Figure 3.6). *Then $f = g$ on the set $S \subset \mathrm{Dom}\,f$ ($= \mathrm{Dom}\,g$) of all x such that $-1 \leqq x \leqq 0$.*

4. ADDITION AND MULTIPLICATION

We lay down the following definitions of addition and multiplication of functions.

Definition. *Let f and g be functions with domains $\mathrm{Dom}\,f$ and $\mathrm{Dom}\,g$ respectively. Then $f + g$ and fg are functions with domain $(\mathrm{Dom}\,f) \cap (\mathrm{Dom}\,g)$ and rules of correspondence*

$$(f + g)(x) = f(x) + g(x)$$
$$(fg)(x) = f(x)g(x).$$

In other words, the value of $f + g$ at x is the sum of the values of f and g at x (see Figure 3.7), and the value of fg at x (see Figure 3.8), is the product of the values of f and g at x. Thus

$$f + g = \{(x, f(x) + g(x))\} \quad \text{for} \quad x \in (\mathrm{Dom}\,f) \cap (\mathrm{Dom}\,g)$$

and

$$fg = \{(x, f(x)g(x))\} \qquad \text{for} \quad x \in (\mathrm{Dom}\,f) \cap (\mathrm{Dom}\,g).$$

For a simple numerical example, let

$$f = \{(1, 2), (2, 5), (3, 6), (4, 8)\}$$

and

$$g = \{(1, -3), (2, 2), (3, 7), (6, 9)\}.$$

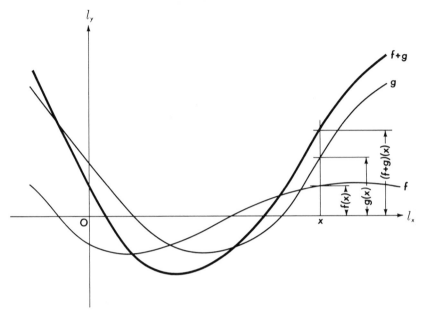

Figure 3.7

Then
$$(\text{Dom}\, f) \cap (\text{Dom}\, g) = \{1, 2, 3, 4\} \cap \{1, 2, 3, 6\} = \{1, 2, 3\}$$
and
$$f + g = \{(1, -1), (2, 7), (3, 13)\}$$
$$fg = \{(1, -6), (2, 10), (3, 42)\}.$$

We obtain as an immediate consequence of the above definition and the corresponding field axioms for the real numbers the following properties relating to the operations of addition and multiplication of functions:

$$f + g = g + f \tag{1}$$

$$(f + g) + h = f + (g + h) \tag{2}$$

$$fg = gf \tag{3}$$

$$(fg)h = f(gh) \tag{4}$$

$$f(g + h) = fg + fh. \tag{5}$$

We refer to (1) as "commutativity of addition," to (2) as "associativity of addition," to (3) as "commutativity of multiplication," to (4) as "associativity of multiplication," to (5) as "distributivity of multiplication with respect to addition." We leave as exercises the proofs of the uniqueness of the *zero function* **0**, such that $f + \mathbf{0} = f$, and the *unity function* **1**, such that $f\mathbf{1} = f$.

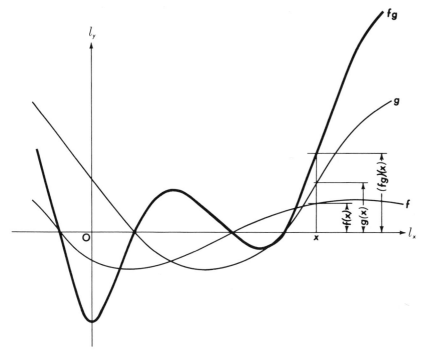

Figure 3.8

Note that we have *additive inverses* (Axiom **F₅**) and *multiplicative inverses* (Axiom **F₁₀**). With these axioms in mind we lay down the following definition.

Definition. *If f is a function, then* $-f = \{(x, -f(x))\}$ *for* $x \in \mathrm{Dom}\, f$ *and* $f^{-1} = \{(x, 1/f(x))\}$ *for* $x \in \mathrm{Dom}\, f$ *and such that* $f(x) \neq 0$.

The multiplicative inverse f^{-1} is frequently written I/f:

$$f^{-1} \equiv \frac{I}{f}.$$

Thus

$$f^{-1}(x) = \frac{I}{f}(x) = \frac{I(x)}{f(x)} = \frac{1}{f(x)}$$

since $I(x) = 1$.

5. COMPOSITION

We denote the operation of the *composition* of the function f with the function g by $f \circ g$ (read f composition g).

Definition. *If f and g are two functions, $f \circ g$ is the function whose domain is all $x \in \mathrm{Dom}\, g$ such that $g(x) \in \mathrm{Dom}\, f$ and whose rule of correspondence is $f \circ g(x) = f(g(x))$.*

For example, if

$$f = \sin$$
$$g = j^2,$$

then

$$f \circ g = \sin \circ j^2$$

and

$$f \circ g(x) = \sin x^2.$$

Note that if $\text{Dom} f \circ g = \text{Dom} f$, then $\text{Ran} f \circ g = \text{Ran} f$. However, in general, $\text{Dom} f \circ g \neq \text{Dom} f$. Consider, for example, the two functions

$$f = \{(1, 4), (2, 6), (3, -7), (4, 5)\}$$

and

$$g = \{(1, 5), (2, 1), (6, 3), (7, 4)\}.$$

Then

$$f \circ g = \{(2, 4), (6, -7), (7, 5)\}$$

and

$$\text{Dom} f \circ g = \{2, 6, 7\}$$
$$\text{Ran} f \circ g = \{4, -7, 5\}.$$

We see that in $\text{Dom} f \circ g$ there are numbers not in $\text{Dom} f$ and that $\text{Ran} f$ contains numbers not in $\text{Ran} f \circ g$. In fact $\text{Ran} f \circ g$ is a subset of $\text{Ran} f$. On the other hand, $g \circ f = \{(2, 3)\}$. In this case both $\text{Dom} g \circ f$ and $\text{Ran} g \circ f$ are subsets of $\text{Dom} g$ and $\text{Ran} g$ respectively.

Another illustration that will bring out the same point is the composition, say of tan with **5**. We have

$$\tan \circ \mathbf{5} = \{(x, \tan 5)\}$$

for all x whereas

$$\mathbf{5} \circ \tan = \{(\tan x, 5)\} = \mathbf{5}$$

for $x \neq [(2n + 1)\pi]/2$ and $n \in I$.

With regard to composition of a function f with the constant function **k**, it should be noted that this can be done only when $k \in \text{Dom} f$. Then

$$f \circ \mathbf{k} = \{(x, f(k))\}$$

for all x. On the other hand,

$$\mathbf{k} \circ f = \{(f(x), k)\} = \mathbf{k}$$

only for $x \in \text{Dom} f$. (Clearly $\text{Ran} f \subset \text{Dom} \mathbf{k}$ since $\text{Dom} \mathbf{k}$ is the set of all x.)

From the above examples we may also conclude that *in general the operation* "composition" *is not commutative*. There are, of course, examples for which this operation *is* commutative. For instance, let $f = j^2$ and $g = j^4$. In this case Dom $f \circ g$ = Dom $g \circ f$ = the set of all x. Also

$$j^2 \circ j^4(x) = j^2(j^4(x)) = j^2(x^4) = x^8$$

and

$$j^4 \circ j^2(x) = j^4(j^2(x)) = j^4(x^2) = x^8.$$

Although the composition operation is not commutative, it *is* associative. That is,

$$(f \circ g) \circ h = f \circ (g \circ h). \tag{1}$$

To show this we first prove that Dom $(f \circ g) \circ h$ = Dom $f \circ (g \circ h)$ and then that $(f \circ g) \circ h(x) = f \circ (g \circ h)(x)$.

Now Dom $(f \circ g) \circ h$ = the set of all x in Dom h such that $h(x) \in$ Dom $f \circ g$. This in turn is the same as the set of all $x \in$ Dom h such that $h(x) \in$ Dom g *and* $g(h(x)) \in$ Dom f. On the other hand, Dom $f \circ (g \circ h)$ = the set of all x in Dom $g \circ h$ such that $g \circ h(x) \in$ Dom f. This in turn is the same as the set of all $x \in$ Dom h such that $h(x) \in$ Dom g *and* $g(h(x)) \in$ Dom f. Hence we have shown that

$$\text{Dom } (f \circ g) \circ h = \text{Dom} f \circ (g \circ h).$$

For each x belonging to their common domain we have

$$(f \circ g) \circ h(x) = f \circ g(h(x)) = f(g(h(x)))$$

and

$$f \circ (g \circ h)(x) = f(g \circ h(x)) = f(g(h(x)))$$

which proves the second part of our statement.

As an illustration let

$$f = \{(1, 2), (2, 3), (3, 4), (4, 5)\}$$
$$g = \{(0, 3), (1, 2), (2, 1), (3, 4)\}$$
$$h = \{(1, 0), (2, 3), (3, 1), (4, 2)\}.$$

Then

$$f \circ g = \{(0, 4), (1, 3), (2, 2), (3, 5)\}$$

and

$$(f \circ g) \circ h = \{(1, 4), (2, 5), (3, 3), (4, 2)\}$$

while

$$g \circ h = \{(1, 3), (2, 4), (3, 2), (4, 1)\}$$

and

$$f \circ (g \circ h) = \{(1, 4), (2, 5), (3, 3), (4, 2)\}.$$

Strangely, for the operation substitution, we have two distributive laws—one for addition:

$$(f + g) \circ h = f \circ h + g \circ h \tag{2}$$

and one for multiplication:

$$(fg) \circ h = (f \circ h)(g \circ h). \tag{3}$$

To prove (2) we have by definition that

Dom $(f + g) \circ h$ = the set of all $x \in \text{Dom } h$ such that $h(x) \in \text{Dom } (f + g)$.

But by the definition of Section 4,

$$\text{Dom } (f + g) = (\text{Dom } f) \cap (\text{Dom } g).$$

Hence Dom $(f + g) \circ h$ is the set of all $x \in \text{Dom } h$ such that $h(x) \in (\text{Dom } f) \cap (\text{Dom } g)$. On the other hand,

$$
\begin{aligned}
\text{Dom } (f \circ h + g \circ h) &= (\text{Dom } f \circ h) \cap (\text{Dom } g \circ h) \\
&= (\text{the set of all } x \in \text{Dom } h \text{ such that } h(x) \in \text{Dom } f) \\
&\quad \cap (\text{the set of all } x \in \text{Dom } h \text{ such that} \qquad (4) \\
&\quad h(x) \in \text{Dom } g) \\
&= \text{the set of all } x \in \text{Dom } h \text{ such that } h(x) \in (\text{Dom } f) \\
&\quad \cap (\text{Dom } g).
\end{aligned}
$$

Thus we have shown that

$$\text{Dom } (f + g) \circ h = \text{Dom } (f \circ g + g \circ h).$$

And for all x in this common domain

$$(f + g) \circ h(x) = (f + g)(h(x)) = f(h(x)) + g(h(x)) \qquad (5)$$

by definition of addition (cf. Section 4). Furthermore,

$$(f \circ h + g \circ h)(x) = f \circ h(x) + g \circ h(x) = f(h(x)) + g(h(x)). \qquad (6)$$

Equations (5) and (6) now complete the proof of (2).

We now turn to the proof of the multiplicative distributive law of (3). First

$$\text{Dom } (fg) \circ h = \text{the set of all } x \in \text{Dom } h \text{ such that } h(x) \in \text{Dom } fg. \qquad (7)$$

But Dom $fg = (\text{Dom } f) \cap (\text{Dom } g)$. Hence

Dom $(fg) \circ h$ = the set of all $x \in \text{Dom } h$ such that $h(x) \in (\text{Dom } f) \cap (\text{Dom } g)$.

On the other hand

$$
\begin{aligned}
\text{Dom } (f \circ h)(g \circ h) &= (\text{Dom } f \circ h) \cap (\text{Dom } g \circ h) \\
&= \text{the set of all } x \in \text{Dom } h \text{ such that} \\
&\quad h(x) \in (\text{Dom } f) \cap (\text{Dom } g) \qquad (8)
\end{aligned}
$$

[cf. (4)]. Thus (7) and (8) show that

$$\text{Dom } (fg) \circ h = \text{Dom } (f \circ h)(g \circ h).$$

To complete the proof we see that for all x in this common domain

$$(fg) \circ h(x) = (fg)(h(x)) = f(h(x))g(h(x))$$

by definition of multiplication (cf. Section 4). Also

$$(f \circ h)(g \circ h)(x) = [f \circ h(x)][g \circ h(x)] = f(h(x))g(h(x))$$

and (3) is proved.

6. FURTHER PROPERTIES OF FUNCTIONS

We have seen earlier that associated with the operations of addition and multiplication we have *neutral functions*. That is

$$f + \mathbf{0} = f$$

and

$$f\mathbf{1} = f.$$

Thus the zero function, $\mathbf{0}$, is the "neutral" function for addition and the unity function, $\mathbf{1}$, is the "neutral" function for multiplication. The operation of composition also has a neutral function, say g, such that

$$f \circ g = g \circ f = f.$$

We assert that g is the identity function j. To prove this we merely note that

$$\mathrm{Dom}\, f \circ j = \mathrm{Dom}\, f = \mathrm{Dom}\, j \circ f$$

and for each $x \in \mathrm{Dom}\, f$,

$$f \circ j(x) = f(j(x)) = f(x) = j(f(x)) = j \circ f(x).$$

Thus the function j on $\mathrm{Dom}\, f$ is the neutral element for substitution.

In the case of addition we were able to define a function $-f$ such that

$$f + (-f) = \mathbf{0},$$

the neutral function for addition. Under the mild restriction $f(x) \neq 0$ for $x \in \mathrm{Dom}\, f$ we were able to define a function f^{-1} such that

$$ff^{-1} = \mathbf{1},$$

the neutral function for multiplication. We shall now show that under certain conditions we can define a function h with the analogous property, namely, that

$$f \circ h = j,$$

where j is the neutral function for composition. To do this we must màke certain additional definitions.

Definition.   *A function f is called* **one–one** *if $f(a) = f(b)$ for any a, b in $\mathrm{Dom}\, f$ implies $a = b$.*

Hence, if a function is one–one, it belongs to that class of functions whose distinct ordered pairs all have different second elements as well as different first elements.

If f is one–one, then we shall call f^*, where

$$f^* = \{(f(x), x)\}$$

(for $x \in \mathrm{Dom}\, f$), the *inverse* of f. It is clear from the above definition of $f*$ that $\mathrm{Dom}\, f* = \mathrm{Ran}\, f$ and $\mathrm{Dom}\, f = \mathrm{Ran}\, f*$. Notice that if f were not one–one, as for example $\mathbf{2} = \{(x, 2)\}$, then the inverse of the ordered pairs would not yield a function—for then we would have distinct ordered pairs with equal first members. As an immediate consequence we also note that

$$f** = f.$$

We shall now show that, in a certain sense, f and $f*$ are inverses. That is, we shall show that

$$f* \circ f = j \quad \text{for} \quad x \in \mathrm{Dom}\, f \tag{1}$$

and

$$f \circ f* = j \quad \text{for} \quad x \in \mathrm{Dom}\, f* = \mathrm{Ran}\, f. \tag{2}$$

To prove (1), let $x \in \mathrm{Dom}\, f$. Then $f* \circ f(x) = f*(f(x)) = x = j(x)$. To prove (2), let $x \in \mathrm{Dom}\, f*$. Then $f \circ f*(x) = f** \circ f*(x) = f**(f*(x)) = x = j(x)$.

As an illustration let

$$f = \frac{\mathbf{I}}{j + \mathbf{I}}$$

where $\mathrm{Dom}\, f$ is all $x \neq -1$. We wish to find $f*$.

Since $f \circ f* = j$ we have

$$j = \frac{\mathbf{I}}{f* + \mathbf{I}}$$

or $j(f* + \mathbf{I}) = \mathbf{I}$ and

$$f* + \mathbf{I} = \frac{\mathbf{I}}{j}.$$

Thus

$$f* = \frac{\mathbf{I}}{j} - \mathbf{I} = \frac{\mathbf{I} - j}{j}$$

for $x \neq 0$.

The *inverse* of a function, as we have just defined it, should not be confused with the *multiplicative inverse* as defined on page 75. (Rarely is there any likelihood of confusion with the *additive inverse*.) If a function f is given where $\mathrm{Dom}\, f$ is tacitly assumed to be all x for which $f(x)$ is defined, then there may exist various subsets of $\mathrm{Dom}\, f$ on which f is one–one. Thus if we ask for the inverse of a function f that is not one–one on its entire domain, we mean the inverse (with specified domain) on the subset (or subsets) of $\mathrm{Dom}\, f$ where f *is* one–one. This is analogous to, but more complicated than the definition of f^{-1}, that is, f^{-1} exists for all $x \in \mathrm{Dom}\, f$ *such that* $f(x) \neq 0$.

EXERCISES

1. Which of the following sets of ordered pairs are functions? For each function find its domain and range.

(i) $\{(3, 2), (6, 8), (7, 9), (8, 10), (2, 3)\}$
(ii) $\{(1, 2), (2, 1), (5, 6), (2, 3), (7, 8)\}$
(iii) $\{(8, -5), (6, 5), (8, 1), (3, 2)\}$.

2. Find the domain and range of the functions whose rules of correspondence are:

(i) $f(x) = 3x - 9$

(ii) $f(x) = x^2 + 5$

(iii) $f(x) = \sqrt{x^2 - 1}$

(iv) $f(x) = \dfrac{x^2 + 5x - 1}{2x - 1}$

(v) $f(x) = \dfrac{5x^2 + 4x}{x^2 + 1}$.

3. On what set $\mathscr{S}$ are the functions $f = \dfrac{j^2 - 1}{j - 1}$ and $g = j + 1$ equal?

4. Sketch the graphs of the functions whose rules of correspondence are:

(i) $f(x) = 3x - 5$
(ii) $f(x) = x^2$
(iii) $f(x) = 4x^2$
(iv) $f(x) = 4x^2 + 1$
(v) $f(x) = \sqrt{9 - x^2}$
(vi) $f(x) = \cos x$
(vii) $f(x) = [x]$
(viii) $f(x) = x^3$
(ix) $f(x) = 3|x|$
(x) $f(x) = \operatorname{sgn} x$.

5. Let $g = 3j + 5$ and $h = 2j - 1$. For each f given in Exercise 4, find $\operatorname{Dom} f \cap \operatorname{Dom} g$ and $\operatorname{Dom} f \cap \operatorname{Dom} h$.

6. Let $f = \sqrt{9 - j^2}$ and $g = aj + 6$. For what values of a will the graph of g be tangent to the graph of f? [*Note:* Strictly speaking we should write $f = \sqrt{} \circ (9 - j^2)$. However, for compactness we shall frequently write f as above, that is, as $f = \sqrt{9 - j^2}$.]

7. Given the functions $f = \{(3, -1), (2, 3), (7, -2), (5, 8)\}$ and $g = \{(5, 3), (1, 5), (7, 2), (3, 5)\}$ find:

(i) $f + g$

(ii) fg.

8. Given the functions $f = j^2 - 1$ and $g = 3j - j^2$.
(i) What is $\operatorname{Dom} f \cap \operatorname{Dom} g$?
(ii) What are the rules of correspondence for $f + g$ and fg?

9. (i) Determine $f + g$ and fg for

$$f = \frac{j^3 - 8}{j + 1} \quad \text{and} \quad g = \frac{j^2 - 1}{j - 1}.$$

(ii) Determine the rules of correspondence for $f + g$ and fg.

10. For the functions f and g defined in Exercise 7, determine $f \circ g$ and $g \circ f$.

11. Prove that the functions **0** and **I** (that is, the neutral functions for addition and multiplication) are unique.

12. Let $f = \mathbf{3}$, $g = j$ and $h = j^{1/2}$. Evaluate the following at the indicated value of x.

(i) $(fg)h$	at $x = 9$		(vi) $(h + g) \circ f$ at $x = 5$	
(ii) $f(hg)$	at $x = 3$		(vii) $(fg) \circ h$	at $x = 1$
(iii) $(f + g)h$	at $x = 1$		(viii) $(g \circ f) \circ h$ at $x = 4$	
(iv) $g(f + h)$	at $x = 7$		(ix) $(f \circ g) \circ h$ at $x = 4$	
(v) $(f + g) \circ f$ at $x = 2$			(x) $(h \circ g) \circ f$ at $x = 4$.	

13. Let $\mathscr{S} \subset \mathrm{Dom}\, f$. In each of the following cases define $\mathscr{S}$ so that f will be one–one on $\mathscr{S}$.

(i) $f = j$	(vi) $f = |\ \ |$
(ii) $f = j^2$	(vii) $f = \sin$
(iii) $f = \mathbf{4}j^2 - \mathbf{6}j + \mathbf{2}$	(viii) $f = \tan$
(iv) $f = j^3$	(ix) $f = j \sin$
(v) $f = [\ \ ]$	(x) $f = |\ \ |j^2$.

14. What are the domains of the following functions?

(i) $\sqrt{\ \ } \circ j$	(vi) $j \circ \sqrt{\ \ }$
(ii) $\sqrt{\ \ } \circ j^2$	(vii) $\sin \circ \cos$
(iii) $|\ \ | \circ \sin$	(viii) $j^3 \circ \sin$
(iv) $\sin \circ |\ \ |$	(ix) $\dfrac{\mathbf{I}}{\mathbf{I} + j} \circ \sin$
(v) $j^2 \circ \sqrt{\ \ }$	(x) $\tan \circ \dfrac{\mathbf{I}}{j}$.

15. Give the domains and ranges for the inverses of the functions given in Exercise 12.

16. Find the inverses of the following functions. (Specify the domains and the ranges of the inverse in each case.)

(i) $f = \mathbf{2}j - \mathbf{3}$	(vi) $f = \dfrac{\mathbf{I} - j^2}{\mathbf{I} + j^2}$
(ii) $f = \dfrac{j + \mathbf{I}}{j - \mathbf{I}}$	(vii) $f = (\mathbf{I} + j^2)^{1/2}$
(iii) $f = \dfrac{j - \mathbf{I}}{j + \mathbf{I}}$	(viii) $f = j^3$
(iv) $f = \dfrac{\mathbf{I}}{\mathbf{I} + j^2}$	(ix) $f = j^2 - \mathbf{4}j + \mathbf{4}$
(v) $f = \dfrac{\mathbf{I} + j^2}{\mathbf{I} - j^2}$	(x) $f = j^4 - \mathbf{I}$.

4

LIMITS AND CONTINUITY

Our study of function theory proper begins in this chapter. The work of earlier chapters presented known material—but perhaps in a format unfamiliar to some readers. The reason for this procedure was to make the transition to the more advanced theory smoother—and we hope, more palatable. Some of the new ideas we are to introduce are quite subtle; but we have behind us a firm logical structure upon which to build.

To avoid digressions at critical points in our arguments we shall introduce certain auxiliary concepts in this present introduction. This is a necessary prelude to the satisfactory development of any nontrivial discipline. We shall endeavor to keep these preliminaries to a minimum. Fortunately, for the immediate future, we need introduce only two new definitions. One is an extension of the definition of *interval* given in Chapter 2, the other is the meaning of an *accumulation point*.

We recall that the set of all points x such that $a < x < b$ was called an interval and was denoted by $I(a, b)$. For clarity in future expositions we shall now call $I(a, b)$ an *open interval*. The notation $I[a, b]$ will refer to the set of all real numbers x such that $a \leq x \leq b$ and will be called a *closed interval*. The difference between a closed interval and an open interval is that a closed interval includes the end points. The difference in notation is that we use *brackets* for closed intervals and *parentheses* for open intervals. If one desires to be fancy—and occasionally it is convenient to do so—we shall write $I(a, b]$ to indicate the set of all real numbers x such that $a < x \leq b$ and write $I[a, b)$ to indicate the set of

83

Figure 4.1

all real numbers x such that $a \le x < b$. The intervals $I(a, b]$ and $I[a, b)$ are neither open nor closed intervals.

We call α an *accumulation point* or *limit point* of a set S if every open interval J containing α, contains at least one point (distinct from α) of S. Thus if $\alpha \in S$, every open interval J containing α contains at least one other distinct point of S. If $\alpha \notin S$, every open interval J containing α contains at least one point of S. If $S = I[a, b]$, then every x in $I[a, b]$ is an accumulation point and no point not in $I[a, b]$ is an accumulation point. For if x is in $I[a, b]$ and I' is an open interval containing $x \in I[a, b]$, then the intersection of $I[a, b]$ and I' is not empty. On the other hand, suppose c is *not* in $I[a, b]$—say to the left of a as in Figure 4.1. Then $a - c > 0$. Thus the open interval $I(c - \varepsilon, c + \varepsilon)$ [where $\varepsilon = \frac{1}{2}(a - c) > 0$] contains no points of $I[a, b]$, and hence c is not a point of accumulation.

If $S = I(a, b)$, an open interval, then all x in the *closed* interval $I[a, b]$ are accumulation points of S, and no point not in $I[a, b]$ is an accumulation point. Thus we see that the sets of accumulation points of $I[a, b]$ and $I(a, b)$ {as well as $I(a, b]$ and $I[a, b)$} are identical and all equal to $I[a, b]$.

When S is referred to as $\mathrm{Dom}\, f$ for some function f, we use the phrase "α is an accumulation point of $\mathrm{Dom}\, f$" to mean that there is a nonempty open interval J such that $J \subset \mathrm{Dom}\, f$ and α is an accumulation point of J.

We could discourse further on this topic; but the elementary facts we have presented above are sufficient for our purposes. Additional results will be found in the exercises at the end of the chapter.

I. LIMITS

Let us introduce the notion of *limit* by means of a concrete example. Towards this end consider the simple function

$$f = j^2 + 3. \tag{1}$$

Now if x is close to 2, then we would expect $f(x)$ to be close to 7. In fact, we readily see that $f(x)$ may be made arbitrarily close to 7 if x is sufficiently close to 2. For instance, suppose we demand that $f(x)$ differ from 7 by less than 0.041 in absolute value. Then we need only take x between $2 - 0.01$ and $2 + 0.01$, that is,

$$|x - 2| < 0.01.$$

More generally, if one were to demand that $|f(x) - 7| < \varepsilon$ where ε is any positive number no matter how small, then it would be sufficient to choose x so close to 2 that

$$|x - 2| < \frac{\varepsilon}{5}$$

as well as

$$|x - 2| < 1$$

were satisfied. Then since the last inequality implies $|x| < 3$,

$$|f(x) - 7| = |x^2 + 3 - 7| = |x^2 - 4| = |x - 2|\,|x + 2|$$

$$< |x - 2|[|x| + 2] < \frac{\varepsilon}{5}\,(5) = \varepsilon$$

as we desired.

We describe the above situation by saying that 7 is the limit of f as x approaches 2. However, to say that f can be made arbitrarily close to 7 provided x is sufficiently close to 2 is—to say the least—not a workable definition of limit. For the terms "arbitrarily close" and "sufficiently close" make the statement vague and useless. We therefore lay down the following precise definition of limit:

Definition. *The* **limit** *of the function f at a is the number b, if for each number $\varepsilon > 0$ there is a number $\delta > 0$ such that $|f(x) - b| < \varepsilon$ whenever $x \in \mathrm{Dom}\,f$ and $0 < |x - a| < \delta$.*

We write

$$\lim_a f = b$$

or

$$\lim_{x \to a} f(x) = b$$

to denote that b is the limit of f at a.

The concept of limit is without doubt the single most important idea in all analysis. Limits, in one form or another, will be our major topic of discussion throughout the remainder of this book.

Let us examine the above definition of limit. An obvious first comment is that we must assume that a is an accumulation point of $\mathrm{Dom}\,f$; otherwise, the definition would be meaningless. Thus we may consider situations where a *is* in the $\mathrm{Dom}\,f$ or a is *not* in $\mathrm{Dom}\,f$. (Of course in either case, a *must be* a point of accumulation.) A second, not quite so obvious comment, is that a function need not *have* a limit at an accumulation point a; and furthermore, even if $a \in \mathrm{Dom}\,f$, $\lim_a f$ may exist and be unequal to $f(a)$. Let us give examples to illustrate all these phenomena:

Example 1. *Let $f = j^2$, $a = 3$. Then certainly $a \in \mathrm{Dom}\,f$, and*

$$\lim_a f = \lim_3 j^2 = 9.$$

Example 2.   *Let*

$$g = \frac{j^2 - 1}{j - 1}.$$

Then $1 \notin \mathrm{Dom}\, g$, *(although 1 is an accumulation point of* $\mathrm{Dom}\, g$). *In this case*

$$\lim_1 g = 2.$$

Example 3.   *Let* $h = [\ \ ]$, *the greatest integer function. Then the domain of h is all real numbers, yet if n is an integer,*

$$\lim_n h$$

does not exist.

Example 4.   *Let* $\phi = \sin \circ 1/j$ *on the open interval* $I(0, 1)$. *Then* $0 \notin \mathrm{Dom}\, \phi$ *(although 0 is an accumulation point of* $\mathrm{Dom}\, \phi$) *and*

$$\lim_{x \to 0} \sin \frac{1}{x}$$

does not exist.

Example 5.   *Let* $\psi = 1 - (\mathrm{sgn})^2$ *where* sgn *is the signum function. Then certainly* $0 \in \mathrm{Dom}\, \psi$ *since* $\mathrm{Dom}\, \psi$ *is the set of all real numbers. Now*

$$\lim_0 \psi = 0$$

although $\psi(0) = 1$. *That is, the limit of* ψ *at 0 exists and is unequal to* $\psi(0)$.

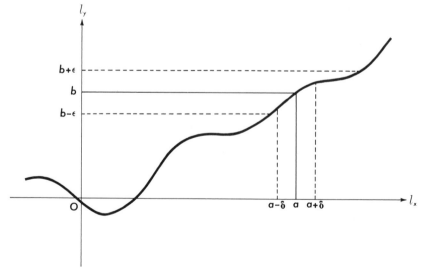

Figure 4.2

A geometric interpretation of limit is given by Figure 4.2. Intuitively we say $f(x)$ is close to b when x is close to a. If properly interpreted in terms of the above definition of limit, the last sentence expresses a very quantitative fact.

We also notice in the above definition of limit that we require $|x - a|$ to be positive. That is, we do not allow x to be equal to a. There are two reasons for this. The first is that a may not be in Dom f. This is illustrated by Example 2 (cf. Figure 4.3). The other reason is brought out by Example 5, namely, even if $a \in$ Dom f and $\lim_a f$ exists, we may have $\lim_a f \neq f(a)$.

Let us now turn to the proofs of a few simple general theorems regarding limits.

Theorem 1. *If f is the constant function $\{(x, k)\}$, then*

$$\lim_a f = k.$$

PROOF. Choose any $\varepsilon > 0$. Then if δ is any positive number,

$$|f(x) - k| = |k - k| = 0 < \varepsilon$$

whenever $0 < |x - a| < \delta$.

Theorem 2. *If j is the identity function, then*

$$\lim_a j = a.$$

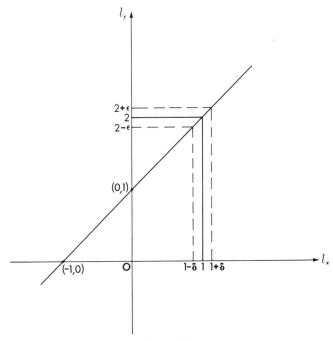

Figure 4.3

PROOF. For any $\varepsilon > 0$ we must show that there is a $\delta > 0$ such that $|j(x) - a| < \varepsilon$ whenever $0 < |x - a| < \delta$. In this case we may take $\delta = \varepsilon$. Then $0 < |x - a| < \delta = \varepsilon$ implies

$$|x - a| = |j(x) - a| < \varepsilon.$$

Next we should like to generalize Theorem 2 so as to include the functions j^n (with $n \in N$). However, a question that may have bothered the reader even after the first illustrative example [namely, $f = j^2 + \mathbf{3}$ of (1)] is the following: Given an epsilon greater than zero, how do we *find* a delta? The answer is a combination of experience, hindsight, intelligence, and practice. To illustrate, let us prove that

$$\lim_a j^5 = a^5, \quad (a \neq 0).$$

That is, let $\varepsilon > 0$ be assigned. We must determine a $\delta > 0$ such that $|x^5 - a^5| < \varepsilon$ if $0 < |x - a| < \delta$.

To do this, let us first write

$$|x^5 - a^5| = |x - a| \, |x^4 + ax^3 + a^2x^2 + a^3x + a^4|. \tag{2}$$

Now $\delta > 0$ can be as small as we choose. Hence there is no loss of generality in assuming that $\delta < |a|$. But $0 < |x - a| < \delta$ implies

$$|x| < \delta + |a|,$$

and if we assume $\delta < |a|$, the above inequality yields

$$|x| < 2|a|.$$

Thus, under the assumption

$$0 < \delta < |a|,$$

equation (2) may be written

$$\begin{aligned}
|x^5 - a^5| &< |x - a|[(2a)^4 + |a|(2|a|)^3 + a^2(2a)^2 + |a|^3(2|a|) + a^4] \\
&< |x - a|[|2a|^4 + |2a|^4 + |2a|^4 + |2a|^4 + |2a|^4] \\
&= |x - a|[5|2a|^4] \tag{3}
\end{aligned}$$

where we have replaced $|a|(2|a|)^3 = 8a^4$ by $16a^4$; replaced $a^2(2a)^2 = 4a^4$ by $16a^4$; replaced $2a^4$ by $16a^4$; replaced a^4 by $16a^4$—in all cases strengthening our inequality.

Now if we let δ be less than $\varepsilon/5(2a)^4$ then $0 < |x - a| < \delta$ (and $\delta < |a|$) together with (3) imply

$$|x^5 - a^5| < \delta[5(2a)^4] < \frac{\varepsilon}{5(2a)^4} 5(2a)^4 = \varepsilon.$$

Thus we see that

$$\lim_a j^5 = a^5, \quad (a \neq 0)$$

(and we have also demonstrated where the "magic" factor $1/80a^4$ comes from).

We shall now prove the general theorem.

Theorem 3. *If j is the identity function, then for any positive integer n,*

$$\lim_a j^n = a^n.$$

PROOF. It is convenient to divide the theorem into the cases $a = 0$ and $a \neq 0$. Suppose first that $a = 0$. Then we must show that for any $\varepsilon > 0$ there is a $\delta > 0$ such that $|x^n| < \varepsilon$ whenever $0 < |x| < \delta$. But this is easily accomplished by letting $\delta = \sqrt[n]{\varepsilon}$.

We now turn to the nontrivial part of the theorem where we assume $a \neq 0$. Since the theorem has been shown to be true for $n = 1$ (cf. Theorem 2) we may assume without loss of generality that n is a positive integer greater than 1.

To prove our theorem we must show that for any given $\varepsilon > 0$ there is a $\delta > 0$ such that

$$|x^n - a^n| < \varepsilon$$

whenever

$$0 < |x - a| < \delta.$$

We assert that any positive δ less than $|a|$ which has the property

$$\delta < \frac{\varepsilon}{n|2a|^{n-1}} \tag{4}$$

will serve our purpose. (The factor $1/n|2a|^{n-1}$ was of course suggested by an argument analogous to the one that led to the factor $1/5|2a|^{5-1}$ for the case j^5.) To prove this contention consider the identity

$$x^n - a^n = (x - a)(x^{n-1} + ax^{n-2} + a^2x^{n-3} + \cdots + a^{n-1}). \tag{5}$$

If $0 < |x - a| < \delta$, then

$$|x| < |a| + \delta < 2|a|$$

and

$$|a^p x^q| < 2^q |a|^{p+q} \leq |2a|^{p+q} \tag{6}$$

for any nonnegative integers p and q. Thus, applying the triangle inequality to (5) and invoking (6) we obtain

$$|x^n - a^n| < |x - a|[n|2a|^{n-1}] < \delta[n|2a|^{n-1}] < \varepsilon$$

for $0 < |x - a| < \delta$.

In order to acquire a little more familiarity (and confidence) with manipulating "epsilons and deltas" we solve in detail two illustrative examples.

Example 6.   *Prove that* $\lim_a \mathbf{k}j^3 = ka^3$ *where* $k \neq 0$ *is a constant.*

To show this it is sufficient to exhibit a $\delta > 0$ such that for $0 < |x - a| < \delta$ we have

$$|kx^3 - ka^3| < \varepsilon \tag{7}$$

for any preassigned number $\varepsilon > 0$.

If $a = 0$, we may let $\delta = \sqrt[3]{\varepsilon/|k|}$. Then for $0 < |x - a| = |x - 0| = |x| < \delta$ we have

$$|kx^3 - ka^3| = |kx^3 - k0^3| = |k|\,|x|^3 < |k|\delta^3 = \varepsilon.$$

To treat the case $a \neq 0$ we first consider the identity

$$kx^3 - ka^3 = k(x - a)(x^2 + ax + a^2),$$

and by the triangle inequality

$$|kx^3 - ka^3| \leq |k|\,|x - a|\,[|x|^2 + |a|\,|x| + |a|^2]. \tag{8}$$

Now if $\delta > 0$ is chosen less than $|a|$, the inequality $0 < |x - a| < \delta$ implies

$$|x| < |a| + \delta < 2|a|$$

and (8) becomes

$$|kx^3 - ka^3| < |k|\delta[4|a|^2 + 2|a|^2 + |a|^2] = 7a^2|k|\delta.$$

(Of course, following the pattern of Theorem 3, we could write $|kx^3 - ka^3| < 3|2a|^2|k|\delta$.) Thus if we choose a $\delta > 0$ less than $|a|$ and also less than

$$\frac{\varepsilon}{7a^2|k|}$$

our equation (7) will be established.

Example 7.   *Prove that* $\lim_2 (3j^4 + 5j^2) = 68$.

It is sufficient to exhibit a number $\delta > 0$ such that if $0 < |x - 2| < \delta$, then $|3x^4 + 5x^2 - 68| < \varepsilon$, for any preassigned number $\varepsilon > 0$. Now

$$\begin{aligned} |3x^4 + 5x^2 - 68| &= |3x^4 - 48 + 5x^2 - 20| \\ &\leq |3x^4 - 48| + |5x^2 - 20| \\ &= 3|x^4 - 16| + 5|x^2 - 4|. \end{aligned} \tag{9}$$

But

$$|x^4 - 16| = |x - 2|\,|x^3 + 2x^2 + 4x + 8|$$

and if $\delta > 0$ is less than 2, the inequality $0 < |x - 2| < \delta$ implies $|x| < 4$ and

$$|x^4 - 16| \leq \delta[64 + 32 + 16 + 8] = 120\delta.$$

Hence

$$3|x^4 - 16| \leq 360\delta.$$

Thus if $\delta < 2$ and also less than $\frac{1}{2}(\varepsilon/360)$, we have

$$3|x^4 - 16| < \frac{\varepsilon}{2}.$$

[We multiply $\varepsilon/360$ by $1/2$ because there are two terms involved on the right-hand side of inequality (9).] Similarly we write

$$|x^2 - 4| = |x - 2|\,|x + 2|$$

and for $0 < |x - 2| < \delta$,

$$|x^2 - 4| < 6\delta < 6\left(\frac{\varepsilon}{720}\right) = \frac{\varepsilon}{120}.$$

Hence

$$5|x^2 - 4| < \frac{\varepsilon}{24}.$$

Finally, if $\delta > 0$ has the properties

$$\delta < 2$$

and

$$\delta < \frac{\varepsilon}{720},$$

then

$$|3x^4 + 5x^2 - 68| \leqq 3|x^4 - 16| + 5|x^2 - 4| < \frac{\varepsilon}{2} + \frac{\varepsilon}{24} < \varepsilon$$

for $0 < |x - 2| < \delta$.

2. LIMITS OF COMPOUND FUNCTIONS

Since $\lim_2 j^2 = 4$ and $\lim_2 3j = 6$, it is reasonable to assume that $\lim_2 (j^2 + 3j) = 10$ and $\lim_2 3j^3 = 24$. Indeed, these results may be proved by the methods employed in the previous section. It is natural however, to ask whether for two functions f and g such that $\lim_a f = b_1$ and $\lim_a g = b_2$ rules analogous to those for obtaining values for the addition, multiplication, and quotient of two functions are also true about limits. The answer is yes, as we shall demonstrate in Theorems 6 and 7 of this section. First, however, we shall show (Theorem 4) that if $\lim_a f$ exists (where a is a point of accumulation of Dom f), then this limit is unique. We need the trivial but useful lemma:

Lemma. *If $|a| \leqq \varepsilon$ for all numbers $\varepsilon > 0$, then $a = 0$.*

PROOF. Suppose $a \neq 0$. Then $|a|/2 > 0$. Let

$$\varepsilon = \frac{|a|}{2}.$$

Then $|a| \leqq |a|/2$, which is a contradiction.

We are now in a position to prove the uniqueness of the limit.

Theorem 4. *If the limit of f at a exists, it is a unique number. That is, if $\lim_a f = b_1$ and $\lim_a f = b_2$, then $b_1 = b_2$.*

PROOF. Let $\varepsilon > 0$ be given. Since

$$\lim_a f = b_1$$

there is a $\delta_1 > 0$ such that $|f(x) - b_1| < \varepsilon/2$ for $x \in \mathrm{Dom}\, f$ and $0 < |x - a| < \delta_1$. Similarly there is a $\delta_2 > 0$ such that

$$|f(x) - b_2| < \frac{\varepsilon}{2}$$

for $x \in \mathrm{Dom}\, f$ and $0 < |x - a| < \delta_2$. Now let $\delta = \min(\delta_1, \delta_2)$. Then for $0 < |x - a| < \delta$,

$$|b_1 - b_2| = |b_1 - f(x) + f(x) - b_2| \leq |b_1 - f(x)| + |f(x) - b_2|$$

$$< \frac{\varepsilon}{2} + \frac{\varepsilon}{2} = \varepsilon.$$

By the previous lemma this implies $|b_1 - b_2| = 0$ or $b_1 = b_2$.

Before proving one of our main theorems—Theorem 6—we establish two simple but useful results (Theorem 5 and Corollary) that will be used in various future proofs.

Theorem 5. *If $\lim_a f = b$ and $s_1 < b < s_2$, then there is a number $\delta > 0$ such that for $x \in \mathrm{Dom}\, f$ and satisfying $0 < |x - a| < \delta$, we have*

$$s_1 < f(x) < s_2.$$

PROOF. Let $\varepsilon = \min(b - s_1, s_2 - b) > 0$. Then

$$s_1 \leq b - \varepsilon < b < b + \varepsilon \leq s_2. \tag{1}$$

But $\lim_a f = b$. Therefore there exists a $\delta > 0$ such that

$$|f(x) - b| < \varepsilon$$

for $x \in \mathrm{Dom}\, f$ and $0 < |x - a| < \delta$. In other words, for this δ,

$$b - \varepsilon < f(x) < b + \varepsilon.$$

By virtue of (1), the above inequality implies

$$s_1 < f(x) < s_2$$

for $x \in \mathrm{Dom}\, f$ and $0 < |x - a| < \delta$.

Corollary. *If $\lim_a f = b$ and $b \neq 0$, then there is a $\delta > 0$ such that*

$$|f(x)| > \frac{|b|}{2}$$

for $x \in \mathrm{Dom}\, f$ and $0 < |x - a| < \delta$.

PROOF. We distinguish two cases:

Case 1. $b > 0$.

In this case $b/2 < b < 3b/2$ and by Theorem 5 there is a $\delta > 0$ such that for $x \in \mathrm{Dom}\, f$ and $0 < |x - a| < \delta$,

$$\frac{b}{2} < f(x) < \frac{3b}{2}, \tag{2}$$

and hence $|f(x)| > |b|/2$.

Case 2. $b < 0$.

In this case $3b/2 < b < b/2$ and again by Theorem 5, there is a $\delta > 0$ such that for $x \in \mathrm{Dom}\, f$ and $0 < |x - a| < \delta$,

$$\frac{3b}{2} < f(x) < \frac{b}{2}.$$

So

$$-\frac{3b}{2} > -f(x) > -\frac{b}{2} \tag{3}$$

and hence $|f(x)| > |b|/2$.

Finally we prove one of the main results of this chapter, Theorem 6, which establishes the facts that the limit of the sum is the sum of the limits, and the limit of the product is the product of the limits.

Theorem 6. *If* $\lim_a f = b_1$ *and* $\lim_a g = b_2$ *where* a *is an accumulation point of* $(\mathrm{Dom}\, f) \cap (\mathrm{Dom}\, g)$, *then:*

(i) $\lim\limits_{a} (f + g) = \lim\limits_{a} f + \lim\limits_{a} g = b_1 + b_2$.

(ii) $\lim\limits_{a} fg = [\lim\limits_{a} f][\lim\limits_{a} g] = b_1 b_2$.

PROOF. (i) We must show that for each $\varepsilon > 0$ there is a $\delta > 0$ such that for $x \in (\mathrm{Dom}\, f) \cap (\mathrm{Dom}\, g)$ and $0 < |x - a| < \delta$ we have

$$|(f + g)(x) - (b_1 + b_2)| < \varepsilon. \tag{4}$$

Since $\lim_a f = b_1$, there exists a $\delta_1 > 0$ such that for $x \in (\mathrm{Dom}\, f) \cap (\mathrm{Dom}\, g)$ and $0 < |x - a| < \delta_1$

$$|f(x) - b_1| < \frac{\varepsilon}{2}.$$

Similarly, since $\lim_a g = b_2$, there is a number $\delta_2 > 0$ such that

$$|g(x) - b_2| < \frac{\varepsilon}{2}$$

for $x \in (\mathrm{Dom}\, f) \cap (\mathrm{Dom}\, g)$ and $0 < |x - a| < \delta_2$.
Now

$$|(f + g)(x) - (b_1 + b_2)|$$
$$= |f(x) + g(x) - b_1 - b_2|$$
$$= |[f(x) - b_1] + [g(x) - b_2]| \leq |f(x) - b_1| + |g(x) - b_2| \quad (5)$$

and for $x \in (\mathrm{Dom}\, f) \cap (\mathrm{Dom}\, g)$ and $0 < |x - a| < \min (\delta_1, \delta_2)$ we have

$$|f(x) - b_1| + |g(x) - b_2| < \frac{\varepsilon}{2} + \frac{\varepsilon}{2} = \varepsilon.$$

Using this result in (5) we have established (4) and hence (i).

(ii) Let $\varepsilon > 0$ be given. Since $\lim_a g = b_2$ there exists a $\delta_1 > 0$ such that

$$|g(x) - b_2| < 1 \qquad\qquad (6)$$

for $x \in \mathrm{Dom}\, g$ and $0 < |x - a| < \delta_1$. (The number "1" in (6) is not critical, any positive number would do as well.) Now from (6)

$$|g(x)| - |b_2| < |g(x) - b_2| < 1$$

or

$$|g(x)| < |b_2| + 1$$

for $x \in \mathrm{Dom}\, g$ and $0 < |x - a| < \delta$.

Also by hypothesis there exists a $\delta_2 > 0$ such that

$$|f(x) - b_1| < \frac{\varepsilon}{2(|b_2| + 1)}$$

for $x \in (\mathrm{Dom}\, f) \cap (\mathrm{Dom}\, g)$ and $0 < |x - a| < \delta_2$. Similarly there is a $\delta_3 > 0$ such that for $x \in (\mathrm{Dom}\, f) \cap (\mathrm{Dom}\, g)$ and $0 < |x - a| < \delta_3$,

$$|g(x) - b_2| < \frac{\varepsilon}{2(|b_1| + 1)}.$$

Now let $\delta = \min (\delta_1, \delta_2, \delta_3)$ and $x \in (\mathrm{Dom}\, f) \cap (\mathrm{Dom}\, g)$. Then if $0 < |x - a| < \delta$ we have

$$|(fg)(x) - b_1 b_2| = |f(x)g(x) - b_1 b_2| = |f(x)g(x) - b_1 g(x) + b_1 g(x) - b_1 b_2|$$
$$\leqq |g(x)|\,|f(x) - b_1| + |b_1|\,|g(x) - b_2|$$
$$< (|b_2| + 1) \frac{\varepsilon}{2(|b_2| + 1)} + |b_1| \frac{\varepsilon}{2(|b_1| + 1)}$$
$$< \frac{\varepsilon}{2} + \frac{\varepsilon}{2} = \varepsilon.$$

As an immediate corollary of (ii) of the above theorem and Theorem 1 we have:

Corollary 1. *If* $\lim_a f = b$ *and if* **k** *is a constant function, then*

$$\lim_a \mathbf{k}f = kb.$$

Also (i) of Theorem 6 and the above corollary lead immediately to:

Corollary 2. *If* $\lim_a f = b_1$ *and* $\lim_a g = b_2$, *then*

$$\lim_a (f - g) = \lim_a f - \lim_a g = b_1 - b_2.$$

Before continuing further we consider a concrete illustration.

Example 1. *Find* $\lim_3 (j^3 + 2j^2 + 5)$.

By Theorem 6

$$\lim_3 (j^3 + 2j^2 + 5) = \lim_3 j^3 + \lim_3 2j^2 + \lim_3 5. \qquad (7)$$

By Theorem 3

$$\lim_3 j^3 = 3^3 = 27.$$

By Corollary 1 to Theorem 6 and Theorem 3

$$\lim_3 2j^2 = 2 \lim_3 j^2 = 2(3^2) = 18,$$

while Theorem 1 implies

$$\lim_3 5 = 5.$$

Thus (7) becomes

$$\lim_3 (j^3 + 2j^2 + 5) = 27 + 18 + 5 = 50.$$

We consider now the theorem that essentially states: the limit of the reciprocal is the reciprocal of the limit.

Theorem 7. *If* a *is an accumulation point of* $\text{Dom } f$ *and* $\lim_a f = b \neq 0$, *then* $\lim_a f^{-1} = 1/b$.

PROOF. Let $\varepsilon > 0$ be given. We must show the existence of a $\delta > 0$ such that for $x \in \text{Dom } f^{-1}$ and $0 < |x - a| < \delta$ we have

$$\left| \frac{1}{f(x)} - \frac{1}{b} \right| < \varepsilon.$$

From the corollary to Theorem 5 we know there exists a $\delta_1 > 0$ such that for $x \in \text{Dom } f$ and $0 < |x - a| < \delta_1$ we have

$$|f(x)| > \frac{|b|}{2}$$

and hence

$$\frac{1}{|f(x)|} < \frac{2}{|b|}.$$

Also by hypothesis there is a $\delta_2 > 0$ such that for $x \in \mathrm{Dom}\, f$ and $0 < |x - a| < \delta_2$,

$$|f(x) - b| < \frac{\varepsilon |b|^2}{2}.$$

Let $\delta = \min\,(\delta_1, \delta_2)$. Then if $0 < |x - a| < \delta$, and $x \in (\mathrm{Dom}\, f) \cap (\mathrm{Dom}\, f^{-1})$:

$$\left| \frac{1}{f(x)} - \frac{1}{b} \right| = \frac{1}{|f(x)|\,|b|} \, |b - f(x)| < \frac{2}{|b|\,|b|} \, \frac{\varepsilon |b|^2}{2} = \varepsilon.$$

The above result and (ii) of Theorem 6 immediately establish the following corollary:

Corollary. *If* $\lim_a f = b_1$ *and* $\lim_a g = b_2 \neq 0$, *then*

$$\lim_a \frac{f}{g} = \frac{b_1}{b_2}.$$

If $\lim_a f = b_1 \neq 0$ and $\lim_a g = b_2 = 0$, then $\lim_a f/g$ does not exist. If, however, $b_1 = 0 = b_2$, then no such categorical statement may be made. For example:

(i) If $f = \mathbf{a}j$ and $g = \mathbf{b}j$ with $a \neq 0 \neq b$, then $\lim_0 f = 0$, $\lim_0 g = 0$ while

$$\lim_0 \frac{f}{g} = \frac{a}{b}.$$

(ii) If $f = \mathbf{a}j^2$ and $g = \mathbf{b}j$ with $a \neq 0 \neq b$, then $\lim_0 f = 0$, $\lim_0 g = 0$ while

$$\lim_0 \frac{f}{g} = 0.$$

(iii) If $f = \mathbf{a}j$ and $g = \mathbf{b}j^2$, with $a \neq 0 \neq b$, then $\lim_0 f = 0$, $\lim_0 g = 0$ while

$$\lim_0 \frac{f}{g}$$

does not exist. In the next chapter we shall exhibit a systematic procedure for determining such limits (L'Hospital's Rule).

We consider now an explicit problem that exploits Theorem 7.

Example 2. *Find* $\lim_3 \dfrac{j^3 - 6}{2j + 1}$.

By Corollary 2 to Theorem 6, Theorem 3, and Theorem 1,

$$\lim_3 (j^3 - 6) = \lim_3 j^3 - \lim_3 6 = 27 - 6 = 21.$$

By Theorem 6, Corollary 1 to Theorem 6, Theorem 2, and Theorem 1,

$$\lim_3 (2j + 1) = \lim_3 2j + \lim_3 1 = 2 \lim_3 j + \lim_3 1$$
$$= 2(3) + 1 = 7.$$

Finally, invoking Theorem 7,

$$\lim_{3} \frac{j^3 - 6}{2j + 1} = \frac{\lim_3 (j^3 - 6)}{\lim_3 (2j + 1)} = \frac{21}{7} = 3.$$

3. LIMITS OF COMPOSITE FUNCTIONS

Suppose that $f = j^2$ and $g = j + 3$. Then $\lim_2 g = 5$ and $\lim_5 f = 25$. Now $f \circ g = g^2 = (j + 3)^2 = j^2 + 6j + 9$ and

$$\lim_{2} (j^2 + 6j + 9) = 25.$$

So in this case we have

$$\lim_{2} f \circ g = 25.$$

This observation might lead one to make the following unjustified statement: If $\lim_a g = b$ and if $\lim_b f = L$, then

$$\lim_{a} f \circ g = L. \tag{1}$$

But this statement is *not* always true. For instance, consider

$$f = 1 - (\mathrm{sgn})^2$$

where sgn is the signum function. We have

$$\lim_{0} [1 - (\mathrm{sgn})^2] = 0,$$

and if g is the zero function, **0**,

$$\lim_{0} g = 0.$$

Now

$$f \circ g = (1 - (\mathrm{sgn})^2) \circ 0 = 1 - 0 = 1,$$

the constant function, so that

$$\lim_{0} f \circ g = 1$$

and not 0 as the unqualified statement of (1) might lead us to believe.

In Theorem 8 below we give sufficient conditions under which (1) *is* true. The crucial part of the theorem has been set in boldface type. There are other sufficient conditions we could employ—see, for example, Theorem 11.

Theorem 8. *If* $\lim_a g = b$ *and* $\lim_b f = L$ *where* a *is a point of accumulation of* $\mathrm{Dom}\, f \circ g$, *and* **if there is a number** $c > 0$ **such that** $g(t) \neq b$ **whenever** $0 < |t - a| < c$, *then*

$$\lim_{a} f \circ g = L.$$

PROOF. By definition $\lim_b f = L$. Hence for any $\varepsilon > 0$ there is an $\varepsilon' > 0$ such that

$$|f(x) - L| < \varepsilon \tag{2}$$

for $x \in \text{Dom} f$ and $0 < |x - a| < \varepsilon'$. But (2) implies

$$|f \circ g(t) - L| < \varepsilon$$

for $g(t) \in \text{Dom} f$ and $0 < |g(t) - b| < \varepsilon'$.

Since $\lim_a g = b$, there is a number $\delta_1 > 0$ such that

$$|g(t) - b| < \varepsilon' \tag{3}$$

whenever $t \in \text{Dom} g$ and $0 < |t - a| < \delta_1$. Now by hypothesis $|g(t) - b| > 0$ whenever $0 < |t - a| < c$. So if we let

$$\delta = \min(\delta_1, c)$$

we have

$$0 < |g(t) - b| < \varepsilon'$$

whenever $t \in \text{Dom} g$ and $0 < |t - a| < \delta$. Combining the inequalities (2) and (3) we obtain

$$|f(g(t)) - L| < \varepsilon$$

for $t \in \text{Dom} g$, $g(t) \in \text{Dom} f$ and $0 < |t - a| < \delta$. Thus by definition of limit we have

$$\lim_a f \circ g = \lim_{t \to a} f(g(t)) = L.$$

4. LIMITS OF SOME SPECIAL FUNCTIONS

So far, in all our examples of limits of functions, we have dealt mainly with polynomials or rational functions. In these cases we were able to give an algorithm for "finding the $\delta > 0$ for any given $\varepsilon > 0$." There are many functions, however, for which this technique is not feasible—for example in the case of the trigonometric functions. In this section we shall establish the following limits, which will be useful in future work:

(i) $\lim_0 \sin = 0$

(ii) $\lim_0 \cos = 1$

(iii) $\lim_0 \dfrac{\sin}{j} = 1.$

In proving the above one must resort to devices other than those applicable to rational functions. We shall need the following preliminary theorem.

Theorem 9.   *Let f, g, h be three functions with common domain the open interval $I(x_1, x_2)$. Let $a \in I(x_1, x_2)$ and for every $x \in I(x_1, x_2)$ let $f(x) \leq g(x) \leq h(x)$. Then if*

$$\lim_a f = b = \lim_a h$$

we must have

$$\lim_a g = b.$$

PROOF.   By definition, for any $\varepsilon > 0$, there is a $\delta_1 > 0$ such that $b - \varepsilon < f(x) < b + \varepsilon$ for $0 < |x - a| < \delta_1$, and a $\delta_2 > 0$ such that $b - \varepsilon < h(x) < b + \varepsilon$ for $0 < |x - a| < \delta_2$. Let

$$\delta = \min (a - x_1, x_2 - a, \delta_1, \delta_2).$$

Then for $0 < |x - a| < \delta$ we have

$$b - \varepsilon < f(x) \leq g(x) \leq h(x) < b + \varepsilon. \tag{1}$$

That is,

$$b - \varepsilon < g(x) < b + \varepsilon$$

or

$$|g(x) - b| < \varepsilon$$

for $0 < |x - a| < \delta$. Hence our theorem is proved.

We shall now prove statements (i), (ii), (iii) above. On the unit circle with center at $O = (0, 0)$ we consider the arc from $Q = (1, 0)$ to $(0, 1)$ (see Figure 4.4). A point $P = (x, y)$, $0 < x < 1$, on this arc is also given by $P = (\cos \theta, \sin \theta)$ where θ is the length of $\widehat{QP}$ (hence $0 < \theta < \pi/2$). Let T be the point of intersection of the tangent to the circle at Q with Ray OP and let S be the point of intersection of

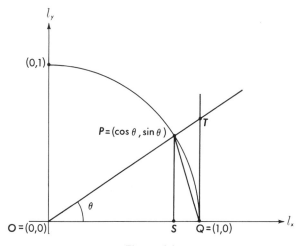

Figure 4.4

the perpendicular from P with the x-axis. Now from our discussion in the Appendix to Chapter 2 we see that

$$d(P, S) < \theta < d(Q, T). \tag{2}$$

But (2) is equivalent to

$$0 < \sin \theta < \theta < \tan \theta \tag{3}$$

for $0 < \theta < \pi/2$.

From the first half of (3), namely

$$0 < \sin \theta < \theta \tag{4}$$

and the facts that $\lim_0 j = 0$, $\lim_0 \mathbf{0} = 0$, we conclude by Theorem 9 that

$$\lim_0 \sin = 0. \tag{5}$$

Thus we have established (i).

Now consider the segment $I(P, Q)$, see Figure 4.4. Then $d(P, Q) < \theta$. Also

$$d(P, Q) = \sqrt{(\cos \theta - 1)^2 + (\sin \theta - 0)^2} = \sqrt{2 - 2 \cos \theta}.$$

Hence

$$0 < 2 - 2 \cos \theta < \theta^2$$

or

$$1 - \tfrac{1}{2}\theta^2 < \cos \theta < 1. \tag{6}$$

Since $\lim_0 \mathbf{I} = 1$ and $\lim_0 \tfrac{1}{2} j^2 = 0$, Theorem 9 may again be invoked to establish (ii):

$$\lim_0 \cos = 1. \tag{7}$$

Returning to (3) and recalling that $\tan \theta = \sin \theta / \cos \theta$ we may write the second half of (3) as

$$\sin \theta < \theta < \frac{\sin \theta}{\cos \theta}. \tag{8}$$

Since $\sin \theta > 0$ for $0 < \theta < \tfrac{1}{2}\pi$, the above equation implies

$$1 > \frac{\sin \theta}{\theta} > \cos \theta.$$

But $\lim_0 \mathbf{I} = 1$ and by (7), $\lim_0 \cos = 1$. Hence

$$\lim_0 \frac{\sin}{j} = 1$$

and we have proved (iii).

5. CONTINUOUS FUNCTIONS

Our intuitive notion of a *continuous* function is a function whose graph has no breaks or jumps. If a curve *does* have breaks, such as the function [ ], then we say that the function is not continuous at the points where the breaks occur. If the graph has no breaks or jumps in a given interval, then it will be defined for each point in the interval and we see, for example (cf. Figure 4.2) that if x is sufficiently close to a then $f(x)$ is arbitrarily close to $b = f(a)$. In other words,

$$\lim_a f = f(a).$$

A precise, more general, definition of continuity is given below. This definition implies this intuitive concept, although the converse may not be true.

Definition. *The function f is* **continuous** *at a point $a \in \text{Dom} f$ if for each $\varepsilon > 0$ there is a $\delta > 0$ such that $|f(x) - f(a)| < \varepsilon$ if $|x - a| < \delta$ (and $x \in \text{Dom} f$).*

If $\lim_a f = f(a)$ we do not need the restriction $0 < |x - a|$. It will be recalled that this restriction was put in the definition of limit to cover the case where $f(x)$ was arbitrarily close to b when x was sufficiently close to a—a being a point of accumulation of $\text{Dom} f$ even though $a \notin \text{Dom} f$; or if a were in $\text{Dom} f$ and we had $f(a) \neq b$. (Cf. the examples of pages 85–86.) In the case of a continuous function, however, if $a \in \text{Dom} f$, then f is defined at a; and if $\lim_a f = f(a)$, then $|f(a) - f(a)| = 0$ (which is less than any preassigned positive ε) when $x = a$.

In the second example of page 86, namely

$$g = \frac{j^2 - 1}{j - 1},$$

we saw that

$$\lim_1 g = 2.$$

But g is not continuous at $x = 1$ since $g(1)$ is not defined. Similarly, the fifth example of page 86, namely

$$\psi = 1 - (\text{sgn})^2,$$

is not continuous at $x = 0$, although the limit exists:

$$\lim_0 \psi = 0 \neq \psi(0).$$

Another example is furnished by the function

$$f = j \sin \circ \frac{1}{j}$$

which is defined and continuous for all $x \neq 0$. Although 0 is a point of accumulation of $\text{Dom} f$, the function is *not* continuous at $x = 0$. (The limit does exist,

$$\lim_0 f = 0$$

even though $f(0)$ is not defined.) *However*, if we add the definition $f(0) = 0$, then Dom f is the set of all real x and f *is* continuous at $x = 0$ (and hence for all x). (We remark that if we *define* $g(1)$ as 1, then the function g of the previous page also becomes continuous for all x.)

For continuous functions we have theorems similar to Theorems 6, 7, and 8 for limits. Theorem 10 below parallels Theorems 6 and 7.

Theorem 10. *Let f and g be continuous at an accumulation point a of* $(\mathrm{Dom}\, f) \cap (\mathrm{Dom}\, g)$. *Then*

(i) $\lim\limits_{a} (f + g) = \lim\limits_{a} f + \lim\limits_{a} g = f(a) + g(a)$.

(ii) $\lim\limits_{a} fg = [\lim\limits_{a} f][\lim\limits_{a} g] = f(a)g(a)$.

(iii) $\lim\limits_{a} f^{-1} = \dfrac{1}{\lim\limits_{a} f} = \dfrac{1}{f(a)}$ provided $f(a) \neq 0$.

The proofs of these results follow the same pattern as the proofs of Theorems 6 and 7, and hence will be left as exercises for the reader.

The "function of a function" rule, Theorem 8, for continuous functions is expressed in Theorem 11 below.

Theorem 11 (*Continuity of a composite function*). *Let g have a limit at a, and let f be continuous at $b = \lim_a g$ where a is a point of accumulation in the domain of $f \circ g$. Then*

$$\lim_a f \circ g = f(\lim_a g) = f(b).$$

PROOF. Since f is continuous at b, then for every $\varepsilon > 0$ there is an $\varepsilon' > 0$ such that

$$|f(x) - f(b)| < \varepsilon$$

whenever $|x - b| < \varepsilon'$ and $x \in \mathrm{Dom}\, f$. This implies

$$|f(g(t)) - f(b)| < \varepsilon$$

for $g(t) \in \mathrm{Dom}\, f$ and $|g(t) - b| < \varepsilon'$. But $\lim_a g = b$, and therefore corresponding to $\varepsilon' > 0$ there is a $\delta > 0$ such that $|g(t) - b| < \varepsilon'$ whenever $t \in \mathrm{Dom}\, g$ and $0 < |t - a| < \delta$. Hence for every $\varepsilon > 0$ there is a $\delta > 0$ such that

$$|f \circ g(t) - f(b)| < \varepsilon$$

whenever $0 < |t - a| < \delta$, $t \in \mathrm{Dom}\, g$, $g(t) \in \mathrm{Dom}\, f$. This completes the proof of the theorem.

Corresponding to Theorem 5 we have the following analogous result for continuity:

Theorem 12. *If the function f is continuous at a with $a \in \mathrm{Dom}\, f$ and $s_1 < f(a) < s_2$ then there is a number $\delta > 0$ such that $s_1 < f(x) < s_2$ provided $|x - a| < \delta$ and $x \in \mathrm{Dom}\, f$.*

As a corollary to the above theorem we have:

Corollary. *If f is continuous at a and $f(a) > 0$, $[f(a) < 0]$, then there is a number $\delta > 0$ such that $f(x) > 0$, $[f(x) < 0]$, provided $x \in \text{Dom} f$ and $|x - a| < \delta$.*

6. CONTINUITY ON AN INTERVAL

Thus far we have restricted our discussion of continuity of a function f to properties at a *point* in the domain of f. Now we should like to set up a norm for determining when a function is continuous over an entire set or interval on which the function is defined. We make the following definition:

Definition. *Let f be a function with domain $\text{Dom} f$. Let $S \subset \text{Dom} f$ be a subset of $\text{Dom} f$. Let $f_S = f$ for all $x \in S$. Then we say f is* **continuous** *on S if f_S is continuous at each point of S.*

If S is an *open interval*, and $S \subset \text{Dom} f$, the function f is continuous on S if it is continuous at each point of S. Similarly if S is a *closed interval*, say $S = I[a, b]$, then a function f is continuous on $I[a, b]$ if it is continuous at every point of S.

Occasionally some confusion arises in the minds of some readers about the meaning of continuity at the end points a and b. For by saying that f is continuous at a do we not imply that for each $\varepsilon > 0$ there is a $\delta > 0$ such that $|f(x) - f(a)| < \varepsilon$ if $|x - a| < \delta$? And are there not values of x satisfying $|x - a| < \delta$ and not in S for any $\delta > 0$ no matter how small? However, if one looks more carefully at the definition of continuity, one sees that $|f(x) - f(a)| < \varepsilon$ if $|x - a| < \delta$ and $x \in \text{Dom} f$. Thus to say f is continuous at a (where a is an end point of the closed interval $I[a, b]$) we mean that for every $\varepsilon > 0$ there is a $\delta > 0$ such that $|f(x) - f(a)| < \varepsilon$ provided $0 \leq x - a < \delta$. This statement implies $x \geq a$, that is, $x \in \text{Dom} f$. In the "limit form" we frequently express this fact by writing

$$\lim_{a+} f = f(a).$$

Similar remarks apply at the right-hand end-point b. Continuity at b means $|f(x) - f(b)| < \varepsilon$ provided $0 \leq b - x < \delta$, or

$$\lim_{b-} f = f(b).$$

We conclude this chapter with four important (and classical) theorems about functions that are continuous on closed intervals. First we define *bounded* function:

Definition. *If f is defined on an interval I (open, closed, or neither) and if there is a number M such that $|f(x)| \leq M$ for all $x \in I$, then we shall say that f is* **bounded** *on I.*

Theorem 13. *If f is continuous on $I[a, b]$, then f is bounded on $I[a, b]$.*

PROOF. Let S be the set of all $s \in I[a, b]$ such that for some number N_s (which may depend on s) we have $|f(x)| \leq N_s$ for $x \in I[a, s]$. Clearly, if $s \in S$ and $a \leq x < s$, then $x \in S$. The set S is not empty since it contains a and is bounded above by b. Therefore S has a least upper bound, say s', and every $x \in I[a, s']$ is in S. We prove the theorem by showing that $s' \in S$ and that $s' = b$.

Since f is continuous on $I[a, b]$ there is, for $\varepsilon = 1$, a $\delta' > 0$ such that

$$|f(s') - f(x)| < 1 \qquad\qquad (1)$$

whenever $x \in I[a, b]$ and

$$|s' - x| < \delta'.$$

Choose $\delta < \min (\delta', b - s')$. Now let $x \in I(s' - \delta, s']$. Then

$$|s' - x| < \delta < \delta'$$

and we have

$$|f(s')| - |f(x)| \leq |f(s') - f(x)| < 1$$

or

$$|f(s')| < 1 + |f(x)|.$$

But $x \in I[a, s')$ so that $x \in S$ and there is a number N_x such that $|f(x')| \leq N_x$ for $x' \in I[a, x]$. Thus

$$|f(s')| < 1 + N_x.$$

Now let $t \in I(s' - \delta, s']$. Then

$$|f(t)| - |f(s')| \leq |f(t) - f(s')| < 1$$

or

$$|f(t)| < 1 + |f(s')| < 2 + N_x = N_{s'}.$$

Hence $s' \in S$.

Next we prove that $s' = b$. If it were not, then for any number $t \in I[s', s' + \delta)$ we should have again that

$$|f(t)| < 1 + |f(s')| < N_{s'}.$$

If $x \in I[s', t]$ we obtain

$$|f(x)| < 1 + |f(t)| < 1 + N_{s'}$$

so that t, which is greater than s', also belongs to S. This contradicts the fact that s' was the least upper bound of S.

Theorem 14. *If f is continuous on $I[a, b]$, then there is an $x^* \in I[a, b]$ such that $f(x^*) \geq f(x)$ for all x in $I[a, b]$.*

PROOF. By Theorem 13, there exists an N such that $|f(x)| \leq N$ for all $x \in I[a, b]$. Therefore f has a least upper bound (say M) on $I[a, b]$. We shall show that there is an $x^* \in I[a, b]$ such that $f(x^*) = M$.

If there were no such x^*, then $M - f(x)$ would exceed zero for all $x \in I[a, b]$ and

$$g(x) = \frac{1}{M - f(x)}$$

would be continuous and bounded on $I[a, b]$. Again by Theorem 13, there would exist an $L > 0$ such that

$$|g(x)| = \frac{1}{M - f(x)} \leq L.$$

But this last inequality implies

$$f(x) \leq M - \frac{1}{L},$$

which contradicts the fact that M is the least upper bound of f on $I[a, b]$.

Theorem 15 (*Intermediate Value Theorem*). *Let f be continuous on $I[a, b]$, let M be its least upper bound and m its greatest lower bound on $I[a, b]$. If y is any number such that $m < y < M$, then there is a number $e \in I[a, b]$ such that $f(e) = y$.*

PROOF.   Theorem 14 tells us that there are numbers c and d in $I[a, b]$ such that $f(c) = m$ and $f(d) = M$. (We shall assume $c < d$. A similar proof holds if $d < c$.) Let S be the set of all $x \in I[c, d]$ such that $f(x) < y$. The set is not empty, for example $c \in S$ and S is bounded (by d). Let e be the least upper bound of S. We claim that $f(e) = y$.

Suppose $f(e) \neq y$. Then either $f(e) < y$ or $f(e) > y$. Let us first dispose of the case $f(e) < y$.

If $f(e) < y$, let $\varepsilon = y - f(e)$. Then by the continuity of f on $I[a, b]$ there is a $\delta' > 0$ such that

$$|f(x) - f(e)| < \varepsilon = y - f(e),$$

whenever

$$|x - e| < \delta'.$$

This last condition is satisfied if $x \in I(e, e + \delta)$ where $\delta < \min(\delta', d - e)$, so that

$$f(x) - f(e) < y - f(e)$$

or

$$f(x) < y.$$

This contradicts the fact that e was an upper bound for S.

The case $f(e) > y$ also leads to a contradiction. The proof is left as an exercise for the reader.

For an application of the Intermediate Value Theorem we should like to consider a result, known as a Fixed Point Theorem, which itself also has many interesting applications.

Theorem 16. *Let f be a continuous function whose domain is the closed unit interval $I[0, 1]$ and whose range is contained in $I[0, 1]$. Then there is at least one point $x' \in I[0, 1]$ such that $f(x') = x'$. (Such a point is called a* **fixed point** *of f.)*

PROOF. If either $f(0) = 0$ or $f(1) = 1$, we are through. Suppose, then, neither is true. Then we must have $f(0) > 0$ and $f(1) < 1$. Define the function g by the rule of correspondence $g(x) = x - f(x)$ where Dom $g = I[0, 1]$. Then $g(0) = -f(0) < 0$ and $g(1) = 1 - f(1) > 0$. Therefore by Theorem 15 there is an x' in $I[0, 1]$ such that $g(x') = 0$. But $g(x') = x' - f(x')$. Thus

$$x' = f(x').$$

A generalization of this theorem to two dimensions tells us, that a continuous function that maps each point of a disc onto a point of the disc must leave at least one point fixed.

EXERCISES

1. Let $\mathscr{S}$ be a subset of the real numbers. Prove that s is an accumulation point of $\mathscr{S}$ if and only if every open interval containing s contains infinitely many points of $\mathscr{S}$.

2. Let $\mathscr{S} = \{1, 2, \cdots, n\}$. Show that $\mathscr{S}$ has no point of accumulation.

3. Does every unbounded subset of the real numbers have a point of accumulation? Justify your answer.

4. For each of the following cases determine a $\delta > 0$ such that:

(i) If $0 < |x - 2| < \delta$, then $f(x) = x^3 - 2x$ differs from 4 by less than 0.004.

(ii) If $0 < |x - 3| < \delta$, then $f(x) = 2x^2 - 3x + 1$ differs from 10 by less than 0.002.

(iii) If $0 < |x - 1| < \delta$, then $f(x) = 3x^4 - 2x + 2$ differs from 3 by less than 0.003.

5. For the following functions prove that $\lim_a f = f(a)$

(i) $f = 3j^3 - 2j + 2$ all a

(ii) $f = 5j^2 + 3j + 1$ all a

(iii) $f = \dfrac{j^2 - 2j + 1}{j^2 + 2}$ all a

(iv) $f = \dfrac{3j - 1}{j^2 - 4}$ $a \neq \pm 2$

(v) $f = \dfrac{3j^2 - 2}{j + 1}$ $a \neq -1$

(vi) $f = \dfrac{4j - 2}{3j}$ $a \neq 0$.

6. Find $\lim\limits_{h \to 0} \dfrac{f(a + h) - f(a)}{h}$ if

(i) $f = 3j^2$
(ii) $f = j^{-2}$

(iii) $f = j^3$
(iv) $f = \mathbf{k}$.

7. Find $\lim_0 f$ if:

(i) $f = \dfrac{(2 + j)^3 - 8}{j}$

(ii) $f = \dfrac{1}{j}\left(\dfrac{1}{2 + j} - \dfrac{1}{2}\right)$

(iii) $f = \dfrac{(5 - j)^{1/2} - 5^{1/2}}{j}$

(iv) $f = \dfrac{j[(3 + j)^{1/2} - 3^{1/2}]}{j^2}$

(v) $f = \dfrac{|\ |^2}{j}$

(vi) $f = \dfrac{\sin \circ \mathbf{k}j}{j}$.

8. Let $f = [\ \ ]$ and let p be an integer. Prove that $\lim_p f$ does not exist.

9. Let $f = \sin \circ 1/j$. Prove that $\lim_0 f$ does not exist.

10. (i) Give examples of functions which are defined at a (for some a) but for which $\lim_a f \neq f(a)$.

(ii) Give examples of functions which are not defined at a (for some a), but for which $\lim_a f$ does exist.

11. Show that $\lim_a f = \ell$ if and only if $\lim_a |f - \ell| = 0$.

12. Prove that $\lim_a f = b$ if and only if $\lim_0 f \circ (\mathbf{a} + j) = b$.

13. Let $f = j \sin \circ 1/j$ if $x \neq 0$ and let $f = 0$ if $x = 0$. Prove that f is continuous at $x = 0$.

14. (i) Let $f = j$ on $I(0, 1)$ and let $f = 1$ for all $x \geq 1$. Prove that f is continuous at $x = 1$.

(ii) Does $\lim\limits_{h \to 0} \dfrac{f(1 + h) - f(1)}{h}$ exist?

15. Let f be continuous on $I[0, 1]$ and let $f(x) = 0$ for all rational numbers $x \in I[0, 1]$. Prove that f is identically zero on $I[0, 1]$.

16. Assume that

$$\lim_{h \to 0} \frac{\sin (a + h) - \sin a}{h} = b$$

for any finite a. Prove that $\sin$ is continuous at a.

17. Prove Theorem 12.

18. Prove the case "$f(e) > y$" of Theorem 15.

19. Prove that

$$\lim_{h \to 0} \frac{\cos h - 1}{h} = 0.$$

20. Which of the following expressions are numbers and which are meaningless symbols?

(i) $\lim\limits_{0} \dfrac{|\ |}{j^2}$

(v) $\lim\limits_{\frac{1}{2}\pi} \sec$

(ii) $\lim_{0} \dfrac{j^2 - 2j}{j}$

(vi) $\lim_{0} \csc$

(iii) $\lim_{0} \tan$

(vii) $\lim_{0} \dfrac{j}{|\ \ |}$.

(iv) $\lim_{\frac{1}{2}\pi} \tan$

21.   (i) Find two disjoint intervals on each of which f assumes the value zero exactly once:

$$f = j^2 - 3j + 2.$$

(ii) Find three disjoint intervals on each of which g assumes the value zero exactly once:

$$g = 2j^3 - j^2 - 13j - 6.$$

22.   Prove that if f is one–one and continuous at each $x \in \mathrm{Dom}\, f$, then $f*$ is continuous at each $y \in \mathrm{Dom}\, f* = \mathrm{Ran}\, f$. [*Hint:* First show that either: (i) $\xi_1 > \xi_2$ for all ξ_1, ξ_2 in $\mathrm{Dom}\, f$ implies $f(\xi_1) > f(\xi_2)$, *or* (ii) $\xi_1 > \xi_2$ for all ξ_1, ξ_2 in $\mathrm{Dom}\, f$ implies $f(\xi_1) < f(\xi_2)$. (In other words f is either an "increasing" or "decreasing" function.) One can then use the Intermediate Value Theorem (Theorem 15) to complete the proof of the exercise.]

5

DERIVATIVES

The two main problems of the calculus are:

Problem 1. *Given:* The graph of a function f. *Find:* The slope of the tangent line to the graph at a point $P = (a, f(a))$

and

Problem 2. *Given:* Two vertical lines, $\lambda(1, 0, c_1)$ and $\lambda(1, 0, c_2)$ and the graph of a function f. *Find:* The area bounded by these two lines, the graph of f and the x-axis. (See Figure 5.1.)

These two problems are as old as the study of geometry, and for a few special cases, the ancient Greeks devised methods for obtaining the answers. The great advance made by Newton and Leibnitz was that they discovered an intimate connection between the two problems. The insight enabled them to devise a method for giving precise answers to these problems for a wide variety of functions—functions that have important applications in physics, astronomy, engineering, and economics.

For example, suppose the motion of a projectile fired from the ground is given by the formula $s = v_0 t - 16t^2$, where s (feet) is the distance above the ground, t (seconds) is the time, and v_0 (feet/second) is the initial velocity. The answer to the first Problem will enable us to predict the instantaneous velocity at any time t_1, as well as when the projectile will reach its maximum height and what that height will be. If on the other hand, the velocity v (feet/second) of the projectile is given by the formula $v = v_0 - 32t$, then the answer to the second Problem will enable us to predict its height above the ground at any time t_1, as well as when it will land. Again, if the velocity v (centimeters/second) of a

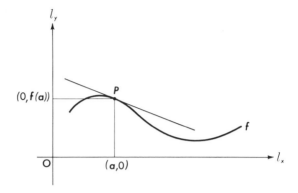

Problem 1

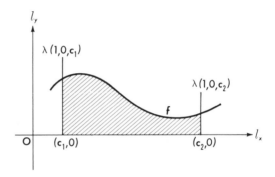

Problem 2
Figure 5.1

nuclear particle at any time t (seconds) is given by $v = 2 \times 10^{10} - 10^4 t^{-2}$, say, the answer to the first Problem will give us the acceleration of the particle at any time t. And if the force of attraction f (dynes) between two particles carrying electric charges is given by $f(x) = 10x^{-2}$ when they are x centimeters apart, the answer to the second Problem will tell us the work necessary to move them y centimeters apart. Economists also make use of the calculus—for instance—to predict production rates for maximum profits.

It is no exaggeration, therefore, to say that the calculus is one of the great inventions of the human mind and has become a major factor in the development of modern society.

In this chapter we shall center our attention on the first of the two basic problems (Problem 1) and certain ramifications that arise from its study. Chapter 6 will be concerned with Problem 2 and some of its attendant complications.

Let us explore the meaning of "tangent to a curve" in an informal manner before making a precise definition (see Section 1). We shall use the word "curve" as synonymous with "graph of a function."

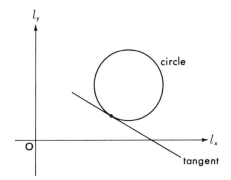

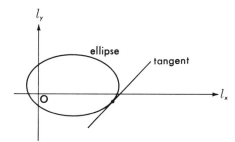

Figure 5.2

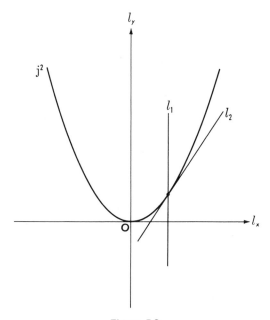

Figure 5.3

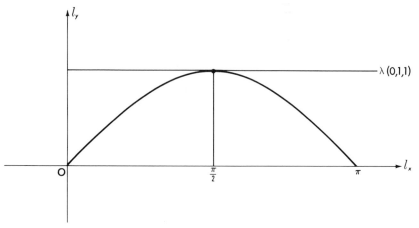

Figure 5.4

This imparts a slight geometric flavor to our discussions and makes them appear somewhat less sterile.

In elementary and high school, students sometimes are given the impression that a tangent to a curve is a line that intersects the curve only once. This is indeed true for a curve such as a circle or an ellipse (cf. Figure 5.2). But a curve such as the graph of the function j^2, for instance, has at least two lines that intersect the curve only once at each of its points (cf. Figure 5.3). Which of these lines (ℓ_1 or ℓ_2), if either, shall we call the tangent line to the curve?

Another problem is presented by the graph of the sine function. If we consider the graph of the sine function on the domain $I[0, \pi]$, then the line $\lambda(0, 1, 1)$ intersects the curve only once at the point $(\frac{1}{2}\pi, 1)$, see Figure 5.4. Now extend the domain to the whole real line. Then the line $\lambda(0, 1, 1)$ intersects the curve on infinitely many points (cf. Figure 5.5). Does $\lambda(0, 1, 1)$ now cease to be the tangent at the point $(\frac{1}{2}\pi, 1)$?

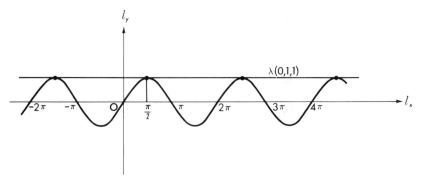

Figure 5.5

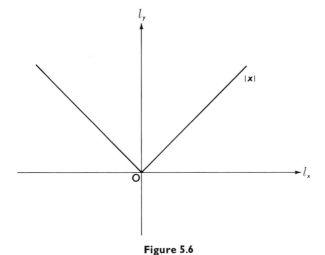

Figure 5.6

Consider also the absolute value function, | | (cf. Figure 5.6). Can one draw a tangent at the point (0, 0) that will not violate the intuitive notion of tangent?

Admittedly there is a need for a more general definition of tangent line to a curve—one that will apply to a more general class of curves than merely the circle and ellipse. We shall arrive at a suitable definition in Section 1.

I. DEFINITION OF THE DERIVATIVE

As we mentioned above, "curve," is synonymous with "graph of a function." Sometimes we shall speak simply of the "curve f" instead of the "graph of the function f." Referring to Figure 5.7, let f be a

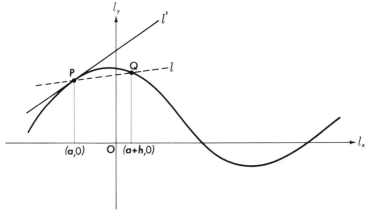

Figure 5.7

function with an interval as domain, let $P = (a, f(a))$ be a fixed point and $Q = (a + h, f(a + h))$ any other distinct point. This of course implies $h \neq 0$, $a \in \text{Dom} f$, $a + h \in \text{Dom} f$. Now construct the line ℓ joining P and Q. If we take $|h|$ smaller and smaller, the point Q gets closer and closer to the point P. The resulting line ℓ through P and Q approaches the solid line ℓ' through P. That is, the solid line through P is the "limiting position" of the line through P and Q as $|h|$ gets close to zero; and the slope

$$\frac{f(a + h) - f(a)}{h}$$

of ℓ must get close to the slope of ℓ'.

With the above considerations in mind we make the following definition of tangent line to a point $(a, f(a))$ on the curve f.

Definition. *Let f be a function with domain $\text{Dom} f$. Let the interval $I(a - |h|, a + |h|)$ be in $\text{Dom} f$. Then if*

$$\lim_{h \to 0} \frac{f(a + h) - f(a)}{h}$$

*exists, the line through the point $(a, f(a))$ with slope $m = \lim_{h \to 0}[f(a + h) - f(a)]/h$ is called the **tangent line** to the curve f at $(a, f(a))$.*

If the limit does not exist, then either the graph of f does not have a tangent at $(a, f(a))$ or the tangent exists and is parallel to ℓ_y. Usually, an examination of the graph of f will reveal which alternative obtains.

Example 1. *What is the slope of the tangent line to the parabolic curve j^2 through the point $P = (3, 3^2)$?*

Let h be any number unequal to zero and consider the point $Q = (3 + h, (3 + h)^2)$. (Since $\text{Dom} j^2$ is the set of all real numbers; 3, $3 + h$, and $\langle 3, x, 3 + h \rangle$ are all in $\text{Dom} j^2$.) Then the slope of the line through P and Q is

$$\frac{(3 + h)^2 - 3^2}{h} = \frac{9 + 6h + h^2 - 9}{h} = \frac{6h + h^2}{h} = 6 + h$$

and the slope of the tangent line to the curve j^2 (if it exists) is

$$\lim_{h \to 0} (6 + h).$$

(See Figure 5.8.) But clearly the above limit does exist and its value is 6. Thus the slope m of the tangent line to the parabolic curve j^2 at the point $(3, 9)$ is

$$m = 6.$$

Example 2. *Draw the graph of $g = j^2 + 3j + 1$ and find the slope of the tangent line to this graph at the point $P = (a, a^2 + 3a + 1)$.*

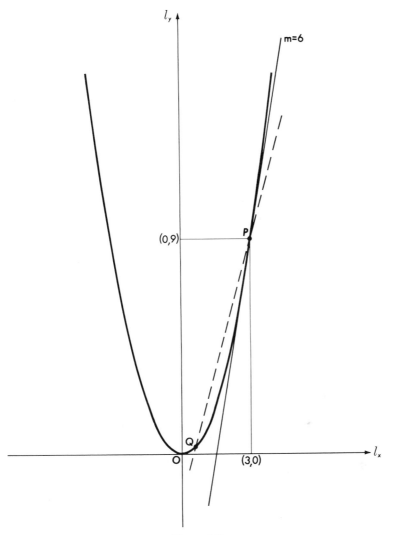

Figure 5.8

The graph of g appears in Figure 5.9 below. If the slope exists at P, it is, by definition,

$$m = \lim_{h \to 0} \frac{[(a + h)^2 + 3(a + h) + 1] - [a^2 + 3a + 1]}{h}$$

$$= \lim_{h \to 0} \frac{2ah + h^2 + 3h}{h} = \lim_{h \to 0} (2a + h + 3) = 2a + 3.$$

Let us examine the result of Example 2 more closely. We see that for each number a for which

$$\lim_{h \to 0} \frac{g(a + h) - g(a)}{h}$$

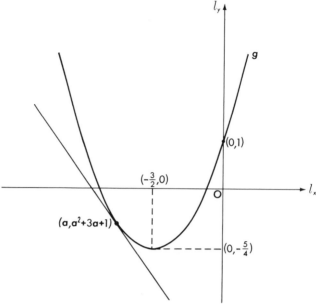

Figure 5.9

exists we shall obtain the slope $2a + 3$. In general, therefore, if f is any
function defined on an interval we can consider the set $\mathscr{S}$ of numbers
x such that $\lim_{h \to 0} [f(x + h) - f(x)]/h$ exists. (Clearly $\mathscr{S} \subset \mathrm{Dom}\, f$,
and it is possible for $\mathscr{S}$ to be empty.) On $\mathscr{S}$ we define a new function
which we shall call the *derivative function*. The derivative function of f,
denoted by Df, is the set of ordered pairs

$$\left\{ \left(x, \lim_{h \to 0} \frac{f(x + h) - f(x)}{h} \right) \right\}$$

for $x \in \mathscr{S}$. Alternatively we can say that Df is the function whose rule
of correspondence is

$$(Df)(x) = \lim_{h \to 0} \frac{f(x + h) - f(x)}{h}, \quad x \in \mathscr{S}.$$

This derivative function Df—which is more often called the *derivative
of f*—has the property that the height of its graph above the point
$(a, 0)$, that is $(Df)(a)$, is the slope of the tangent line to the graph of f
at the point $(a, f(a))$. For this reason the curve Df is sometimes
referred to as the *slope curve* of f. Having defined the slope of the curve
of f at $P = (a, f(a))$ as $(Df)(a)$, we see that the equation of the tangent
line to f at P is given by $(Df)(a)(a - x) + y = f(a)$. Later on (Chapter
6) we shall see that the rise in f from $(a, f(a))$ to $(b, f(b))$ is a measure
of the area bounded by Df, the lines $\lambda(1, 0, a)$, $\lambda(1, 0, b)$ and the x-axis.
Thus f is sometimes referred to as an *area curve* of Df.

If $g = Df$ is the derivative of f, it is possible that g itself has a derivative. In particular, if Dg exists at a we write

$$(Dg)(a) = \lim_{h \to 0} \frac{g(a + h) - g(a)}{h} = \lim_{h \to 0} \frac{(Df)(a + h) - (Df)(a)}{h}.$$

An alternate notation for Dg is $D(Df)$ or simply D^2f. We call D^2f the *second derivative* of f. It is of course possible that $D^3f, D^4f, \cdots$ exist. We shall occasionally use D^2f, but we shall have little use for the higher derivatives of f in this text. A geometric interpretation of the second derivative can be made in terms of the *curvature* of f. Geometric explanations of higher derivatives are more difficult to analyze. The study of the properties and applications of derivatives is referred to as the *differential calculus*.

2. DERIVATIVES OF SOME SPECIAL FUNCTIONS

To gain familiarity with the operation of finding the derivative of a function f we consider some special cases that frequently arise in practice. In all the illustrations of this section $\text{Dom}\, f = \text{Dom}\, Df$. For simplicity in notation we shall write the derivative of f at a as $Df(a)$ rather than use the previously employed more complex notation $(Df)(a)$. No confusion should arise.

Example 1. *If $f = \mathbf{k}$ (where k is any real number) then*

$$Df = \mathbf{0}.$$

By definition

$$Df(a) = \lim_{h \to 0} \frac{f(a + h) - f(a)}{h} = \lim_{h \to 0} \frac{k - k}{h} = \lim_{h \to 0} \frac{0}{h} = 0.$$

Example 2. *If $f = j$, then*

$$Df = \mathbf{1}.$$

By definition

$$Df(a) = \lim_{h \to 0} \frac{j(a + h) - j(a)}{h} = \lim_{h \to 0} \frac{a + h - a}{h} = \lim_{h \to 0} 1 = 1.$$

If $f = j^2$, then we saw in Example 1 of the previous section that $Df(3) = 6$. More generally:

Example 3. *If $f = j^2$, then*

$$Df = \mathbf{2j}.$$

Again, by definition,

$$Df(a) = \lim_{h \to 0} \frac{j^2(a+h) - j^2(a)}{h} = \lim_{h \to 0} \frac{a^2 + 2ah + h^2 - a^2}{h}$$

$$= \lim_{h \to 0} (2a + h) = 2a = 2j(a).$$

Suppose now we consider the more general problem of finding Df when $f = j^n$ and n is a positive integer. We have the following elegant result:

Example 4. *If $f = j^n$ (where $n > 0$ is an integer), then*

$$Df = \mathbf{n} j^{n-1}. \tag{1}$$

From our definition,

$$Df(a) = \lim_{h \to 0} \frac{j^n(a+h) - j^n(a)}{h}$$

and by the binomial theorem

$$Df(a) = \lim_{h \to 0} \frac{\left[a^n + n a^{n-1}h + \dfrac{n(n-1)}{2} a^{n-2}h^2 + \cdots + h^n \right] - a^n}{h}$$

$$= \lim_{h \to 0} \left[n a^{n-1} + \frac{n(n-1)}{2} a^{n-2}h + \cdots + h^{n-1} \right] = n j^{n-1}(a).$$

The above result raises the further question: Is the above formula [equation (1)] valid for n a *negative integer*? The answer is "yes", as we demonstrate in Example 5 below.

Example 5. *If $f = j^{-n}$ (where $n > 0$ is an integer), then*

$$Df = -\mathbf{n} j^{-n-1}.$$

Assume $a \neq 0$. Then as usual

$$Df(a) = \lim_{h \to 0} \frac{j^{-n}(a+h) - j^{-n}(a)}{h} = \lim_{h \to 0} \frac{1/(a+h)^n - 1/a^n}{h}$$

$$= \lim_{h \to 0} \frac{a^n - (a+h)^n}{a^n(a+h)^n h}.$$

Now apply the binomial theorem to the term $(a+h)^n$ in the numerator of the above limit. Then

$$Df(a) = \lim_{h \to 0} \frac{\left[-n a^{n-1} - \dfrac{n(n-1)}{2} a^{n-2}h - \cdots - h^{n-1} \right]}{a^n (a+h)^n}$$

where we have canceled h. But by the corollary to Theorem 7 of Chapter 4,

$$Df(a) = \frac{\lim\limits_{h \to 0} \left[-na^{n-1} - \dfrac{n(n-1)}{2} a^{n-2}h - \cdots - h^{n-1} \right]}{\lim\limits_{h \to 0} a^n(a+h)^n}$$

$$= \frac{-na^{n-1}}{a^{2n}} = -na^{-n-1} = -nj^{-n-1}(a).$$

The results of Examples 1, 4, and 5 imply that if

$$f = j^n$$

then

$$Df = nj^{n-1} \tag{2}$$

where n is an integer—positive, negative, or zero. One would like to extend this result to the case where n is *any* real number. In Example 6 below we shall establish (2) for n a positive rational number. The case of n a negative rational number will be left as an exercise for the reader. If n is *not* a rational number, the result is still true; but in this case we have to resort to other techniques. (For example, the use of logarithms is appropriate. See the exercises at the end of the chapter as well as Chapter 7.)

Example 6. *If $f = j^{p/q}$ (where p and q are positive integers), then*

$$Df = \frac{p}{q} j^{(p/q)-1}.$$

To prove this result let h be any nonzero number and define, for $a > 0$,

$$u(h) = (a+h)^{1/q}$$

and

$$v(a) = a^{1/q}.$$

Then

$$\lim_{h \to 0} u(h) = v(a).$$

Also, since $a + h = u^q(h)$ and $a = v^q(a)$ we may write

$$h = u^q(h) - v^q(a).$$

Using these facts, we see that the difference quotient

$$\frac{j^{p/q}(a+h) - j^{p/q}(a)}{h}$$

becomes

$$\frac{u^p(h) - v^p(a)}{u^q(h) - v^q(a)}$$

and

$$Df(a) = \lim_{h \to 0} \frac{[u(h) - v(a)][u^{p-1}(h) + u^{p-2}(h)v(a) + \cdots + v^{p-1}(a)]}{[u(h) - v(a)][u^{q-1}(h) + u^{q-2}(h)v(a) + \cdots + v^{q-1}(a)]}.$$

After canceling $u(h) - v(a)$, we see that the numerator of the above expression contains p terms, the denominator, q terms. Since

$$\lim_{h \to 0} u^{p-i}(h)v^{i-1}(a) = v^{p-1}(a)$$

and

$$\lim_{h \to 0} u^{q-j}(h)v^{j-1}(a) = v^{q-1}(a)$$

we infer

$$Df(a) = \frac{pv^{p-1}(a)}{qv^{q-1}(a)} = \frac{p(a^{1/q})^{p-1}}{q(a^{1/q})^{q-1}} = \frac{p}{q}(a^{1/q})^{p-q}$$

$$= \frac{p}{q}a^{(p/q)-1} = \frac{p}{q}j^{(p/q)-1}(a)$$

for any positive a.

For our last illustration let us turn our attention to the calculation of the derivative of a different kind of function. We choose the sine function.

Example 7. *If $f = \sin$, then*

$$D \sin = \cos. \tag{3}$$

By definition

$$Df(a) = \lim_{h \to 0} \frac{\sin (a + h) - \sin a}{h}$$

$$= \lim_{h \to 0} \frac{2 \cos \frac{1}{2}(2a + h) \sin \frac{1}{2}h}{h}$$

$$= [\lim_{h \to 0} \cos (a + \tfrac{1}{2}h)]\left[\lim_{h \to 0} \frac{\sin \frac{1}{2}h}{\frac{1}{2}h}\right].$$

But from Section 4 of the previous chapter

$$\lim_{h \to 0} \cos (a + \tfrac{1}{2}h) = \cos a$$

and

$$\lim_{h \to 0} \frac{\sin \frac{1}{2}h}{\frac{1}{2}h} = 1.$$

Thus (3) is established.

3. SOME GENERAL RULES OF DIFFERENTIATION

In Section 2 of Chapter 4 we saw, under suitable hypotheses, that if $\lim_a f$ and $\lim_a g$ exist, then so does $\lim_a (f \pm g)$, $\lim_a fg$, and $\lim_a f/g$. The same situation prevails for derivatives, although the results are not necessarily as simple. For example, if Df and Dg exist, then $D(fg)$ exists, but $D(fg)$ is not necessarily equal to $(Df)(Dg)$. The easiest case, of course, is the sum.

Theorem 1.   *Let $I(a, b) \subset \mathrm{Dom}\ (g_1 + g_2)$ and let Dg_1 and Dg_2 exist at a point c in $I(a, b)$. Then if $f = g_1 + g_2$, Df exists and*

$$Df(c) = Dg_1(c) + Dg_2(c).$$

PROOF.   By definition

$$\frac{f(c + h) - f(c)}{h} = \frac{(g_1 + g_2)(c + h) - (g_1 + g_2)(c)}{h}$$

$$= \frac{g_1(c + h) + g_2(c + h) - g_1(c) - g_2(c)}{h}$$

$$= \frac{g_1(c + h) - g_1(c)}{h} + \frac{g_2(c + h) - g_2(c)}{h}.$$

Hence Df exists and

$$Df(c) = \lim_{h \to 0} \frac{g_1(c + h) - g_1(c)}{h} + \lim_{h \to 0} \frac{g_2(c + h) - g_2(c)}{h}$$

$$= Dg_1(c) + Dg_2(c).$$

For a simple illustration of the above theorem we note that if

$$f = j^2 + \sin$$

then

$$Df = Dj^2 + D \sin$$

and by Example 3 and Example 7 of the previous section

$$Df = 2j + \cos.$$

Before proceeding with the formula for the derivative of the product, we would like to mention a relation between *continuity* and *differentiability*. The two notions are not identical in content. For example, $|x|$ is continuous but not differentiable at $x = 0$. (Prove this!) On the other hand we shall prove in Theorem 2 below that if f is differentiable at a, it is continuous at a. In other words, as might be suspected, differentiability implies continuity (but not conversely), and hence is a more restrictive classification of functions.

Theorem 2. *Let $I(a, b) \subset \text{Dom } f$. Let Df exist at $c \in I(a, b)$. Then f is continuous at c.*

PROOF. By definition

$$Df(c) = \lim_{h \to 0} \frac{f(c + h) - f(c)}{h}$$

for $c + h \in I(a, b)$. In other words, given any $\varepsilon > 0$ there is a $\delta > 0$ such that

$$\left| \frac{f(c + h) - f(c)}{h} - Df(c) \right| < \varepsilon \tag{1}$$

whenever $0 < |h| < \delta$. Now for $h > 0$, (1) is equivalent to

$$[Df(c) - \varepsilon]h < f(c + h) - f(c) < [Df(c) + \varepsilon]h$$

and

$$\lim_{h \to 0} [Df(c) - \varepsilon]h = 0 = \lim_{h \to 0} [Df(c) + \varepsilon]h.$$

Hence by Theorem 9 of Chapter 4,

$$\lim_{h \to 0} [f(c + h) - f(c)] = 0$$

or

$$\lim_{h \to 0} f(c + h) = f(c). \tag{2}$$

If $h < 0$, a similar argument again yields (2). (See also Exercise 11 of Chapter 4.) But (2) is the definition of continuity of f at c, viz.:

$$\lim_{c} f = f(c).$$

We now derive the formula for the derivative of the product of two functions.

Theorem 3. *Let $I(a, b) \subset (\text{Dom } g_1) \cap (\text{Dom } g_2)$. Let Dg_1 and Dg_2 exist at a point $c \in I(a, b)$. Then if $f = g_1 g_2$, Df exists and,*

$$Df(c) = g_1(c)Dg_2(c) + g_2(c)Dg_1(c).$$

PROOF. By definition

$$\frac{f(c + h) - f(c)}{h} = \frac{(g_1 g_2)(c + h) - (g_1 g_2)(c)}{h}$$

$$= \frac{g_1(c + h)g_2(c + h) - g_1(c)g_2(c)}{h}.$$

In the numerator of the above expression subtract and add $g_1(c + h)g_2(c)$:

$$\frac{g_1(c + h)g_2(c + h) - g_1(c + h)g_2(c) + g_1(c + h)g_2(c) - g_1(c)g_2(c)}{h}$$

$$= g_1(c + h)\left[\frac{g_2(c + h) - g_2(c)}{h} \right] + g_2(c)\left[\frac{g_1(c + h) - g_1(c)}{h} \right].$$

Hence Df exists and

$$Df(c) = \left[\lim_{h \to 0} g_1(c + h)\right] \lim_{h \to 0} \frac{g_2(c + h) - g_2(c)}{h}$$
$$+ g_2(c) \lim_{h \to 0} \frac{g_1(c + h) - g_1(c)}{h}.$$

By Theorem 2, $\lim_{h \to 0} g_1(c + h) = g_1(c)$ and by hypothesis,

$$\lim_{h \to 0} \left[\frac{g_1(c + h) - g_1(c)}{h}\right] \quad \text{and} \quad \lim_{h \to 0} \left[\frac{g_2(c + h) - g_2(c)}{h}\right]$$

exist. The proof of our theorem is complete.

For a simple illustration of the above theorem, we note that if

$$f = j^2 \sin$$

then

$$Df = j^2 D \sin + \sin Dj^2$$

or

$$Df = j^2 \cos + (\sin)(2j).$$

Since $D\mathbf{k} = \mathbf{0}$ by Example 1 of Section 2, we immediately obtain the following corollary to Theorem 3:

Corollary. *Let $c \in \text{Dom } g$ and let $Dg(c)$ exist. Then for any real number k, $D\mathbf{k}g$ exists and*

$$D\mathbf{k}g = \mathbf{k}Dg.$$

PROOF.   By Theorem 3,

$$D\mathbf{k}g = \mathbf{k}Dg + gD\mathbf{k}.$$

But $D\mathbf{k} = \mathbf{0}$.

We now turn to the "function of a function rule" or "chain rule" of differentiation. Essentially it states (Theorem 4 below) that

$$Df \circ g(c) = Df(g(c))Dg(c).$$

Suppose f has a derivative at a point d in its domain. Consider now the expression

$$\frac{f(d + k) - f(d)}{k} - Df(d). \tag{3}$$

If $k \neq 0$ is small, the above difference will be small. Call it $\varepsilon(k)$. Now (3) is not defined at $k = 0$ since $[f(d + k) - f(d)]/k$ is not defined. However,

$$\lim_{k \to 0} \varepsilon(k) = \lim_{k \to 0} \frac{f(d + k) - f(d) - kDf(d)}{k} \tag{4}$$

exists and equals zero. Thus if we define $\varepsilon(0)$ to be zero, ε will be continuous at $k = 0$. After these preliminary remarks let us state and prove our "chain rule of differentiation" theorem.

Theorem 4.   *Let f have for its domain the open interval $I(a, b)$. Let Df exist at a point $d \in I(a, b)$. Let g be a function whose range is contained in $I(a, b)$ and also such that $d \in \text{Ran } g$. Let $g(c) = d$. Then if $Dg(c)$ exists, $Df \circ g(c)$ also exists and*

$$Df \circ g(c) = Df(g(c))Dg(c).$$

PROOF.   We show that

$$\lim_{h \to 0} \frac{f(g(c + h)) - f(g(c))}{h} = Df(g(c))Dg(c).$$

Now $d = g(c)$ and let

$$k(h) = g(c + h) - g(c).$$

Since g has a derivative at c, it is continuous at c, and hence

$$\lim_{h \to 0} k(h) = 0.$$

Let

$$\varepsilon(k(h)) = \frac{f(d + k(h)) - f(d) - kDf(d)}{k(h)}$$

if $k(h) \neq 0$ and let $\varepsilon(k(h)) = 0$ if $k(h) = 0$, [cf. (4).]. Then

$$\lim_{h \to 0} \varepsilon(k(h)) = 0,$$

[cf. Theorem 8 of Chapter 4.] Hence

$$\lim_{h \to 0} \frac{f(g(c + h)) - f(g(c))}{h}$$

$$= \lim_{h \to 0} \frac{f(d + k(h)) - f(d)}{h}$$

$$= \lim_{h \to 0} \frac{k(h)\varepsilon(k(h)) + k(h)Df(d)}{h}$$

$$= \lim_{h \to 0} \left[\frac{g(c + h) - g(c)}{h}\right][\varepsilon(k(h)) + Df(d)]$$

$$= \lim_{h \to 0} \left[\frac{g(c + h) - g(c)}{h}\right]\left[\lim_{h \to 0} \varepsilon(k(h))\right] + \lim_{h \to 0} \left[\frac{g(c + h) - g(c)}{h}\right]Df(d)$$

$$= Dg(c) \cdot 0 + Dg(c) \cdot Df(d)$$

$$= Dg(c)Df(g(c)).$$

For an application of the chain rule we shall derive the very useful formula for the derivative of f^n.

Theorem 5.   *Let $I(a, b) \subset \text{Dom } f$. Let $c \in I(a, b)$ and let $Df(c)$ exist. Let n be an integer: positive, negative, or zero. If n is negative, let $f(c) \neq 0$. Then*

$$Df^n(c) = nf^{n-1}(c)Df(c). \tag{5}$$

PROOF.   We may write

$$f^n = j^n \circ f$$

so that

$$Df^n(c) = Dj^n \circ f(c).$$

Applying Theorem 4 to $j^n \circ f$ and recalling (2) of Section 2, we find

$$Dj^n \circ f(c) = [nj^{n-1} \circ f(c)]Df(c).$$

The formula for the derivative of the reciprocal, f^{-1} of f is an immediate consequence:

Corollary 1.   *Let $I(a, b) \subset \text{Dom } f$. Let $c \in I(a, b)$ and let $Df(c)$ exist. If $f(c) \neq 0$, then $Df^{-1}(c)$ exists and*

$$Df^{-1}(c) = -\frac{Df(c)}{f^2(c)}.$$

PROOF.   Let $n = -1$ in Theorem 5.

Of course this result can be proved without recourse to the function of a function rule. We leave this alternate proof to the reader.

A few simple examples will illustrate the use of the above theorems.

Example 1.   *If $f = (j^2 + 5)^9$, find Df.*

By (5),

$$\begin{aligned} Df &= 9(j^2 + 5)^8 D(j^2 + 5) \\ &= 9(j^2 + 5)^8(2j) \\ &= 18j(j^2 + 5)^8. \end{aligned}$$

Example 2.   *Let $f = \sin \circ 1/j$ on some interval excluding zero. Find $Df(c)$ for $c \neq 0$.*
By Theorem 4

$$\begin{aligned} D \sin \circ \frac{1}{j}(c) &= \left(\cos \frac{1}{c}\right) D \frac{1}{j}(c) \\ &= \left(\cos \frac{1}{c}\right)\left(-\frac{1}{c^2}\right) \\ &= -\frac{1}{c^2} \cos \frac{1}{c}. \end{aligned}$$

Example 3. *Let $f = \sin$, find $D\csc$ at any x which is not an integral multiple of π.*

Since $\csc = f^{-1}$ we can use Corollary 1 to Theorem 5 to write

$$D \csc = -\frac{D\sin}{(\sin)^2} = -\frac{\cos}{(\sin)^2} = -\csc\cot.$$

Theorem 3 for the derivative of the product and Corollary 1 to Theorem 5 immediately yield the additional corollary:

Corollary 2. *Let $(\text{Dom} f) \cap (\text{Dom} g)$ contain $I(a, b)$. Let $c \in I(a, b)$ and let $Df(c)$ and $Dg(c)$ both exist. Then if $g(c) \neq 0$, $D(f/g)(c)$ exists and*

$$D\frac{f}{g}(c) = \frac{g(c)Df(c) - f(c)Dg(c)}{g^2(c)}. \tag{6}$$

For example,

$$D\frac{x^3 + 4x}{3x + 2} = \frac{(3x + 2)(3x^2 + 4) - (x^3 + 4x)(3)}{(3x + 2)^2}$$

$$= \frac{6x^3 + 6x^2 + 8}{(3x + 2)^2}$$

if $x \neq -2/3$.

We prove one final result on the derivative of the inverse f^* of f. First we observe that if $Df^*(c)$ exists and if $Df \neq 0$ at $f^*(c)$, then using Theorem 4, we get

$$1 = Dj(c) = Df \circ f^*(c) = Df(f^*(c))Df^*(c)$$

or

$$Df^*(c) = \frac{1}{Df(f^*(c))}. \tag{7}$$

The following theorem gives the conditions for the existence of Df^*.

Theorem 6. *Let f be one–one on $\text{Dom} f = I(a, b)$. If f has a derivative on $I(a, b)$ and if $Df \neq 0$ on $I(a, b)$, then its inverse f^* has a derivative on $\text{Ran} f = \text{Dom} f^*$ and*

$$Df^* = \frac{1}{(Df) \circ f^*}.$$

PROOF. Let x and $x + h$ be in $\text{Dom} f^*$ and let

$$k(h) = f^*(x + h) - f^*(x).$$

Since f^* is one–one, $k(h) \neq 0$ when $h \neq 0$. The continuity of f^* (see Exercise 22 of Chapter 4) implies that $k(h)$ approaches zero as h approaches zero. Now

$$f(f^*(x + h)) = x + h = f(f^*(x) + k(h))$$

[since $f*(x + h) = f*(x) + k(h)$] and furthermore

$$x = f(f*(x)).$$

Thus for $h \neq 0$,

$$\frac{f*(x + h) - f*(x)}{h} = \frac{1}{\dfrac{h}{f*(x + h) - f*(x)}}$$

$$= \frac{1}{\dfrac{f(f*(x) + k(h)) - f(f*(x))}{k(h)}}. \qquad (8)$$

As $h \to 0$, the limit of the right-hand side of (8) exists and equals

$$\frac{1}{(Df)(f*(x))}$$

(since $Df \neq 0$). Therefore the limit of the left-hand side of (8) exists, and by definition is $Df*(x)$.

For an example of Theorem 6, consider the sine function. Now sin is one–one on $I(-\pi/2, \pi/2)$ and $D \sin = \cos \neq 0$ on $I(-\pi/2, \pi/2)$. Thus for $c \in \operatorname{Ran} \sin = \operatorname{Dom} \sin^* = I(-1, 1)$,

$$D \sin^* (c) = \frac{1}{\cos(\sin^* c)} = \frac{1}{\sqrt{1 - [\sin \circ \sin^* (c)]^2}}$$

$$= \frac{1}{\sqrt{1 - c^2}}.$$

Of course, a more common name for $\sin^*$ is Arcsin.

4. MAXIMA AND MINIMA, ROLLE'S THEOREM, AND CONSEQUENCES

One of the first and most elementary applications of the differential calculus is the problem of determining *maxima* and *minima* of functions. Let us first define these terms. Let f be a function. Let x_0 be a point in Dom f. If for all $x \in \operatorname{Dom} f$ we have $f(x_0) \geq f(x)$, then we call $f(x_0)$ a *maximum* of f (on Dom f). If $f(x_0) \leq f(x)$ for all $x \in \operatorname{Dom} f$, then $f(x_0)$ is called a *minimum* of f (on Dom f). The relation between maxima (minima) and derivative will be clearly brought out in Theorem 7 below.

The crucial fact needed in the proof of Theorem 7 is Theorem 14 of Chapter 4. This theorem states that if f is continuous on $I[a, b]$, then for some $x_0 \in I[a, b]$, $f(x_0)$ is a maximum for f on $I[a, b]$. Of course, Theorem 14 of Chapter 4 also implies that f has a minimum on $I[a, b]$; for a minimum of f is a maximum of $-f$. It is also noteworthy that

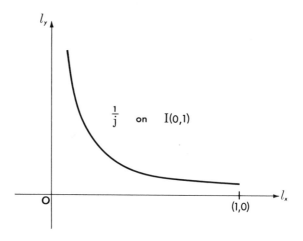

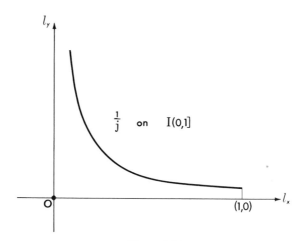

Figure 5.10

both the conditions (i) The interval be closed, and (ii) The function be continuous on the interval, are required. For if either of these conditions is violated, then the theorem is no longer necessarily true. For an illustration of (i), let $f = 1/j$ on $I(0, 1)$. Then f is continuous on the *open* interval $I(0, 1)$, but has no maximum on $I(0, 1)$. For an illustration of (ii), let $f = 1/j$ on $I(0, 1]$ and $f(0) = 0$. Then f is defined on the closed interval $I[0, 1]$, but is *not* continuous there. Clearly f is unbounded on $I[0, 1]$. (See Figure 5.10.)

We now turn to the proof of Theorem 7, which establishes the connection between maxima (minima) and derivatives.

Theorem 7. *Let f be defined on I[a, b] and let x' ∈ I(a, b). If f(x') is a maximum or a minimum for f on I[a, b] and if Df(x') exists, then Df(x') = 0.*

PROOF.   Since $f(x')$ is a maximum for f on $I[a, b]$, Theorem 14 of Chapter 4 implies

$$f(x' + h) - f(x') \leq 0 \tag{1}$$

for all h such that $x' + h \in I[a, b]$. If $h > 0$, then

$$\frac{f(x' + h) - f(x')}{h} \leq 0 \tag{2}$$

and if $h < 0$

$$\frac{f(x' + h) - f(x')}{h} \geq 0. \tag{3}$$

But by hypothesis $Df(x')$ exists. Therefore the left-hand members of (2) and (3) must have a common limit, which must be zero.

Clearly, by reversing the inequality in (1) we establish Theorem 7 if $f(x')$ is a minimum.

The converse of Theorem 7 requires a bit more discussion. For example, if

$$g(x) = 3x^3 + 8x^2 + 3x - 2$$

then

$$Dg(x) = 9x^2 + 16x + 3$$

and setting Dg equal to zero yields

$$x = \frac{-8 \pm \sqrt{37}}{9} = -0.213, -1.565.$$

It is clear from the graph of g (cf. Figure 5.11) that $x = -1.565$ is a maximum and $x = -0.213$ is a minimum only if Dom g is suitably restricted. We shall return to a more detailed discussion of maxima and minima later in this section.

Two important theorems involving derivatives are Rolle's Theorem (Theorem 8) and the mean value theorem (Theorem 9). Applications of these two theorems abound throughout the remainder of this book. (The mean value theorem is often referred to as the "Law of the Mean".)

Theorem 8 (*Rolle's Theorem*). *If f is continuous on I[a, b] and differentiable on I(a, b), and if f(a) = f(b), then there exists at least one point x' ∈ I(a, b) such that Df(x') = 0.*

PROOF.   If $f = \mathbf{k}$, where k is a real number, then for any $x \in I(a, b)$ we have $Df = 0$ and our theorem is true.

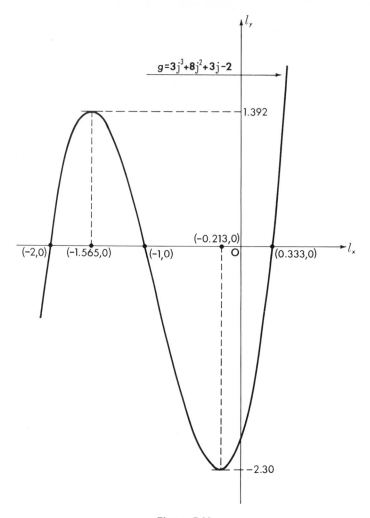

Figure 5.11

Suppose now that f is not a constant function. Then for some $x \in I(a, b)$ either $f(x) > f(a)$ or $f(x) < f(a)$. In either case Theorem 14 of Chapter 4 implies the existence of an $x_0 \in I(a, b)$ such that $f(x_0)$ is a maximum or a minimum on $I[a, b]$. By Theorem 7

$$Df(x_0) = 0.$$

Theorem 9 (*The mean value theorem*). *Let f be continuous on $I[a, b]$ and differentiable on $I(a, b)$. Then there is an $x' \in I(a, b)$ such that*

$$f(b) - f(a) = (b - a)Df(x').$$

PROOF. Let $x \in I(a, b)$ and consider

$$A(x) = \frac{1}{2} \begin{vmatrix} a & f(a) & 1 \\ b & f(b) & 1 \\ x & f(x) & 1 \end{vmatrix}$$

$$= \frac{a}{2} [f(b) - f(x)] - \frac{b}{2} [f(a) - f(x)] + \frac{x}{2} [f(a) - f(b)].$$

(Recall the "area function" of Section 4 of Chapter 2.) We note that A is continuous on $I[a, b]$, differentiable on $I(a, b)$, and $A(a) = 0 = A(b)$. Thus all the conditions of Rolle's Theorem are satisfied. Hence there exists an x' in the open interval $I(a, b)$ such that $DA(x') = 0$. But

$$DA(x) = -\frac{a}{2} Df(x) + \frac{b}{2} Df(x) + \frac{1}{2} [f(a) - f(b)].$$

Hence

$$0 = -aDf(x') + bDf(x') + [f(a) - f(b)],$$

which proves Theorem 9.

Theorems 7, 8, and 9 are basic theorems exploiting and illuminating certain properties of continuous and differentiable functions. We have also seen examples of functions that are not continuous, that are continuous and not differentiable, that are neither continuous nor differentiable. (Of course, by Theorem 2, if a function is differentiable it must be continuous.) Are there any other classes of functions of interest in pure mathematics and of practical use in applied mathematics? The answer is yes. One such class of functions is the class of *monotone functions*. We shall define what is meant by a monotone function and prove various interesting results concerning monotone functions. In particular, we shall show, using the above theorems, various relations that exist among monotone, continuous, and differentiable functions.

Definition. *If for all a, $b \in$ Dom f with $a < b$ we have $f(a) < f(b)$, then we say f is **strictly increasing**. If $a < b$ implies $f(a) > f(b)$, we say f is **strictly decreasing**. If $a < b$ implies $f(a) \le f(b)$, we say f is **monotone increasing**. If $a < b$ implies $f(a) \ge f(b)$, we say f is **monotone decreasing**. The term **monotone function** is used to describe functions in any of the four situations above.*

Using this definition and the mean value theorem we may prove:

Theorem 10. *Let f be continuous on $I[a, b]$. Let $Df(x) > 0$ for all $x \in I(a, b)$. Then f is strictly increasing on $I[a, b]$.*

PROOF. Let $x', x'' \in I[a, b]$ with $x' < x''$. Then by Theorem 9,

$$f(x'') - f(x') = (x'' - x')Df(x^*) \tag{4}$$

where $x' < x* < x''$. Hence $x* \in I(a, b)$, and by hypothesis $Df(x*) > 0$. By construction $x'' > x'$. Therefore (4) implies $f(x'') - f(x') > 0$ or

$$f(x'') > f(x')$$

for all $x'' > x'$ in $I[a, b]$.

The reader may readily establish the following analogous results for f continuous on $I[a, b]$:

(i) If $Df(x) < 0$ for $x \in I(a, b)$, then f is strictly decreasing on $I[a, b]$.
(ii) If $Df(x) \geq 0$ for $x \in I(a, b)$, then f is monotone increasing on $I[a, b]$.
(iii) If $Df(x) \leq 0$ for $x \in I(a, b)$, then f is monotone decreasing on $I[a, b]$.

The reader may also prove that if f is strictly increasing on $I[a, b]$ and Df exists on $I(a, b)$, then $Df \geq 0$ on $I(a, b)$. Note that this result cannot be strengthened to read "$Df > 0$". For example, $f = j^3$ is strictly increasing on $I[-1, 1]$, but $Df(0) = 0$ (see Figure 5.12).

The concept of a *relative maximum* (*minimum*) is important in many problems. We define these terms.

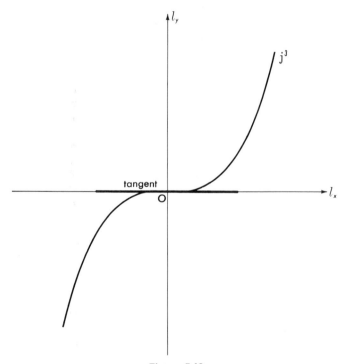

Figure 5.12

Definition. *Let $I[a, b]$ be a closed interval contained in the domain of a function f. Then $f(x_0)$ is called a **relative maximum** of f if for $x_0 \in I[a, b] \subset \operatorname{Dom} f$, the maximum of f on $I[a, b]$ is $f(x_0)$. A **relative minimum** is defined analogously.*

The above definition leads to the following theorem.

Theorem 11. *Let f be continuous on $I[a, b] \subset \operatorname{Dom} f$, let $a < x_0 < b$, and let $Df(x) \geqq 0$ for $x \in I(a, x_0)$ and $Df(x) \leqq 0$ for $x \in I(x_0, b)$. Then $f(x_0)$ is a relative maximum of f.*

PROOF. Since $Df(x) \geqq 0$ for $x \in I(a, x_0)$, it follows that f is monotone increasing on $I[a, x_0]$. Hence $f(x_0) \geqq f(x)$ for all $x \in I[a, x_0]$. Similarly, since $Df(x) \leqq 0$ for $x \in I(x_0, b)$, we conclude that f is monotone decreasing on $I[x_0, b]$. Hence $f(x_0) \geqq f(x)$ on $I[x_0, b]$. Thus $f(x_0) \geqq f(x)$ for all $x \in I[a, b]$.

Reversing the inequalities in the above theorem we can prove an analogous statement for a relative minimum of f.

Note that nothing was said about the existence of $Df(x_0)$. Thus the theorem is still true whether or not $Df(x_0)$ exists. For example, if $f = |\ \ |$ (see Figure 5.6), $Df(0)$ does not exist, yet $f(0)$ is a relative minimum of f.

Let f be continuous on $I[a, b] \subset \operatorname{Dom} f$, and differentiable on $I(a, b)$. Then a *necessary* condition that f have a relative maximum or a relative minimum at a point x_0 in $I(a, b)$ is that $Df(x_0) = 0$. The condition is *not* sufficient. For example, if $I(a, b)$ is any open interval containing the point $x = 0$, then $Dj^3(0) = 0$; yet $j^3(0)$ is neither a relative maximum nor a relative minimum of j^3 on $I[a, b]$ (see Figure 5.12). However, we do have the following theorem:

Theorem 12. *Let f be continuous on $I[a, b] \subset \operatorname{Dom} f$ and twice differentiable on the interval $I(a, b)$. Let x_0 be the only point in $I(a, b)$ for which $Df(x_0)$ vanishes. Furthermore, let $D^2f(x_0) < 0$. Then $f(x_0)$ is a relative maximum.*

PROOF. By hypothesis

$$D^2f(x_0) = \lim_{h \to 0} \frac{Df(x_0 + h) - Df(x_0)}{h} = \lim_{h \to 0} \frac{Df(x_0 + h)}{h} < 0$$

since $Df(x_0) = 0$. For $h > 0$ and sufficiently small

$$Df(x_0 + h) < 0.$$

But $Df(x)$ vanishes only at x_0; and since D^2f exists, Df must be continuous on $I(a, b)$. Thus $Df(x_0 + h) < 0$ for all $h > 0$ such that $x_0 + h \in I(a, b)$. Similarly $Df(x_0 + h) > 0$ for all $h < 0$ such that $x_0 + h \in I(a, b)$. An application of Theorem 11 completes the proof.

Theorem 12 may be more convenient to apply in practice than Theorem 11 for checking the existence of a relative maximum. It is not as general, though, since it demands the existence of the second derivative. If we change the hypothesis in Theorem 12 to $D^2f(x_0) > 0$, then the same argument establishes $f(x_0)$ as a relative minimum. If $D^2f(x_0) = 0$, we can draw no conclusions. For example, if $f = j^4$, then $D^2f(0) = 0$, but $f(0)$ is a relative minimum. If $f = -j^4$, then $D^2f(0) = 0$, but $f(0)$ is a relative maximum. Finally, if $f = j^3$, then $D^2f(0) = 0$, but $f(0)$ is neither a relative maximum nor a relative minimum (on any closed interval having zero as an interior point).

We continue our discussion of applications of the mean value theorem. From Section 2 we recall that if $f = \mathbf{k}$, then $Df = \mathbf{0}$. The question may be raised: "Is this the only class of functions which has a derivative function equal to zero?" The mean value theorem answers this question in the affirmative.

Theorem 13.   *Let f be continuous on $I[a, b]$ and let Df exist and equal zero on $I(a, b)$. Then $f = \mathbf{k}$.*

PROOF.   Let $x \in I(a, b)$. Then by Theorem 9

$$f(x) - f(a) = (x - a)Df(x')$$

for some $x' \in I(a, x)$. But $Df(x') = 0$ by hypothesis. Therefore $f(x) = f(a)$ for all $x \in I(a, b)$. Hence f is a constant function.

From this theorem we immediately obtain the following:

Theorem 14.   *If f and g are differentiable and $Df = Dg$ on $(\text{Dom } f) \cap (\text{Dom } g)$, then $f = g + \mathbf{k}$ on $(\text{Dom } f) \cap (\text{Dom } g)$.*

PROOF.   Since $Df = Dg$ we have $Df - Dg = \mathbf{0}$ or

$$D(f - g) = \mathbf{0}.$$

By Theorem 13, $f - g = \mathbf{k}$, or

$$f = g + \mathbf{k}.$$

We now see that the question: "What is the function whose derivative is $2j$?" cannot be given a unique answer any more than the question: "What is the number whose square is 4?" admits of a unique answer. Similarly, the class of functions $j^2 + \mathbf{k}$ for each real number $\mathbf{k}$ has a derivative equal to $2j$. If f is a function whose derivative is g, we call f an *antiderivative* of g. By Theorem 14, an antiderivative is unique up to an additive constant. Thus if $Df = g$, the set of antiderivatives of g is the set of all $f + \mathbf{k}$. For example, for any function of the form $\mathbf{a}j^n$, the set of antiderivatives is $\{[\mathbf{a}/(\mathbf{n} + \mathbf{1})]j^{n+1} + \mathbf{k}\}$, while the set of antiderivatives of cos is $\{\sin + \mathbf{k}\}$. The set of antiderivative functions of f is generally denoted by $\int f$. Sometimes it is also written as $D^{-1}f$. This last notation has the advantage that the superscripts on the D's sometimes behave like exponents for the multiplication of numbers. Thus $D^1(D^{-1}f) = f$ and $D^2(D^{-1}f) = Df$. [A word of caution: $D^n(D^{-m}f) = D^{n-m}f$ for $n \geq m \geq 0$, but necessarily for other choices of n and m. For example, $D^{-1}(Dj^2) = \{j^2 + \mathbf{k}\}$.]

5. THE GENERALIZED LAW OF THE MEAN AND L'HOSPITAL'S RULE

The reader will recall that in our discussion of limits (cf. page 96) the question arose as to what can be said about $\lim_a f/g$ when $\lim_a f = 0 = \lim_a g$. We saw that no general answer could be given, and that each case had to be handled separately. The following theorem gives us a very useful criterion for determining such limits (when they exist) for a certain wide class of functions.

Theorem 15 (*Generalized law of the mean*). *Let f and g be continuous on $I[a, b]$ and differentiable on $I(a, b)$. If $Dg(x) \neq 0$ for $x \in I(a, b)$, then there is an $x^* \in I(a, b)$ such that*

$$\frac{f(b) - f(a)}{g(b) - g(a)} = \frac{Df(x^*)}{Dg(x^*)}.$$

PROOF. First note that $Dg(x) \neq 0$ implies $g(b) \neq g(a)$. For by Theorem 9, $g(b) - g(a) = (b - a)Dg(x^*)$, which since $b - a > 0$, implies $g(b) - g(a) \neq 0$.
Now let

$$\phi(x) = \frac{1}{g(b) - g(a)} \begin{vmatrix} f(a) & g(a) & 1 \\ f(b) & g(b) & 1 \\ f(x) & g(x) & 1 \end{vmatrix}$$

$$= \frac{f(b) - f(a)}{g(b) - g(a)} [g(x) - g(a)] - [f(x) - f(a)].$$

Since ϕ is continuous on $I[a, b]$ and differentiable on $I(a, b)$, and furthermore since $\phi(a) = \phi(b)$ $(= 0)$, the conditions of Rolle's Theorem are met. Hence there is an $x^* \in I(a, b)$ such that

$$D\phi(x^*) = \frac{f(b) - f(a)}{g(b) - g(a)} Dg(x^*) - Df(x^*) = 0.$$

Rearranging terms we see the truth of our theorem.

With the aid of the generalized mean value theorem we may prove L'Hospital's Rule.

Theorem 16 (*L'Hospital's Rule*). *Let f and g be continuous on I[a, b] and continuously differentiable on I(a, b). Let Dg ≠ 0 on I(a, b), and let f(x₀) = 0 = g(x₀) for some x₀ ∈ I(a, b). Then*

$$\lim_{h \to 0} \frac{f(x_0 + h)}{g(x_0 + h)} = \frac{Df(x_0)}{Dg(x_0)}.$$

PROOF.   For any interval in $I[a, b]$ with end points x_0 and $x_0 + h$ in $I(a, b)$ we have $Dg \neq 0$. Hence $g(x_0 + h) \neq g(x_0) = 0$. Thus by the generalized law of the mean

$$\frac{f(x_0 + h) - f(x_0)}{g(x_0 + h) - g(x_0)} = \frac{Df(x^*)}{Dg(x^*)}$$

where x^* is between x_0 and $x_0 + h$. Since $f(x_0) = g(x_0) = 0$, the above equation becomes

$$\frac{f(x_0 + h)}{g(x_0 + h)} = \frac{Df(x^*)}{Dg(x^*)}.$$

Now take the limit of both sides of the above equation as h approaches zero. By the continuity of f, g, Df, and Dg, our theorem is established.

Theorem 16 may be used to verify (i) and (ii) of page 96. We consider some further examples.

Example 1.   *Find*

$$\lim_{x \to 1} \frac{x^2 + x - 2}{x - 1}.$$

Since the conditions of L'Hospital's Rule are met,

$$\lim_{1} \frac{j^2 + j - 2}{j - 1} = \frac{D(j^2 + j - 2)(1)}{D(j - 1)(1)} = \frac{(2j + 1)(1)}{1(1)} = \frac{2 + 1}{1} = 3.$$

Example 2.   *Find*

$$\lim_{0} \frac{\sin}{j}.$$

Again, by Theorem 16,

$$\lim_{0} \frac{\sin}{j} = \frac{D \sin 0}{Dj(0)} = \frac{\cos 0}{1} = 1.$$

6. SOME ELEMENTARY APPLICATIONS

The differential calculus is a powerful tool that is helpful in solving many scientific problems. We shall discuss a few simple applications where our theory may be applied; the exercises at the end of the chapter contain additional illuminating illustrations.

A. Maximum and Minimum

We have discussed the relation between derivatives and maxima–minima at some length in Section 4. A simple problem is the following:

From a circular piece of sheet metal it is desired to cut out a rectangle of maximum area. What should the dimensions of the rectangle be?

Let us first draw a picture (Figure 5.13a) and call the radius of the circle a. Draw an inscribed rectangle and call one of the sides x. Then the other side must be $\sqrt{(2a)^2 - x^2}$ since the hypotenuse of the right triangle is $2a$ (see Figure 5.13b). Thus

$$A(x) = x\sqrt{4a^2 - x^2}$$

is the area of a rectangle (with one side x) inscribed in a circle of radius a. Now Dom A is the set of all x such that $|x| \leq 2a$, while DA exists only for $|x| < 2a$. Hence for $x \in I(-2a, 2a)$,

$$DA(x) = \frac{-x^2}{\sqrt{4a^2 - x^2}} + \sqrt{4a^2 - x^2}. \tag{1}$$

If we set $DA(x)$ equal to zero we obtain

$$-x^2 + (4a^2 - x^2) = 0 \tag{2}$$

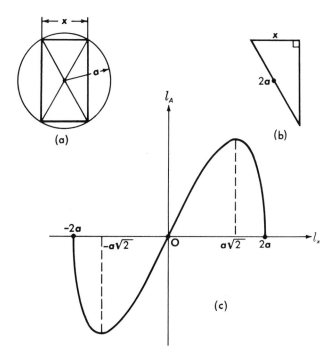

(a)

(b)

(c)

Figure 5.13

for $|x| < 2a$. Trivially, (2) reduces to

$$x = \pm a\sqrt{2}$$

and $\pm a\sqrt{2}$ are interior points of $I[-2a, 2a]$.

Since $DA(\pm a\sqrt{2}) = 0$ and $\pm a\sqrt{2}$ are interior points of $I[-2a, 2a]$ we know that $A(a\sqrt{2})$ and $A(-a\sqrt{2})$ are candidates for a relative maximum or minimum of A on $I[-2a, 2a]$. (Recall that the vanishing of the derivative at an interior point is only a *necessary* condition.) Physically, from Figure 5.13a, we know that A must be a maximum at $a\sqrt{2}$ (and also that $x = -a\sqrt{2}$ must be discarded.) However, we can also verify this fact mathematically. Since D^2A exists for $|x| < 2a$, we can use Theorem 12. From (1)

$$D^2A(x) = \frac{2x^3 - 12a^2x}{(4a^2 - x^2)^{3/2}}$$

and

$$D^2A(a\sqrt{2}) = -4 < 0.$$

Hence $x = a\sqrt{2}$ yields a relative maximum at $A(x)$ on $I[0, 2a]$. (Similarly, $D^2A(-a\sqrt{2}) = 4 > 0$ and $x = -a\sqrt{2}$ yields a relative minimum of $A(x)$ on $I[-2a, 0]$—although from the point of view of the practical problem under consideration, this fact is of no interest.)

The only question that remains is whether $x = a\sqrt{2}$ is a maximum of $A(x)$ on $I[0, 2a]$ and not just a relative maximum. Since Dom $A = I[-2a, 2a]$ and Dom $DA = I(-2a, 2a)$, the only possible value of x (not discovered by solving $DA(x) = 0$ for x) where A could have a maximum is $x = 2a$. (Incidentally, in this problem DA does not exist at $x = 2a$.) But

$$A(2a) = 0$$

(see Figures 5.13a and 5.13c), and hence $x = a\sqrt{2}$ is the length of one side of our maximum area rectangle inscribed in a circle of radius a. The other side of the rectangle is $y = \sqrt{4a^2 - x^2}$, and since $x = a\sqrt{2}$, we have $y = a\sqrt{2}$. That is, our rectangle of maximum area is a square, $a\sqrt{2}$ units on a side. The maximum area is therefore $(a\sqrt{2})^2 = 2a^2$.

B. Falling Bodies

Galileo (1564–1642) found a formula whereby he could predict, for any given time $t \geq 0$, the distance s above the ground of any object dropped from an altitude α. This formula,

$$s = \alpha - 16t^2, \tag{3}$$

associates with each $t \geq 0$ a distance s in such a way that if $s_1 \neq s_2$ then $t_1 \neq t_2$. In other words we may consider the set of ordered pairs $\{(t, \alpha - 16t^2)\}$ a function:

$$s = \{(t, \alpha - 16t^2)\}.$$

(We are assuming t is measured in seconds and that α and s are measured in feet. Thus the "16" in (3) has the dimensions of ft./(sec.)^2). Thus if $\alpha = 500$ ft., the distances of a falling body above the ground for $t = 1$ sec., $t = 2$ sec., $t = 3$ sec. are given by:

$$s(1) = 500 - 16(1)^2 = 484 \text{ ft.}$$
$$s(2) = 500 - 16(2)^2 = 436 \text{ ft.}$$
$$s(3) = 500 - 16(3)^2 = 356 \text{ ft.}$$

The *average* velocity in the interval from 1 sec. to 2 sec. is given by

$$\frac{s(2) - s(1)}{2 - 1} = -48 \text{ ft./sec.} \tag{4}$$

and the average velocity in the interval from 2 sec. to 3 sec. is given by

$$\frac{s(3) - s(2)}{3 - 2} = -80 \text{ ft./sec.} \tag{5}$$

(The negative signs in (4) and (5) indicate that the body is falling.) But the *average* velocity tells us little about the *instantaneous* velocity of the body at a particular time, say $t = t_0$. And a knowledge of the instantaneous velocity of falling bodies is of paramount importance to the scientist. For the case under discussion this problem is easily solved if we keep in mind the fact that there are no sudden jumps in the motion of a freely falling body. That is, both its distance and velocity are changing in a *continuous* manner.

We saw that the average velocity of the falling body during the interval from $t = 1$ sec. to $t = 2$ sec. was -48 ft./sec. And since the average velocity seems to be increasing (in absolute value) during successive intervals [cf. (5)], we surmise that the absolute value of the velocity at $t = 1$ sec. is less than 48 ft./sec. We also infer that if a smaller interval of time is taken, say from $t = 1$ sec. to $t = 1.01$ sec., we should get a better idea of the *instantaneous* velocity at $t = 1$ sec. by computing the average velocity from $t = 1$ sec. to $t = 1.01$ sec. This is easy to do. Thus

$$\frac{s(1.01) - s(1)}{1.01 - 1} = \frac{483.6784 - 484}{0.01} = -32.16 \text{ ft./sec.}$$

is the average velocity in the time interval between $t = 1$ sec. and $t = 1.01$ sec. Similarly,

$$\frac{s(1.001) - s(1)}{1.001 - 1} = -32.016 \text{ ft./sec.}$$

is the average velocity in the time interval between $t = 1$ sec. and $t = 1.001$ sec.

In general, then, if we compute

$$\frac{s(1 + h) - s(1)}{(1 + h) - 1}$$

and pass to the limit as h approaches zero, we obtain the precise velocity at $t = 1$ sec. as

$$\lim_{h \to 0} \frac{s(1 + h) - s(1)}{h}. \tag{6}$$

But (6) is, by definition, $Ds(1)$. Thus, since

$$Ds(t) = D(\alpha - 16t^2) = -32t \text{ ft./sec.} \tag{7}$$

we have $Ds(1) = -32$ ft./sec. From (7) we may also compute the instantaneous value of the velocity at any time t_0. It is $-32t_0$ ft./sec.

Hence we see that in physical problems, velocity can be interpreted as the derivative of distance. We leave to the reader the interpretation of acceleration as the second derivative, D^2s.

C. Marginal Functions

The cost of producing a certain commodity gives rise to a *cost function* C whose domain is the nonnegative integers. The integers in Dom C represent the number of articles produced. It is customary to extend the domain of the function to the interval $I[0, \infty)$, so that the cost function is a continuous function on $I[0, \infty)$.

Among other things, the producer is interested in variations in the cost of production when he increases the number of articles produced. For example, suppose the cost function is

$$C = 10 + 2\sqrt{j} \tag{8}$$

and we are interested in the cost of production when the number of articles produced increases from 25 to 26. Now

$$C(25) = 10 + 2\sqrt{25} = 20$$
$$C(26) = 10 + 2\sqrt{26} = 20.198$$

and the change in C is

$$C(26) - C(25) = 0.198.$$

This cost change when one more article is produced is often referred to as a *marginal cost*. Such a cost change we interpret as an average. The marginal cost is greater than this average when x is 25 and less than this average when $x = 26$.

In practice the above distinction is sometimes important; and the derivative of the cost function, when it exists, can settle the annoying question of whether 0.198 is the marginal cost at 25 or 26. As expected, it tells us that 0.198 is neither the marginal cost at 25 nor at 26, but only an average change in cost. The marginal cost at 25 is given by

$$DC(25) = D(\mathbf{10} + \mathbf{2}\sqrt{j})(25)$$

$$= \frac{\mathbf{1}}{\sqrt{j}}(25) = \frac{1}{\sqrt{25}} = \frac{1}{5} = 0.2 > 0.198$$

and the marginal cost at 26 is

$$DC(26) = \frac{1}{\sqrt{26}} = 0.196 < 0.198.$$

If the cost function were *linear*, say

$$C = \mathbf{a}j + \mathbf{b},$$

then the change in cost when one more unit is produced is equal to a,

$$C(n + 1) - C(n) = [a(n + 1) + b] - [a(n) + b] = a,$$

which in this case happens to be equal to the marginal cost since $DC = \mathbf{a}$.

If R represents the *revenue function*, then as in the case of the cost function, the *marginal revenue* will be given by DR. Now if we define the *profit function* P as

$$P = R - C \quad (R = \text{revenue}, C = \text{cost})$$

then we find that a necessary condition (if profits are to be maximized) is that $DP = \mathbf{0}$. Thus $DR - DC = \mathbf{0}$ or

$$DR = DC.$$

Accordingly, production should be increased if marginal cost is less than marginal revenue, and decreased if marginal cost is greater than marginal revenue. Graphically, the best production level is attained at the point of intersection of the two marginal curves.

EXERCISES

1.   (i) Find the slope of the tangent line to the curve of $f = \mathbf{4}j^2 + \mathbf{4}j - \mathbf{5}$ at $(-1, -5)$.
      (ii) What is the equation of this tangent line?
      (iii) What is the equation of the normal to the curve at $(-1, -5)$?

2.   Prove that $D \cos = -\sin$. [*Hint:* $\cos = \sin \circ (j + \tfrac{1}{2}\pi)$.]

3.   Find the derivative function of each of the following functions and in each case specify the domains.

(i) $f = (j^2 + 5)(j^3 - 2j + 5)$

(ii) $f = \dfrac{j + 3}{j^3 + 4j - 3}$

(iii) $f = \dfrac{\sin}{j^2 - 1}$

(iv) $f = 3 \sin + 2j^2$

(v) $f = \dfrac{2 \cos + j}{\sin - j}$

(vi) $f = j^3 \sin.$

4.   Critical points of f are those values of x in Dom f for which either $Df(x) = 0$ or $Df(x)$ does not exist. Find the critical points of the following functions:

(i) $f = j^4 + 4j^3 + 3j^2 - 22j - 4$

(ii) $f = \dfrac{1}{1 + j}$

(iii) $f = (j - 3)^3$

(iv) $f = j^3 - 2j^2 - 3j.$

5.   Prove that $Dj^{-p/q} = -(p/q)j^{-[(p/q)+1]}$ where p and q are positive integers.

6.   Find D^2f and D^3f for the functions of Exercise 2.

7.   Prove that $f(x) = |x|$ is continuous but not differentiable at $x = 0$.

8.   Show that $f = 1/j$ is continuous on $I(0, 1)$ but has no maximum on $I(0, 1)$.

9.   Let $f = 1/j$ on $I(0, 1]$ and $f(0) = 0$. Show that:

(i) f is not continuous on $I[0, 1]$.

(ii) f is not bounded on $I[0, 1]$.

10.   Find Df for each of the following functions:

(i) $f = (j + 2)^3$

(ii) $f = (j - 1)^7(2j + 5)^{24}$

(iii) $f = \sin^4$

(iv) $f = \sin \circ j^2$

(v) $f = j^2 \circ \sin.$

11.   (i) Find D tan. [*Hint*: tan = sin/cos.]
       (ii) Find D tan*. (Specify the domain on which tan is one–one.)

12.   Let $f = 2j^2 - j$ on $[1, \infty)$. Find $Df^*(6)$.

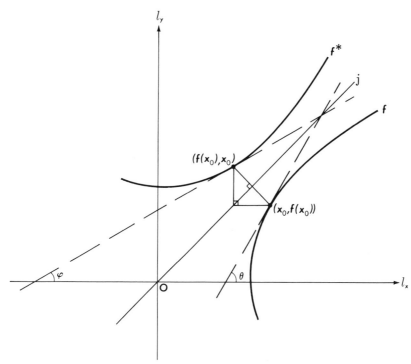

Figure 5.14

13. By referring to Figure 5.14 we can give a geometric interpretation of Theorem 6. Show that the graph of f^* is the mirror image of the graph of f about the graph of j; and from the geometry of the figure deduce that

$$\tan \theta = \frac{1}{\tan \phi}.$$

14. For each of the functions of Exercise 4 find $D^2 f$. Which of the critical points are maximum or minimum points of each function?

15. Prove statements (i), (ii), and (iii) on page 132.

16. If f is continuous and strictly decreasing on $I[a, b]$ and if Df exists on $I(a, b)$, prove that $Df \leq 0$ on $I(a, b)$.

17. (i) Give an example of a function that is one–one but not monotone.

(ii) Prove that if f is one–one and continuous on $I[a, b]$, then f is monotone on $I[a, b]$.

18. Define the area under the curve $1/j$ from 1 to $x > 0$ as $\ln x$, and define $\ln 1$ as zero. That is, the function $\ln$ is the area curve of $1/j$. (In Chapter 6 we shall prove the existence of the area under $1/j$ from 1 to x.)

(i) Prove that the function $\ln$ is continuous at x.

   (ii) Prove that the derivative of ln exists and that $D \ln = 1/j$. [*Hint:* Consider the area of the rectangle that contains $\ln (x + h) - \ln x$ and the area of the rectangle that is contained by $\ln (x + h) - \ln x$. Then use Theorem 9 of Chapter 4 (page 99).]

   (iii) Prove that ln has the properties of the logarithmic function, that is, $\ln xy = \ln x + \ln y$ and $\ln 1/x = -\ln x \ (x, y > 0)$. We frequently write $\log_e \equiv \ln$.

  19.   Our intuitive notion of area shows that ln is one–one and hence has an inverse ln*.

   (i) Show that ln* has the properties of the exponential function, that is, $\ln^* (x + y) = (\ln^* x)(\ln^* y)$. We frequently write $\ln^* \equiv \log_e^* \equiv \exp_e$ or more familiarly, $\ln^* x = e^x$.

   (ii) Show that $D \ln^* = \ln^*$.

  20.   Find Df if:

   (i) $f = \ln \circ j^2$

   (ii) $f = \ln \circ \sin - j$

   (iii) $f = \ln \circ \exp_e$

   (iv) $f = \ln \circ \mathbf{3}$

   (v) $f = j^3 \circ \ln$.

  21.   Find $D \exp_e \circ f$ if

   (i) $f = j^2 - \mathbf{2}j$

   (ii) $f = \cos$

   (iii) $f = \tan$

   (iv) $f = \log_e$

   (v) $f = \mathbf{5}$.

  22.   Find Df for each of the following functions and specify the domain:

   (i) $f = \dfrac{\sin}{\ln}$

   (ii) $f = \ln \circ \cos$

   (iii) $f = \ln \circ (j^2 - \mathbf{2})$

   (iv) $f = \ln \circ (j^2 - \mathbf{9})^{1/2}$

   (v) $f = \sin \circ \ln$.

  23.   (i) If Df exists on some interval, prove that $Df = fD \ln \circ f$.

     (ii) Apply this formula to find Df if $f = j^r$ where r is any real number.

     (iii) Find Df if $f = j^j$.

  24.   (i) Prove that

$$\int (f + g) = \int f + \int g$$

if they exist.

(ii) If g has an antiderivative, prove that

$$\int \mathbf{k} g = \mathbf{k} \int g.$$

25. Very often the reader will encounter the expression $\int f(x)\, dx$ for the set of antiderivatives (or *indefinite integral*) of f, instead of the simple expression $\int f$. The symbol dx is referred to as the differential of x. We shall always consider the two expressions to mean the same thing, viz.: the set of antiderivative functions of f.

Find the following antiderivatives:

(i) $\int (3j^2 + 2j - 1)$

(ii) $\int (\cos + 2j - j^2)$

(iii) $\int (3j^3 - j^4 + 2j^6)$

(iv) $\int (3x^{-2} - 2x + 1)\, dx$

(v) $\int \dfrac{dx}{x + 1}$

(vi) $\int \dfrac{2x}{(1 + x^2)^{1/2}}\, dx$

(vii) $\int \sin 2x\, dx$

(viii) $\int \cos^2 x\, dx$

(ix) $\int \sin^2 x\, dx$

(x) $\int \tan$

(xi) $\int \dfrac{2j}{j^2 + 1}$

(xii) $\int 2j(1 + j^2)^{3/2}$

(xiii) $\int \dfrac{1}{(j + 1)^2}$

(xiv) $\int e^x\, dx$

(xv) $\int j^{-1} \ln.$

26. Let f and g have continuous second derivatives on $I(a, b)$. If x_0 is an interior point of $I(a, b)$ and $f(x_0) = g(x_0) = Df(x_0) = Dg(x_0) = 0$ while $D^2g(x_0) \neq 0$, prove that

$$\lim_{x \to x_0} \frac{f(x)}{g(x)} = \frac{D^2f(x_0)}{D^2g(x_0)}.$$

27. Find the limits (if they exist) of the following functions at the indicated value of a.

(i) $f(x) = \dfrac{2e^{3x} - x - 2}{x^2}$, $\quad a = 0$

(ii) $f(x) = \dfrac{e^x - \cos x}{x}$, $\quad a = 0$

(iii) $f(x) = \dfrac{x \sin x}{x^2 + x}$, $\quad a = \dfrac{\pi}{2}$

(iv) $f(x) = \dfrac{e^{\sin x} - 1}{2 \sin x}$, $\quad a = 0$

(v) $f(x) = \dfrac{2 \cos x - 2}{\sin x}$, $\quad a = 0$

(vi) $f(x) = \dfrac{4 \cos x}{\sin^2 x}$, $\qquad a = 0$

(vii) $f(x) = \dfrac{x \sin x - \frac{1}{2}\pi}{\cos x}$, $\qquad a = \frac{1}{2}\pi$

(viii) $f(x) = \dfrac{\ln x - 1}{x - 1}$, $\qquad a = 1$

(ix) $f(x) = \dfrac{(1 - x)^{1/2} - 1}{x}$, $\qquad a = 0$

(x) $f(x) = \dfrac{1 - \cos x}{x \sin x}$, $\qquad a = 0.$

28. Find the dimensions of the rectangle of largest area that can be made from a wire of given length ℓ.

29. A triangle has vertices $(0, 0)$, $(10, 20)$, $(20, 0)$. What is the area of the largest rectangle with base on the x-axis that can be inscribed in the triangle?

30. Let C be a right circular cone whose base diameter and altitude are equal. What are the dimensions of the right circular cylinder of maximum volume that can be inscribed in C?

31. (i) What is the minimum amount of fencing that will circumscribe a rectangular plot of 10,000 square feet?

(ii) What will be the answer if only three sides of the rectangle need be fenced in?

32. What will be the most economical dimensions of a box (without a top and with a square base) that is to contain 100 cubic inches, if the sides are made of metal costing 4 cents per square inch and the bottom is made of metal costing 10 cents per square inch?

33. A cylindrical can (no top) is to have a volume of 50 cubic inches. What should the height and radius be if the surface area is to be a minimum?

34. If s is distance, interpret $D^2 s$ as acceleration.

35. A projectile is shot upward from the surface of the earth with an initial velocity of 320 feet/second. Its distance s from the earth at any time t (seconds) is given by $s = 320t - 16t^2$ (feet).

(i) At what velocity is the projectile traveling at times $t = 2$ sec., $t = 3$ sec., $t = 4$ sec., $t = 5$ sec., $t = 10$ sec., $t = 20$ sec.?

(ii) When does the projectile reach its maximum height above the earth?

(iii) What is the velocity of the projectile when it reaches this maximum height?

(iv) At what time does the projectile strike the ground?

(v) What is the velocity of the projectile when it strikes the earth?

36. If an article sells for $8 and the cost of producing x units of the article is

$$C(x) = 100 + 2.6x + 0.002x^2,$$

what is the profit function? For what value of x will profits be a maximum and what will the maximum profits be? If the revenue function is $R(x) = 16x$, for what value of x will the profit be maximum?

37. Suppose the cost function for producing x tons of a certain mineral is $C(x) = 80 + 0.01x$. Suppose that the total yearly sales in tons are given by

$$R(t) = 20,000 - 0.02t$$

where t is the price per ton. What price for the mineral yields the best profit?

6

THE DEFINITE INTEGRAL

In the beginning of our discussion of the calculus in Chapter 5 we alluded to the inverse relation between the problem of finding the slope curve of f and the problem of finding the area curve of Df. To illustrate this relationship we consider a few simple examples. We shall speak of the area of certain sets of points, R, that are usually referred to as regions. We shall avoid the long technical discussion of the term region. Rather we shall give analytic definitions of the regions we discuss. Thus, when we speak of a region R bounded by $I[a, b]$, the graph of a continuous function $f > 0$ on $I(a, b)$ and the lines $\lambda(1, 0, a)$, $\lambda(1, 0, b)$ we shall mean that $R = \{(x, y) \mid a < x < b, 0 < y < f(x)\}$ [read: "R is the set of all points (x, y) in the plane such that $a < x < b$ and $0 < y < f(x)$ on $I(a, b)$".] Sometimes we shall speak of the area of such a region simply as "the area under f from a to b". Also we shall speak of the region R bounded by two curves f and g. By this we shall mean that there exist points a and b such that $f(a) = g(a)$, $f(b) = g(b)$, $f > g$ on $I(a, b)$, and $R = \{(x, y) \mid a < x < b, g(x) < y < f(x)\}$. When other types of regions are discussed, their boundaries will be specified and these will clearly indicate their analytic definitions.

Example 1. If $f = \mathbf{k}j$, then $Df = \mathbf{k}$. That is, the height of the graph of $\mathbf{k}$ above any point $(x, 0)$ gives the slope of f at $(x, f(x))$. (See Figure 6.1.) Now consider the area of the region $R = \{(x, y) \mid a < x < b, 0 < y < k\}$—or simply the area under Df from a to b. In this example R is a rectangle and its area is given by $(b - a)k$. But this is precisely the rise in the graph of $f = \mathbf{k}j$ from $(a, f(a))$ to $(b, f(b))$—or simply the rise in f from a to b.

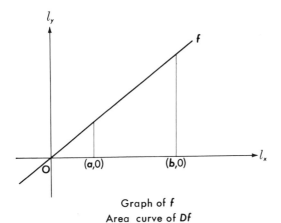

Graph of **f**

Area curve of **Df**

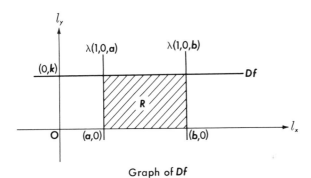

Graph of **Df**

Slope curve of **f**

Figure 6.1

Example 2. Let $f = \frac{1}{2}j^2$. Then $Df = j$. Again $Df(x)$ is the slope of f at $(x, f(x))$. We shall see that the area under Df from a to b is given by the rise in f from $(a, f(a))$ to $(b, f(b))$. From Figure 6.2, the region $R = \{(x, y) \mid a < x < b, 0 < y < x\}$ is a trapezoid whose area is

$$(b - a)\left(\frac{b + a}{2}\right) = \frac{b^2}{2} - \frac{a^2}{2}.$$

But $\dfrac{b^2}{2} - \dfrac{a^2}{2}$ is precisely the rise in f from a to b.

Example 3. Let $f = \frac{1}{3}j^3$. Then $Df = j^2$. (See Figure 6.3.) At the moment we have no ready formula for computing the area of $R = \{(x, y) \mid a < x < b, 0 < y < x^2\}$.

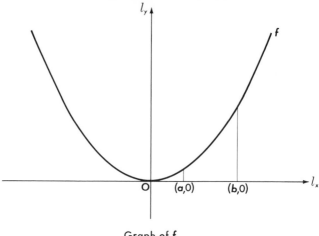

Graph of **f**
Area curve of **Df**

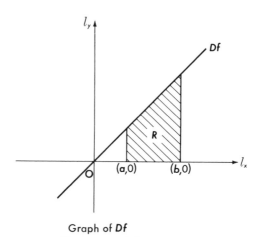

Graph of **Df**
Slope curve of **f**
Figure 6.2

We shall compute, however, a good approximation which will lead us to an educated guess as to what this area should be. First note that the area we are seeking is equal to the area under Df from 0 to b minus the area under Df from 0 to a.

Consider then Figure 6.4 where we have divided the interval $I[0, b]$ into n equal parts or sub-intervals. Each sub-interval is of length b/n and the mid-point of the kth sub-interval is given by

$$\frac{1}{2}\left[(k-1)\frac{b}{n} + k\frac{b}{n}\right] = \frac{(2k-1)b}{2n}.$$

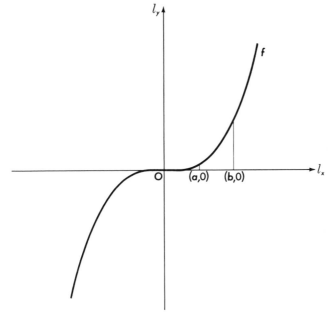

Graph of *f*
Area curve of *Df*

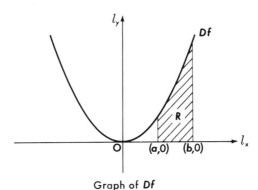

Graph of *Df*
Slope curve of *f*

Figure 6.3

Now consider the sum of the area of the rectangles with base equal to b/n and height equal to $[(2k - 1)b/2n]^2$ for $k = 1, 2, \cdots, n$. The sum of these areas is

$$\sum_{k=1}^{n} \frac{b}{n} \left[\frac{(2k-1)b}{2n} \right]^2 = \frac{b^3}{4n^3} \sum_{k=1}^{n} (2k-1)^2 = \frac{b^3}{4n^3} \frac{(2n-1)(2n)(2n+1)}{6}$$

$$= \frac{b^3}{3} - \frac{b^3}{12n^2}.$$

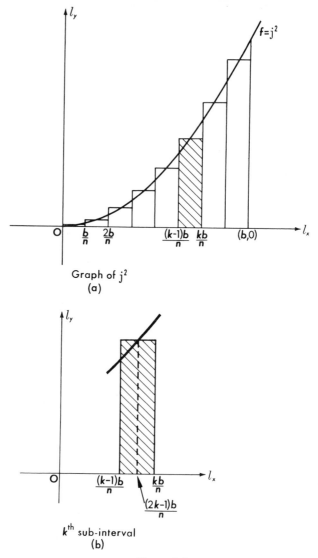

Graph of j^2
(a)

k^{th} sub-interval
(b)

Figure 6.4

(See Exercise 27 (v), of Chapter 1.) Now if the number of these sub-intervals is made larger and larger, then n becomes larger and $1/12n^2$ becomes smaller. So if the region illustrated in Figure 6.4a is to have an area, we would guess it to be $b^3/3$. In the same way we find the area from 0 to a to be $a^3/3$, and subtracting we get

$$\frac{b^3}{3} - \frac{a^3}{3}$$

as a "good guess" for the area under Df from a to b. But $b^3/3 - a^3/3$ is just the rise in f from a to b (cf. Figure 6.3).

Note that Examples 1 and 2 could have been handled in the same manner as that of Example 3, that is, by considering the sums

$$\frac{b-a}{n} \sum_{k=1}^{n} f\left(\frac{(2k-1)(b-a)}{2n}\right)$$

and observing what happens as n becomes large. Indeed, the area under a "smooth" curve f from a to b, with points of subdivision $a = x_0, x_1, \cdots, x_n = b$ is often defined to be

$$\lim_{n \to \infty} \sum_{i=1}^{n} f\left(\frac{x_i + x_{i-1}}{2}\right)(x_i - x_{i-1})$$

and $|x_i - x_{i-1}| \to 0$ for $i = 1, 2, \cdots, n$. This definition does have the advantage of being easily adaptable for certain types of computers; but it has the disadvantage of making the proofs of some of the theorems we want somewhat more complicated.

I. THE DEFINITE INTEGRAL

We now inaugurate a precise discussion of Problem 2 (cf. the introduction to the previous chapter). That is, we shall concern ourselves with the problem of finding the area bounded by a curve f, two vertical lines $\lambda(1, 0, a)$ and $\lambda(1, 0, b)$, and the interval $I[a, b]$ of the x-axis, that is, the area of $R = \{(x, y) \mid a < x < b, 0 < y < f(x)\}$.

Intuitively, "area" is a number—which we associate with a region R in the plane—which gives us a "measure" of the region. It enables us to compare regions "size-wise". For rectangles, the area is *defined* to be the product of the base and altitude. The diagonal of a rectangle divides the rectangle into two congruent (right) triangles; and so we decide that if congruent figures are to have equal areas, the area of a right triangle must be given by one-half the product of its base and altitude. Any triangle may be subdivided into two right triangles. And more generally, a polygon is said to have an area equal to the sum of the areas of the triangles into which it is subdivided. It can be proved too, that the area of a polygon is independent of the particular triangular subdivision.

If the region has one or more boundaries that are graphs of non-linear functions, the problem is more complicated. This is the problem that concerns us at the moment.

Let us begin by formulating the following *axioms for area*:

1 If R is a region, the area of R, written $\mathscr{A}(R)$, is a nonnegative number, and if $R = \varnothing$, the empty set, then $\mathscr{A}(R) = 0$.

2 If R is a rectangle,
$$\mathscr{A}(R) = (\text{base}) \times (\text{altitude}).$$

3   If R_1, R_2 are regions and $R_1 \subset R_2$ (that is, every point (x, y) in R_1 is also in R_2), then

$$\mathscr{A}(R_1) \leqq \mathscr{A}(R_2).$$

4   If R_1 and R_2 are regions,

$$\mathscr{A}(R_1 \cup R_2) = \mathscr{A}(R_1) + \mathscr{A}(R_2) - \mathscr{A}(R_1 \cap R_2).$$

We shall also need the concept of a *partition* of an interval.

Definition.   *Let $I[a, b]$ be a closed interval. Let $x_0, x_1, \cdots, x_n$ be distinct points in $I[a, b]$ such that*

$$a = x_0 < x_1 < \cdots < x_{n-1} < x_n = b.$$

*Then $\pi = [x_0, x_1, \cdots, x_n]$ will denote a **partition** of $I[a, b]$ into n subintervals $I[x_0, x_1], I[x_1, x_2], \cdots, I[x_{n-1}, x_n]$.*

Let π and π' be two partitions of an interval. If every $x_i \in \pi$ is also in π', then we call π' a *refinement* of π. Any two partitions of the same interval $I[a, b]$ clearly have a common refinement. For if $\pi_1 = [x_0, x_1, \cdots, x_n]$ and $\pi_2 = [\xi_0, \xi_1, \cdots, \xi_m]$, we need only arrange the set $\pi_1 \cup \pi_2$ in an increasing sequence to obtain a partition π^* that is a refinement of both π_1 and π_2. For example, if $\pi_1 = [0, 1, 3, 4, 8]$ and $\pi_2 = [0, 2, 4, 6, 7, 8]$, then $\pi^* = [0, 1, 2, 3, 4, 6, 7, 8]$ is a refinement of π_1 and π_2.

We return now to the problem of finding the area under a curve. Consider the graph of a nonnegative continuous function f whose domain of continuity properly contains the interval $I[a, b]$, cf. Figure 6.5. Since f is continuous on $I[a, b]$ it assumes an absolute maximum $f(M)$ and an absolute minimum $f(m)$ on $I[a, b]$, (Theorem 14 of Chapter 4). Then by our "axioms for area",

$$f(m)(b - a) \leqq \mathscr{A}(R) \leqq f(M)(b - a).$$

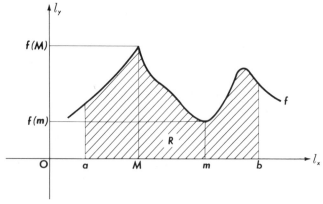

Figure 6.5

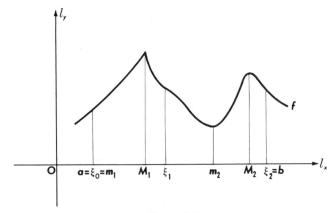

Figure 6.6

Now let $\pi = [\xi_0, \xi_1, \xi_2]$ be a partition of $I[a, b]$ and let $f(M_1), f(M_2)$ be the maximum of f on $I[\xi_0, \xi_1]$ and $I[\xi_1, \xi_2]$ respectively. Similarly define $f(m_1)$ and $f(m_2)$ to be the minimum of f on $I[\xi_0, \xi_1]$ and $I[\xi_1, \xi_2]$ respectively. (Cf. Figure 6.6.) Then

$$\mathscr{A}(R) \leq f(M_1)(\xi_1 - \xi_0) + f(M_2)(\xi_2 - \xi_1) \leq f(M)(b - a)$$

and

$$\mathscr{A}(R) \geq f(m_1)(\xi_1 - \xi_0) + f(m_2)(\xi_2 - \xi_1) \geq f(m)(b - a).$$

If we continue to refine π until we obtain a partition $\pi' = [x_0, x_1, \cdots, x_n]$ of $I[a, b]$ we see that

$$\mathscr{A}(R) \leq \sum_{i=1}^{n} f(M_i)(x_i - x_{i-1}) \leq f(M)(b - a)$$

and likewise that

$$\mathscr{A}(R) \geq \sum_{i=1}^{n} f(m_i)(x_i - x_{i-1}) \geq f(m)(b - a).$$

In the above equations $f(M_i)$ and $f(m_i)$ are the maximum and minimum of f respectively on $I[x_{i-1}, x_i]$.

For simplicity in notation we shall write

$$U(\pi) = \sum_{i=1}^{n} f(M_i)(x_i - x_{i-1})$$

and call it the *upper sum* associated with the partition π. Similarly we write

$$L(\pi) = \sum_{i=1}^{n} f(m_i)(x_i - x_{i-1})$$

and call it the *lower sum* associated with the partition π.

Since $f(M) \geq f(M_i) \geq f(m_i)$ for $i = 1, 2, \cdots, n$, we have

$$L(\pi) \leq f(M) \sum_{i=1}^{n} (x_i - x_{i-1}) = f(M)(b - a).$$

Now the set $\{L(\pi)\}$ obtained for all possible partitions of $I[a, b]$ is bounded from above [by $f(M)(b - a)$] and therefore by Axiom **C** it has a least upper bound, say L:

$$L = \text{l.u.b. } L(\pi).$$

We shall write

$$L = \underline{\int_a^b} f$$

and call it the *lower integral* of f on $I[a, b]$. Similarly, since the set $\{U(\pi)\}$ obtained for all possible partitions π of $I[a, b]$ is bounded from below [by $f(m)(b - a)$], it has a greatest lower bound, U:

$$U = \text{g.l.b. } U(\pi) = \overline{\int_a^b} f.$$

We call $\overline{\int_a^b}$ the *upper integral* of f on $I[a, b]$.

If

$$\underline{\int_a^b} f = \overline{\int_a^b} f$$

we shall call their common value (denoted by $\int_a^b f$) the *definite integral of f on $I[a, b]$* and say f is *integrable* on $I[a, b]$. In the next section we shall prove the interesting and important result that *every continuous function is integrable.*

The region R defined in Figure 6.5, and analytically by the expression $R = \{(x, y) \mid a < x < b, 0 < y < f(x)\}$, has been shown to satisfy the inequalities

$$L(\pi) \leq \mathscr{A}(R) \leq U(\pi)$$

for any partition π, and hence

$$\underline{\int_a^b} f \leq \mathscr{A}(R) \leq \overline{\int_a^b} f.$$

Thus if f is integrable on $I[a, b]$ we must have

$$\mathscr{A}(R) = \int_a^b f.$$

Let f be defined on $I[a, b]$ and let $I[c, d]$ be a subinterval of $I[a, b]$. We find it convenient to define

$$\underline{\int_d^c} f = -\underline{\int_c^d} f$$

and

$$\overline{\int_d^c} f = -\overline{\int_c^d} f.$$

Also, if $I[a, b]$ is a degenerate interval, that is, $a = b$, then we define

$$\overline{\int_a^a} f = \underline{\int_a^a} f = 0 = \int_a^a f.$$

These definitions will prove useful in certain later manipulations.

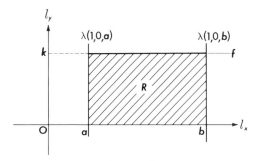

Figure 6.7

We shall now give some concrete examples which illustrate the above concepts. That is, we shall consider certain functions under which the area (integral) from a to b exists in the sense just defined. Furthermore, we shall show that the area so obtained conforms to the areas we usually assign (geometrically) to rectangles and triangles.

Example 1. Let $f = \mathbf{k}$ and let $\pi = [x_0, x_1, \cdots, x_n]$ be a partition of $I[a, b]$. In this case $f(m_i) = f(M_i) = k$, for $i = 1, 2, \cdots, n$, where $f(m_i)$ is the minimum and $f(M_i)$ the maximum of f on $I[x_{i-1}, x_i]$. Then

$$L(\pi) = k \sum_{i=1}^{n} (x_i - x_{i-1}) = k(b - a)$$

$$\leq \mathscr{A}(R) \leq U(\pi) = k \sum_{i=1}^{n} (x_i - x_{i-1}) = k(b - a)$$

where R is the region bounded by f, $\lambda(1, 0, a)$, $\lambda(1, 0, b)$, and $I[a, b]$. (See Figure 6.7.) But

$$\sum_{i=1}^{n} (x_i - x_{i-1}) = b - a$$

for all possible partitions π. Thus

$$\underline{\int_a^b} f = \overline{\int_a^b} f = k(b - a)$$

or

$$\int_a^b f = \mathscr{A}(R) = k(b - a).$$

Example 2. Let $f = j$ on the closed interval $I[a, b]$. Let R be the region bounded by f, $\lambda(1, 0, a)$, $\lambda(1, 0, b)$, and $I[a, b]$. (See Figure 6.8.)

In Example 1 we not only established the existence of the definite integral, but in so doing actually obtained the area in question. In this example we shall first establish the existence of the integral $\int_a^b j$ and then find its value.

Let $\pi = [x_0, x_1, \cdots, x_n]$ be a partition of $I[a, b]$. In this case $x_i = M_i$, $x_{i-1} = m_i$ where $f(M_i)$ and $f(m_i)$ are the maximum and minimum of f on $I[x_{i-1}, x_i]$. Then

$$L(\pi) = \sum_{i=1}^{n} x_{i-1}(x_i - x_{i-1})$$

is the lower sum corresponding to the partition π and

$$U(\pi) = \sum_{i=1}^{n} x_i(x_i - x_{i-1})$$

is the upper sum corresponding to the partition π. We wish to prove first that

$$\underline{\int_a^b} j = \overline{\int_a^b} j.$$

Since x_i exceeds x_{i-1} for all i, we have

$$0 < U(\pi) - L(\pi) = \sum_{i=1}^{n} x_i(x_i - x_{i-1}) - \sum_{i=1}^{n} x_{i-1}(x_i - x_{i-1})$$

$$= \sum_{i=1}^{n} (x_i - x_{i-1})(x_i - x_{i-1})$$

or

$$0 < U(\pi) - L(\pi) \leqq |\pi| \sum_{i=1}^{n} (x_i - x_{i-1}) = |\pi|(b - a)$$

where $|\pi| = \max_i (x_i - x_{i-1})$. Thus if ε is any positive number, we may choose a partition π so that

$$|\pi| < \frac{\varepsilon}{b - a}.$$

Thus we have

$$0 < U(\pi) - L(\pi) < \varepsilon.$$

Now we obtain

$$0 < U(\pi) - L(\pi) = U(\pi) - \overline{\int_a^b} j + \overline{\int_a^b} j - \underline{\int_a^b} j + \underline{\int_a^b} j - L(\pi)$$

$$= \left[U(\pi) - \overline{\int_a^b} j \right] + \left[\overline{\int_a^b} j - \underline{\int_a^b} j \right] + \left[\underline{\int_a^b} j - L(\pi) \right] < \varepsilon \quad (1)$$

by subtracting and adding the upper and lower integrals. From the definitions of $\overline{\int_a^b}$ and $\underline{\int_a^b}$, and from Lemma 2 (of the next section) we see that each of the three terms in brackets on the right-hand side of (1) is nonnegative. In particular we infer

$$0 \leqq \overline{\int_a^b} j - \underline{\int_a^b} j < \varepsilon.$$

Since the above inequality is true for any $\varepsilon > 0$ we infer

$$\overline{\int_a^b} j = \underline{\int_a^b} j,$$

that is, that j is integrable on $I[a, b]$.

Our next problem is to determine the value of $\int_a^b j$. From (1) we deduce

$$0 < U(\pi) - \overline{\int_a^b} j < \varepsilon \tag{2}$$

and

$$0 < \underline{\int_a^b} j - L(\pi) < \varepsilon. \tag{3}$$

Equation (3) may be rearranged to read

$$-\varepsilon < L(\pi) - \int_a^b j < 0. \tag{4}$$

Now add (2) and (4) and recall that $\overline{\int_a^b} j = \underline{\int_a^b} j = \int_a^b j$:

$$-\varepsilon < U(\pi) + L(\pi) - 2\int_a^b f < \varepsilon.$$

Thus

$$\left| \frac{U(\pi) + L(\pi)}{2} - \int_a^b j \right| < \frac{\varepsilon}{2}. \tag{5}$$

But

$$U(\pi) + L(\pi) = \sum_{i=1}^n x_i(x_i - x_{i-1}) + \sum_{i=1}^n x_{i-1}(x_i - x_{i-1})$$

$$= \sum_{i=1}^n (x_i + x_{i-1})(x_i - x_{i-1}) = \sum_{i=1}^n (x_i^2 - x_{i-1}^2)$$

$$= b^2 - a^2.$$

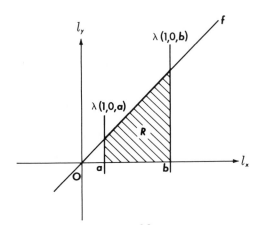

Figure 6.8

Thus (5) becomes

$$\left| \frac{b^2 - a^2}{2} - \int_a^b j \right| < \frac{\varepsilon}{2},$$

and since $\varepsilon > 0$ is arbitrary,

$$\int_a^b j = \frac{b^2 - a^2}{2} = \mathscr{A}(R)$$

(cf. Figure 6.8).

To find areas under all continuous functions by using the definition of integrability would be tedious, and in most cases quite difficult. We therefore proceed to prove a sequence of lemmas in the next section. These will establish the fact that all continuous functions *are* integrable and this will lead us to the *fundamental theorem of the calculus* that relates integrals and derivatives.

2. INTEGRABILITY OF A CONTINUOUS FUNCTION

Our goal in this section is to prove the following result:

Theorem 1. *Let f be continuous on $I[a, b]$. Then*

$$\underline{\int_a^b} f = \overline{\int_a^b} f.$$

In other words Theorem 1 states that every function defined and continuous on a closed finite interval is integrable (and, for $f \geq 0$ on $I[a, b]$, the area under f from a to b is well-defined).

We proceed with the preliminaries. If g is a continuous function defined on $I[a, b]$, then there is a constant k such that

$$f = g + \mathbf{k}$$

is a nonnegative continuous function on $I[a, b]$. Thus with negligible loss of generality (why?) we may assume $f(x) \geq 0$ on $I[a, b]$.

Lemma 1. *Let f be continuous on $I[a, b]$. Let $\pi = [x_0, x_1, \cdots, x_n]$ be a partition of $I[a, b]$ and $\pi' = [\xi_0, \xi_1, \cdots, \xi_m]$ a refinement of π. Then*

$$L(\pi') \geq L(\pi) \tag{1}$$

and

$$U(\pi') \leq U(\pi). \tag{2}$$

PROOF. We prove (1). If $\pi = \pi'$ the lemma is obvious. If $\pi \neq \pi'$, then there is at least one $\xi_j \in \pi'$ which is not in π, and hence for some i,

$$x_{i-1} < \xi_j < x_i.$$

Define

$$\pi_1 = [x_0, x_1, \cdots, x_{i-1}, \xi_j, x_i, \cdots, x_n],$$

and let $f(m^*)$ be the minimum of f on $I[x_{i-1}, \xi_j]$ and $f(m^{**})$ the minimum of f on $I[\xi_j, x_i]$. Now

$$f(m_i) \leq f(m^*)$$

and

$$f(m_i) \leq f(m^{**}),$$

where $f(m_i)$ is the minimum of f on $I[x_{i-1}, x_i]$. Thus

$$f(m_i)(x_i - x_{i-1}) = f(m_i)(\xi_j - x_{i-1}) + f(m_i)(x_i - \xi_j)$$
$$\leq f(m^*)(\xi_j - x_{i-1}) + f(m^{**})(x_i - \xi_j)$$

and

$$L(\pi) = \sum_{k=1}^{n} f(m_k)(x_k - x_{k-1})$$

$$\leq \sum_{k=1}^{i-1} f(m_k)(x_k - x_{k-1}) + f(m^*)(\xi_j - x_{i-1}) + f(m^{**})(x_i - \xi_j)$$

$$+ \sum_{k=i+1}^{n} f(m_k)(x_k - x_{k-1}) = L(\pi_1).$$

In this manner we construct a chain of partitions

$$\pi \subset \pi_1 \subset \pi_2 \subset \cdots \subset \pi'$$

that exhaust the set of ξ_j in π' that are not in π; and finally we obtain

$$L(\pi) \leq L(\pi_1) \leq L(\pi_2) \leq \cdots \leq L(\pi').$$

Similarly we may show that $U(\pi') \leq U(\pi)$.

Lemma 2. *If f is continuous on $I[a, b]$, then*

$$\underline{\int_a^b} f \leq \overline{\int_a^b} f.$$

PROOF.   Let π_1 and π_2 be two partitions of $I[a, b]$ and let π' be a refinement of both. By the previous lemma $L(\pi_1) \leq L(\pi')$ and $U(\pi_2) \geq U(\pi')$. Now $L(\pi') \leq U(\pi')$ so that

$$L(\pi_1) \leq L(\pi') \leq U(\pi') \leq U(\pi_2)$$

for any two partitions π_1 and π_2 of $I[a, b]$. Also

$$L(\pi) \leq \underline{\int_a^b} f$$

for all partitions π since

$$\underline{\int_a^b} f = \text{l.u.b.}_{\pi} L(\pi).$$

But $U(\pi)$, for any π, is an upper bound for $\{L(\pi)\}$. Hence in particular $\overline{\int_a^b} f = \text{g.l.b.}_{\pi} U(\pi)$ is an upper bound for $\{L(\pi)\}$.

Lemma 3. *Let f be continuous on I[a, b], and let μ_1 and μ_2 be numbers such that $\mu_1 \leq f(x) \leq \mu_2$ for all $x \in I[a, b]$. Then*

$$\mu_1(b - a) \leq \underline{\int_a^b} f \tag{3}$$

and

$$\mu_2(b - a) \geq \overline{\int_a^b} f. \tag{4}$$

PROOF. We prove (3). Since $\underline{\int_a^b} f$ is the least upper bound of $L(\pi)$ for all partitions π of $I[a, \ddot{v}]$,

$$f(m_1)(b - a) \leq \underline{\int_a^b} f$$

for the particular partition $\pi = [a, b]$. (As usual $f(m_1)$ is the minimum of f on $I[a, b]$.) But $\mu_1 \leq f(m_1)$. Hence

$$\mu_1(b - a) \leq \underline{\int_a^b} f.$$

The proof of (4) is analogous.

Lemma 4. *Let f be continuous on I[a, b]. Let $c \in I[a, b]$. Then*

$$\underline{\int_a^b} f = \underline{\int_a^c} f + \underline{\int_c^b} f \tag{5}$$

and

$$\overline{\int_a^b} f = \overline{\int_a^c} f + \overline{\int_c^b} f. \tag{6}$$

PROOF. We prove (5). To do this we shall show that

(i) $\underline{\int_a^b} f \geq \underline{\int_a^c} f + \underline{\int_c^b} f$

and

(ii) $\underline{\int_a^b} f \leq \underline{\int_a^c} f + \underline{\int_c^b} f.$

These two inequalities will establish (5).

(i) Let $\pi_1 = [x_0, x_1, \cdots, x_k]$ be a partition of $I[a, c]$ and $\pi_2 = [x_k, x_{k+1}, x_n]$ be a partition of $I[c, b]$. Let $\pi^* = \pi_1 \cup \pi_2$ be a partition of $I[a, b]$. Since

$$\sum_{i=1}^{n} f(m_i)(x_i - x_{i-1}) = \sum_{i=1}^{k} f(m_i)(x_i - x_{i-1}) + \sum_{i=k+1}^{n} f(m_i)(x_i - x_{i-1})$$

where $f(m_i)$ is the minimum of f on $I[x_{i-1}, x_i]$, we have

$$L(\pi_1) + L(\pi_2) = L(\pi^*) \leq \underline{\int_a^b} f \tag{7}$$

for any two partitions π_1 and π_2. The above inequality implies that

$$\underline{\int_a^b} f - L(\pi_2)$$

is an upper bound for $L(\pi_1)$. Since $\overline{\int_a^c} f$ is the least upper bound of $\{L(\pi_1)\}$ we have

$$\overline{\int_a^c} f \leq \overline{\int_a^b} f - L(\pi_2)$$

or

$$L(\pi_2) \leq \overline{\int_a^b} f - \overline{\int_a^c} f. \tag{8}$$

But

$$\underline{\int_c^b} f = \text{l.u.b. } L(\pi_2).$$
$$\phantom{\underline{\int_c^b} f = \text{l.u.b. }}{\scriptstyle \pi_2}$$

Hence (8) implies

$$\underline{\int_c^b} f \leq \overline{\int_a^b} f - \overline{\int_a^c} f$$

which establishes (i).

(ii) Let $\pi = [x_0, x_1, \cdots, x_n]$ be a partition of $I[a, b]$ and π' a refinement of π obtained by adding c to π. Then

$$L(\pi) \leq L(\pi').$$

Let $\pi_1 = [x_0, x_1, \cdots, x_k]$ be that part of π' which is a partition of $I[a, c]$ and let $\pi_2 = [x_k, x_{k+1}, \cdots, x_n]$ be that part of π' which is a partition of $I[c, b]$. Then

$$L(\pi) \leq L(\pi') = L(\pi_1) + L(\pi_2) \leq \overline{\int_a^c} f + \overline{\int_c^b} f \tag{9}$$

and $\overline{\int_a^c} f + \overline{\int_c^b} f$ is an upper bound for $L(\pi)$. But π was an arbitrary partition of $I[a, b]$. Therefore

$$\overline{\int_a^b} f \leq \overline{\int_a^c} f + \overline{\int_c^b} f$$

and the proof of (ii) is complete.

In an analogous fashion we establish (6).

If f is continuous on the interval $I[a, b]$, then we can define a function $\bar{F}$ by the rule of correspondence

$$\bar{F}(c) = \overline{\int_a^c} f, \qquad c \in I[a, b].$$

Similarly we define $\underline{F}$ by the rule of correspondence

$$\underline{F}(c) = \underline{\int_a^c} f, \qquad c \in I[a, b].$$

These remarks lead to the following important (and last) lemma:

Lemma 5. *Let f be continuous on $I[a, b]$ and let $\bar{F}$ and $\underline{F}$ be defined as above. Then*

$$D\bar{F} = f = D\underline{F}$$

on $I[a, b]$.

PROOF. We shall prove that $D\bar{F} = f$ by showing that for each $\varepsilon > 0$ there is a $\delta > 0$ such that

$$\left| \frac{\bar{F}(c + h) - \bar{F}(c)}{h} - f(c) \right| < \varepsilon$$

whenever $0 < |h| < \delta$ and $c, c + h \in I[a, b]$. This of course is equivalent to showing that

$$\lim_{h \to 0} \frac{\bar{F}(c + h) - \bar{F}(c)}{h} = f(c).$$

From Lemma 4,

$$\bar{F}(c + h) - \bar{F}(c) = \overline{\int_a^{c+h}} f - \overline{\int_a^c} f = \overline{\int_a^{c+h}} f. \tag{10}$$

Since by hypothesis f is continuous at c for each $\varepsilon > 0$ there is a $\delta > 0$ such that

$$|f(c + h) - f(c)| < \varepsilon$$

or

$$f(c) - \varepsilon < f(c + h) < f(c) + \varepsilon$$

provided $0 < |h| < \delta$.

Assume first that $0 < h < \delta$. Then by Lemmas 3 and 2,

$$[f(c) - \varepsilon]h \leq \overline{\int_c^{c+h}} f \leq [f(c) + \varepsilon]h$$

or

$$f(c) - \varepsilon \leq \frac{\overline{\int_c^{c+h}} f}{h} \leq f(c) + \varepsilon. \tag{11}$$

If $-\delta < h < 0$, then

$$\overline{\int_c^{c+h}} f = -\overline{\int_{c+h}^c} f$$

and we have

$$[f(c) - \varepsilon](-h) \leq \overline{\int_{c+h}^c} f \leq [f(c) + \varepsilon](-h)$$

or

$$f(c) - \varepsilon \leq \frac{\overline{\int_{c+h}^c} f}{-h} = \frac{\overline{\int_c^{c+h}} f}{h} \leq f(c) + \varepsilon. \tag{12}$$

Equations (11) and (12) together imply

$$\left| \frac{\overline{\int_c^{c+h}} f}{h} - f(c) \right| < \varepsilon$$

if $0 < |h| < \delta$. But from (10) this is the same as

$$\left| \frac{\bar{F}(c + h) - \bar{F}(c)}{h} - f(c) \right| < \varepsilon$$

for $0 < |h| < \delta$. Thus

$$D\bar{F}(c) = \lim_{h \to 0} \frac{\bar{F}(c + h) - \bar{F}(c)}{h} = f(c)$$

for all $c \in I[a, b]$.

A similar argument establishes

$$D\underline{F} = f.$$

We can now prove the major result of this section, namely Theorem 1, which was stated at the beginning:

PROOF OF THEOREM 1.   Let $\bar{F}$ and $\underline{F}$ be defined by the rules of correspondence

$$\bar{F}(x) = \overline{\int_a^x} f$$

and

$$\underline{F}(x) = \underline{\int_a^x} f.$$

By Lemma 5, $D\bar{F} = D\underline{F}$, and hence by Theorem 14 of the previous chapter

$$\bar{F} = \underline{F} + \mathbf{k}.$$

Now $\bar{F}(a) = (\underline{F} + \mathbf{k})(a) = \underline{F}(a) + k$ and $\bar{F}(a) = \underline{F}(a) = 0$. Thus $k = 0$ and $\bar{F} = \underline{F}$. That is,

$$\overline{\int_a^b} f = \underline{\int_a^b} f$$

as we wished to demonstrate.

3. THE FUNDAMENTAL THEOREM OF THE CALCULUS

Our final theorem, which can be regarded as the culmination of the last two chapters, is Theorem 2 below. It is often referred to as the "fundamental theorem of the calculus". It presents the intimate relation between "Problem 1" and "Problem 2" announced at the beginning of Chapter 5. Formally stated the result is:

Theorem 2. *If f is continuous on I[a, b], and if G is any function defined on I[a, b] with the property that DG = f, then*

$$\int_a^b f = G(b) - G(a).$$

PROOF.   First we note that there *do* exist functions G with the property that $DG = f$. For example,

$$F(x) = \int_a^x f, \quad x \in I[a, b]$$

is such a function. Furthermore

$$F(b) - F(a) = \int_a^b f - \int_a^a f = \int_a^b f$$

since $\int_a^a f = 0$.

Now let G be any function with the property that $DG = f$. Then

$$F = G + \mathbf{k}$$

since $DG = DF$. Also

$$F(b) - F(a) = [G(b) + k] - [G(a) + k] = G(b) - G(a)$$

and the proof of our theorem is complete.

This important theorem tells us how to find $\int_a^b f$—namely, we need only find a function G whose derivative is f and evaluate the rise in the graph of G between a and b.

If $DF = f$ is continuous on $I[a, b]$, we shall find it convenient to use the following notation:

$$\int_a^b f = F\big]_a^b = F(b) - F(a).$$

Example 1.   *Calculate the area under* $f = j^2 + 2j - \frac{1}{3}$ *from 1 to 3.*

Since $$D(\tfrac{1}{3}j^3 + j^2 - \tfrac{1}{3}j) = j^2 + 2j - \tfrac{1}{3},$$

$$\int_1^3 (j^2 + 2j - \tfrac{1}{3}) = \tfrac{1}{3}j^3 + j^2 - \tfrac{1}{3}j\big]_1^3 = (9 + 9 - 1) - (\tfrac{1}{3} + 1 - \tfrac{1}{3})$$
$$= 16.$$

Example 2.   *Calculate the area bounded by the curves* $f = -j^2 + 1$ *and* $g = j + 1$. (See Figure 6.9.)

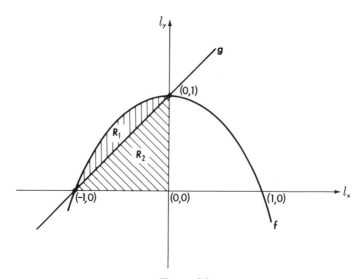

Figure 6.9

We see that the two curves intersect on $(-1, 0)$ and $(0, 1)$. Call R_1 the region bounded by the two curves and call R_2 the region bounded by g, $I[-1, 0]$ and the y-axis. Then by 4. of "axioms for area" (page 154), we have

$$\mathscr{A}(R_1) = \mathscr{A}(R_1 \cup R_2) - \mathscr{A}(R_2).$$

(since $R_1 \cap R_2 = \varnothing$ and $\mathscr{A}(\varnothing) = 0$). Now

$$\mathscr{A}(R_1 \cup R_2) = \int_{-1}^{0} (-j^2 + 1) = -\tfrac{1}{3}j^3 + j\big]_{-1}^{0} = \tfrac{2}{3}$$

and

$$\mathscr{A}(R_2) = \int_{-1}^{0} (j + 1) = \tfrac{1}{2}j^2 + j\big]_{-1}^{0} = \tfrac{1}{2}.$$

Thus

$$\mathscr{A}(R_1) = \tfrac{2}{3} - \tfrac{1}{2} = \tfrac{1}{6}.$$

Of course, since $\int_a^b (f \pm g) = \int_a^b f \pm \int_a^b g$, we could have obtained the same result by writing

$$\int_{-1}^{0} (-j^2 + 1 - j - 1) = \int_{-1}^{0} (-j^2 - j) = -\tfrac{1}{3}j^3 - \tfrac{1}{2}j^2\big]_{-1}^{0} = \tfrac{1}{6}.$$

4. SOME APPLICATIONS

In the foregoing discussions it was assumed that the continuous function f was always nonnegative and that $a < b$. We can remove these restrictions. Suppose $f(x) < 0$ and $x \in I[a, b]$ with $b > a$. Then the graph of f between a and b lies *below* the x-axis (see Figure 6.10). If $\pi = [x_0, x_1, \cdots, x_n]$ is a partition of $I[a, b]$ and $f(m_i)$ is the minimum of f on $I[x_{i-1}, x_i]$ and $f(M_i)$ is the maximum of f on $I[x_{i-1}, x_i]$, then

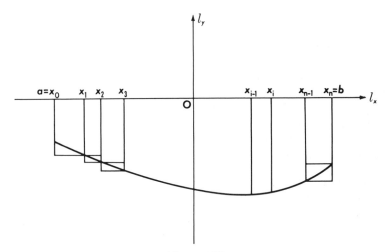

Figure 6.10

the products $f(m_i)(x_i - x_{i-1})$ and $f(M_i)(x_i - x_{i-1})$ are both negative for $i = 1, 2, \cdots, n$. Thus l.u.b.$_\pi L(\pi)$ and g.l.b.$_\pi U(\pi)$, [where as usual,

$$L(\pi) = \sum_{i=1}^{n} f(m_i)(x_i - x_{i-1})$$

and

$$U(\pi) = \sum_{i=1}^{n} f(M_i)(x_i - x_{i-1})]$$

will both be negative. Now $\int_a^b f$ exists and is the *negative* of the area under f from a to b. More generally, then, if the graph of f crosses $I[a, b]$ a finite number of times, we define the definite integral $\int_a^b f$ to be equal to the *algebraic* sum of the areas bounded by f, $I[a, b]$ and the lines $\lambda(1, 0, a)$ and $\lambda(1, 0, b)$. The areas above the x-axis are positive, and those below the x-axis are negative.

Accordingly, to calculate the area under a continuous function f that intersects the x-axis at a finite number of points $a_1, a_2, \cdots, a_n$ on $I[a, b]$ with $f(x) \leq 0$ on $I[a_1, a_2], I[a_3, a_4], \cdots, I[a_{n-1}, a_n]$ and $f(x) \geq 0$ otherwise on $I[a, b]$, we evaluate the sum

$$\int_a^{a_1} f + \int_{a_2}^{a_3} f + \cdots + \int_{a_{n-1}}^{a_{n-2}} f + \int_{a_n}^{b} f - \int_{a_1}^{a_2} f - \int_{a_3}^{a_4} f - \cdots - \int_{a_{n-1}}^{a_n} f.$$

(If n is odd, we take $a_n \equiv b$.) For example, since $\cos \geq 0$ on $I[0, \tfrac{1}{2}\pi]$ and $\cos \leq 0$ on $I[\tfrac{1}{2}\pi, \pi]$, and since $D \sin = \cos$, the area under $\cos$ from 0 to π is given by

$$\int_0^{\pi/2} \cos - \int_{\pi/2}^{\pi} \cos = \sin\Big]_0^{\pi/2} - \sin\Big]_{\pi/2}^{\pi} = 1 + 1 = 2.$$

On the other hand, the definite integral of $\cos$ between 0 and π is zero:

$$\int_0^{\pi} \cos = \sin\Big]_0^{\pi} = 0 - 0 = 0.$$

Our reason for considering the integral of a nonnegative function was to make the connection between "definite integral" and "area" more concrete. However, from the purely mathematical theory of integration such an artifice is not necessary. To remove this restriction we remark that if f and g are nonnegative continuous functions on $I[a, b]$ then $f \pm g$ is integrable on $I[a, b]$. In particular if ϕ is *any* continuous function on $I[a, b]$ and k is a constant such that $\psi = \phi + \mathbf{k}$ is nonnegative, then $\psi - \mathbf{k}$ is integrable on $I[a, b]$. Thus *every* continuous function on a closed finite interval is integrable.

Sometimes we are interested in the area from a to b under a function f having one rule of correspondence from a to c and another from c to b (where $a < c < b$). That is

$$f = \begin{cases} f_1 & \text{on} \quad I[a, c] \\ f_2 & \text{on} \quad I[c, b] \end{cases}$$

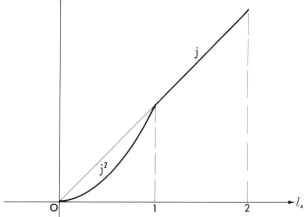

Figure 6.11

where f is continuous on $I[a, b]$ and $f_1(c) = f_2(c)$. In such a case we may again apply 4. of "axioms for area" (page 154) and if $f(x) \geq 0$ on $I[a, b]$, the area is given by

$$\int_a^b f = \int_a^c f_1 + \int_c^b f_2.$$

Thus to find the area from 0 to 2 under

$$f = \begin{cases} j^2 & \text{on} \quad I[0, 1] \\ j & \text{on} \quad I[1, 2] \end{cases}$$

(see Figure 6.11), we write

$$\int_0^2 f = \int_0^1 j^2 + \int_1^2 j = \tfrac{1}{3}j^3\big]_0^1 + \tfrac{1}{2}j^2\big]_1^2 = \tfrac{11}{6}.$$

A word of caution: In the statement of the fundamental theorem of the integral calculus we hypothesized that the function f was *continuous* on $I[a, b]$. This assumption must be respected when calculating the area under a given function from a to b. Suppose we tried to apply the theorem to the function $f = (2 - j)^{-2}$ (see Figure 6.12) between 0 and 4. Now

$$R_1 \cup R_2 \supset R_2$$

and $\mathscr{A}(R_2) = 1$. Thus by 3. of "axioms for area" (page 154) we should expect that

$$\mathscr{A}(R_1 \cup R_2) \geq \mathscr{A}(R_2) = 1.$$

But

$$\int_0^4 (2 - j)^{-2} = (2 - j)^{-1}\big]_0^4 = -\tfrac{1}{2} - \tfrac{1}{2} = -1.$$

Of course the difficulty arises from the discontinuity of f at $x = 2$.

For a further extension we shall apply Theorem 2 to problems of calculating volumes of revolution. We shall show how these problems may be turned into equivalent problems of finding areas under certain curves. Just as area is a number we associate with a set of points in the plane (two-space), so volume is a number that gives a measure of sets

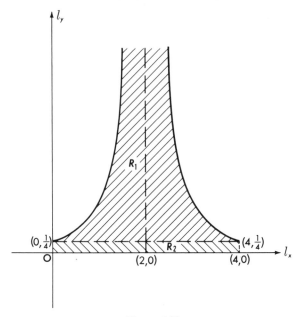

Figure 6.12

of points in three-space. Rather than give a detailed discussion of sets of points in three-space, we shall appeal to the reader's previous knowledge and/or intuition about sets of points that we call *solids* in three-space. Surely it is clear that if a rectangular region $R = \{(x, y) \mid a < x < b, 0 < y < k\}$ is rotated about the x-axis, then the resulting "solid" is cylindrical in shape—we shall call it a *disc*. Its height is $(b - a)$, the base radius is k and its volume is $\mathscr{V}(R) = \pi k^2(b - a)$. In what follows the volume of a disc will play a role (for volumes) analogous to the area of a rectangle (for area).

We consider the problem of finding the volume of the solid generated by rotating the region bounded by $I[a, b]$, a continuous function $f > 0$ on $I(a, b)$, and the lines $\lambda(1, 0, a)$, $\lambda(1, 0, b)$ about the x-axis (see Figure 6.13). Let $\pi = [x_0, x_1, \cdots, x_n]$ be a partition of $I[a, b]$, and as usual let $f(M_i)$ and $f(m_i)$ be the maximum and minimum values of f, respectively, on $I[x_{i-1}, x_i]$. The volume of the outer disc with base radius $f(M_i)$ and height $(x_i - x_{i-1})$ is given by $\pi f^2(M_i)(x_i - x_{i-1})$. Similarly, $\pi f^2(m_i)(x_i - x_{i-1})$ yields the volume of the inner disc with base radius $f(m_i)$ and height $(x_i - x_{i-1})$. It is reasonable to assume that the actual volume of the rotated region $R = \{(x, y) \mid a < x < b, 0 < y < f(x)\}$ is somewhere between the volume of the outer and inner discs. The entire volume $\mathscr{V}(R)$ therefore satisfies the inequalities

$$\pi \sum_{i=1}^{n} f^2(m_i)(x_i - x_{i-1}) \leq \mathscr{V}(R) \leq \pi \sum_{i=1}^{n} f^2(M_i)(x_i - x_{i-1}).$$

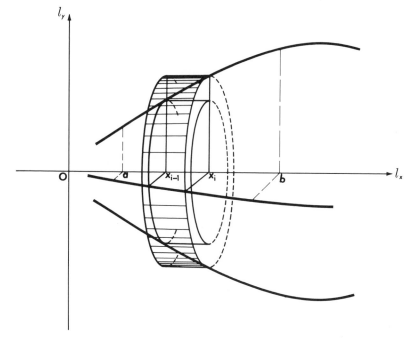

Figure 6.13

Let us now make some assumptions about volume similar to those we made about area (cf. pages 153-154).

1 If R is a region, the volume [written $\mathscr{V}(R)$] of the solid obtained by rotating R about the x-axis is a nonnegative number. If $R = \varnothing$, the empty set, then $\mathscr{V}(R) = 0$.

2 If R is a rectangle, that is, $R = \{(x, y) \mid a < x < b, 0 < y < k\}$,
$$\mathscr{V}(R) = \pi k^2 (b - a).$$

3 If R_1, R_2 are regions and $R_1 \subset R_2$, then
$$\mathscr{V}(R_1) \leqq \mathscr{V}(R_2).$$

4 If R_1 and R_2 are regions,
$$\mathscr{V}(R_1 \cup R_2) = \mathscr{V}(R_1) + \mathscr{V}(R_2) - \mathscr{V}(R_1 \cap R_2).$$

As in the case of area, if $\int_a^b \pi f^2$, the least upper bound of the lower sums exists and equals $\overline{\int_a^b} \pi f^2$, the greatest lower bound of the upper sums, then we shall say that the volume exists and is equal to $\int_a^b \pi f^2$. We note that if f is continuous, then πf^2 is continuous, and so by Theorem 1, $\underline{\int_a^b} \pi f^2$ and $\overline{\int_a^b} \pi f^2$ both exist and are equal. But these sums are precisely the lower and upper integrals of the area under the curve $g = \pi f^2$ from a to b. Thus the volume is equal to the area under g from a to b:

$$\mathcal{V}(R) = \pi \int_a^b f^2 = \int_a^b g.$$

The next example illustrates this result.

Example 1. *Find the volume of the solid generated by rotating the graph of $f = j^2 - j$ between 1 and 3 about the x-axis.*

In our above terminology,

$$\mathcal{V} = \pi \int_1^3 (j^2 - j)^2 = \pi \int_1^3 (j^4 - 2j^3 + j^2)$$

$$= \pi(\tfrac{1}{5}j^5 - \tfrac{1}{2}j^4 + \tfrac{1}{3}j^3)\big]_1^3 = \tfrac{256}{15}\pi.$$

EXERCISES

1. Let π_1 be a partition of $I[0, 1]$ into four subintervals of equal length and π_2 a partition of $I[0, 1]$ into eight subintervals of equal length. Find $L(\pi_1)$, $U(\pi_1)$, $L(\pi_2)$, $U(\pi_2)$ for $f = (1 - j^2)^{1/2}$. What would be the error if we considered $L(\pi_2)$ or $U(\pi_2)$ as the area of the quarter circle with radius 1?

2. Let π_1 and π_2 be as in Exercise 1. Find $L(\pi_1)$, $U(\pi_1)$, $L(\pi_2)$, and $U(\pi_2)$ for $f = j$ and $f = j^2$.

3. Assume $I[a, b]$ is contained in the domain of continuity of f and g and that $f \leq g$ for $x \in I[a, b]$.

(i) Prove that $\int_a^b f \leq \int_a^b g$.

(ii) If in addition $f \neq g$ for at least one point x_0 in $I[a, b]$, prove that $\int_a^b f < \int_a^b g$.

4. Show that $\int_a^b j = \int_{a+c}^{b+c} (j - c)$. Moreover, if f is continuous on $I[a - |c|, b + |c|]$ prove that $\int_a^b f = \int_{a+c}^{b+c} f \circ (j - c)$.

5. Prove that if f is continuous on $I[a, b]$ then for some number $c \in I(a, b)$,

$$f(c)(b - a) = \int_a^b f.$$

[*Hint:* Set $F(x) = \int_a^x f$ for $x \in I[a, b]$ and use the mean value theorem on F.]

6. What is the height of the rectangle with base $I[3, 6]$ and of area equal to

$$\int_3^6 (j^2 - 1)?$$

7. Let f be continuous on $I[a, b]$.

(i) Prove that $|f|$ is integrable on $I[a, b]$.

(ii) Prove that $|\int_a^b f| \leq \int_a^b |f|$. [*Hint:* $|f| \pm f \geq 0$.]

8. Evaluate the following definite integrals

(i) $\int_8^{10} \frac{1}{j^2}$

(ii) $\int_1^2 \left(j^3 + \frac{1}{j^3}\right)$

(iii) $\int_1^2 (j^4 - 2j + 5)$

(iv) $\int_0^1 j^{1/2}$

(v) $\int_0^{\pi/3} \sin$

(vi) $\int_0^{\pi/4} 4 \cos$

(vii) $\int_{(\pi/4)^2}^{(\pi/2)^2} \frac{\sin \circ j^{1/2}}{j^{1/2}}$

(viii) $\int_0^{\pi/3} \sin \circ 2j$

(ix) $\int_0^{\pi} \sin^2$

(x) $\int_0^{\pi/2} (\cos - j \sin)$.

9. Evaluate the following definite integrals

(i) $\int_0^{\pi} \cos$

(ii) $\int_1^4 (j^2 - 2j)$

(iii) $\int_1^2 (j^3 - j + 2)$

(iv) $\int_2^5 \frac{1}{(1-j)^2}$

(v) $\int_{-1}^2 \frac{2j}{(j^2 + 2)^2}$

(vi) $\int_{-1}^3 (j - 1)^2$.

10. In Exercise 9, which, if any, of the definite integrals is equal to the area under the curve for the given intervals?

11. Find the area bounded by:

(i) The parabolas $y = 4 - x^2$ and $y = x^2 + 2$.
(ii) The line $y = x$ and the parabola $y = 5x - x^2$.
(iii) The curves $y = x^3$ and $y = 4x$.
(iv) The curves $y = (x - 8)^2$ and $y = 9x$.

12. For what value of x will $F(x) = \int_1^{x+1} (6j + 8j^{-2})$ be a maximum?

13. In what ratio will the graph of $f = j^n$ (n a positive integer) divide the area of the unit square with vertices $(0, 0)$, $(0, 1)$, $(1, 1)$, $(1, 0)$?

14. Show that

(i) $\int_0^{\pi} \frac{2}{3} \sin \leq \frac{4}{3}\pi^2$

(ii) $\int_1^2 (j^2 - 1)^{1/2} \leq 2$

(iii) $\int_0^1 \frac{j}{(j^2 + 2j + 4)^{1/2}} \leq \frac{1}{4}$

(iv) $\int_0^{\pi/4} \frac{j}{\cos} \leq \frac{1}{16} \pi^2$.

15. The velocity of a body moving along a line is given by $v(t)$. In each of the following cases find the distance traveled by the body between the times t_1 and t_2.

(i) $v(t) = 32t - 8$, $\quad t_1 = 0$, $\quad t_2 = 4$
(ii) $v(t) = t^2 - 2t + 1$, $\quad t_1 = 1$, $\quad t_2 = 3$
(iii) $v(t) = t(t^2 + 4)^{1/2}$, $\quad t_1 = \sqrt{5}$, $\quad t_2 = \sqrt{12}$.

16.   Determine the volume generated by rotating the areas defined below about the x-axis.

(i) $f = \frac{1}{2}j^2$, $x = 0$, $x = 1$

(ii) $f = \cos$, $x = 0$, $x = \frac{1}{2}\pi$, $\left[Hint:\ \cos^2 = \dfrac{1 + \cos \circ 2j}{2} \right]$

(iii) $f = \dfrac{1}{j}$, $x = 1$, $x = 4$

(iv) $f = j^2 + 4j$, $x = 0$, $x = 5$.

17.   Find the volume of the solid generated by rotating about the x-axis the regions defined below.

(i) $f = j^2 + j$, $x = 1$, $x = 4$, $y = 2$

(ii) $f = \dfrac{1}{j}$, $x = \frac{1}{2}$, $x = 2$, $y = \frac{1}{2}$

(iii) $f = j$, $x = 2$, $x = 5$, $y = 1$

(iv) $f = j^{1/2}$, $x = 1$, $x = 4$, $y = 1$.

18.   Show that the volume of:

(i) a sphere is $\frac{4}{3}\pi r^3$ (r = radius of sphere). [*Hint:* The sphere is obtained by rotating $R = \{(x, y) \mid -r < x < r, 0 < y < \sqrt{r^2 - x^2}\}$ about the x-axis.]

(ii) an ellipsoid is $\frac{4}{3}\pi ab^2$ (a = semimajor axis, b = semiminor axis). [*Hint:* The ellipsoid is obtained by rotating $R = \{(x, y) \mid -a < x < a, 0 < y < b\sqrt{1 - x^2/a^2}\}$ about the x-axis.]

(iii) a right circular cone is $\frac{1}{3}\pi r^2 h$ (r = radius of base, h = height). [*Hint:* A cone is right circular if the base is a circle and the line joining the vertex to the center of the base is perpendicular to the base.]

19.   Let f be a continuous function that assumes both positive and negative values on $I[a, b]$. Give a suitable definition of volume if the curve f, bounded by the lines $\lambda(1, 0, a)$ and $\lambda(1, 0, b)$ is rotated about the x-axis.

20.   If for every $x \in \text{Dom}\, f$ we have $f(x) = f(-x)$, then we call f an *even* function. If $f(-x) = -f(x)$ for each $x \in \text{Dom}\, f$, we call f an *odd* function.

(i) If f is continuous and even on $I[-a, a] \subset \text{Dom}\, f$, show that

$$\int_{-a}^{a} f = 2 \int_{0}^{a} f.$$

(ii) If f is continuous and odd on $I[-a, a] \subset \text{Dom}\, f$, prove that

$$\int_{-a}^{a} f = 0.$$

21. Find the areas bounded by

(i) cos, $\lambda(1, 0, 0),$ $\lambda(1, 0, \pi)$
(ii) sin, $\lambda(1, 0, -\pi),$ $\lambda(1, 0, \pi)$
(iii) $j^3 - j,$ $\lambda(1, 0, -4),$ $\lambda(1, 0, 4)$
(iv) $j^2 - 3,$ $\lambda(1, 0, -2),$ $\lambda(1, 0, 2)$
(v) $j^{1/3},$ $\lambda(1, 0, -1),$ $\lambda(1, 0, 1).$

22. A tank is full of water (weighing 62.5 pounds per cubic foot). The shape of the tank is a right circular cone, its altitude is 8 ft. and its base radius is 4 ft.

(i) If the vertex of the tank is down and if all the water is to be pumped to a level 10 ft. above the top of the tank, show that the work done is

$$W = 62.5\pi \int_0^8 (0.5x)^2(18 - x)\, dx \text{ ft.-lbs.}$$

[*Hint:* (The work done in lifting a weight of w lbs. a vertical distance of k ft. is wk ft.-lbs.) Partition the altitude of the tank into n subdivisions $0 = x_0 < x_1 < \cdots < x_n = 8$. Show that the radius of a cross section of the cone at the x_k level is $r_k = 0.5x_k$. Now take cross sections of the cone of thickness $(x_{k+1} - x_k)$ and show that the work done in pumping such a cross section lies between the work done in pumping a disc of radius r_k and a disc of radius r_{k+1}. That is,

$$62.5\pi(0.5x_k)^2(x_{k+1} - x_k)(18 - x_k)$$
$$\leqq 62.5(\text{Volume of the cross section})(18 - x_k)$$
$$\leqq 62.5\pi(0.5x_{k+1})^2(x_{k+1} - x_k)(18 - x_k).]$$

(ii) What is the work done if the vertex of the cone is up?

23. If a hemispherical bowl of radius 6 ft. is full of water, what is the work done in pumping all the water to a level 5 ft. above the top of the bowl?

24. How much work is done in pumping all the water out of a right cylindrical tank of radius 4 ft. and altitude 10 ft. to a height 5 ft. above the top of the tank? (The tank stands on its base.)

25. How much work is done in pumping all the water out of a trough 10 ft. long to a height 6 ft. above the top of the trough, if the vertical cross section of the trough is an isosceles triangle with base 4 ft. and altitude 2 ft?

26. The natural length of a spring is 15 ft.; and a force of $12x$ lbs. is required to hold the spring stretched x ft. beyond its natural length. How much work is done in stretching the spring 5 ft. beyond its natural length?

7

THE LOGARITHMIC FUNCTION AND ITS INVERSE

In Exercises 18 and 19 of Chapter 5 we discussed the logarithmic and exponential functions from a more or less intuitive point of view. Here we shall rigorize what was suggested there and remove any scruples the reader may have about ln and ln*.

The importance of these functions derives from their frequent occurrence in the physical as well as the social sciences. For example, there is a category of problems known as population growth problems. Included are population explosion problems, continuously compounded interest problems, as well as radioactive decay problems. These problems all lead to an equation of the form

$$Df = \mathbf{k}f$$

(where $k < 0$ for decay problems and $k > 0$ for growth problems.) Theorem 2 will lead us to conclude that

$$\ln f = \mathbf{k}j + \mathbf{c}$$

and finally we shall see that

$$f(t) = f_0 \ln^* kt.$$

As we shall see in the examples at the end of this chapter, the above equality will enable us to predict the future population, the amount of capital accumulated at a time t, or the amount of radioactive substance remaining after t years.

Another exciting example of the importance of the functions ln and ln* is given by a rocket in free flight. Such a rocket accelerates itself by the discharge of propellant mass in a direction opposite to the desired acceleration. Conservation of momentum of the rocket and exhaust stream leads to the equation

$$mDv = v_e Dm$$

where m is the total mass of the rocket at time $t \geq 0$; v is the velocity at time t and v_e is the velocity of the exhaust jet relative to the rocket. We generally call $v_e Dm$ the rocket thrust. If it is assumed that v_e is constant, we see that

$$Dv = \mathbf{v}_e \frac{Dm}{m}$$

and we shall show that

$$v(t) = v_e \ln m(t) + k$$

or

$$m(t) = m_0 \ln^* \frac{v(t)}{v_e}$$

(where m_0 is the total mass of the rocket at time $t = 0$.)

I. THE LOGARITHMIC FUNCTION

We have seen that the function $1/j$ is continuous on any interval not containing the origin. Thus by Theorem 1 of Chapter 6

$$\int_1^x \frac{1}{j} \tag{1}$$

exists for any positive x. (That is, the area under the curve $1/j$ from 1 to x is well defined.) The expression in (1) is the rule of correspondence for a function we shall denote by ln. Thus

$$\ln x = \int_1^x \frac{1}{j}. \tag{2}$$

Thus (2) will be our formal definition of the logarithmic function ln. Immediately we obtain from this definition the following properties of the logarithmic function:

(i)
$$\ln 1 = \int_1^1 \frac{1}{j} = 0$$

(ii)
$$D \ln = \frac{1}{j}.$$

From (ii) and the chain rule of differentiation (Theorem 4 of Chapter 5)

(iii)
$$D \ln \circ (-j) = \frac{-1}{-j} = \frac{1}{j}$$

for $x < 0$. Combining properties (ii) and (iii) we have the indefinite integral formula

(iv) $$\int \frac{1}{j} = \ln \circ \mid \ \mid + \mathbf{k}, \quad x \neq 0.$$

By Theorem 10 of Chapter 5 and property (ii) we conclude that:

(v)   ln is strictly increasing and continuous for all positive x.

Exercise 22 of Chapter 4 implies

(vi)   ln* is continuous on Ran ln.

Next we prove the following "addition" property of ln:

(vii)   For $a, b > 0$, $\ln ab = \ln a + \ln b$.

PROOF OF (vii).   We observe that

$$D \ln \circ \mathbf{a}j = \frac{1}{j} = D \ln.$$

Therefore, by Theorem 14 of Chapter 5

$$\ln \circ \mathbf{a}j = \ln + \mathbf{k}.$$

But

$$\ln a = \ln aj(1) = \ln j(1) + \mathbf{k}(1) = 0 + k = k$$

and so

$$\ln \circ \mathbf{a}j = \ln + \ln \circ \mathbf{a}.$$

Thus

$$\ln ab = \ln aj(b) = (\ln + \ln \circ \mathbf{a})(b) = \ln b + \ln a.$$

Property (vii) also implies

(viii) $$\ln x = -\ln \frac{1}{x}, \quad x > 0,$$

$\left[\text{since by property (i), } 0 = \ln \frac{x}{x}, \text{ and } \ln \frac{x}{x} = \ln x + \ln \frac{1}{x}\right]$. Another immediate consequence is

(ix) $$\ln \frac{a}{b} = \ln a - \ln b, \quad a, b > 0.$$

Finally we also conclude from (viii) that

(x)   Ran ln is symmetric about zero: that is, for each number a in Ran ln there is a number $-a$ in Ran ln.

Next we shall show that

(xi)   If $x > 0$ and r is any rational number, then

$$\ln x^r = r \ln x.$$

PROOF OF (xi). By the chain rule of differentiation and Example 6 of Section 2 of Chapter 5,

$$D \ln \circ j^r = \left(\frac{1}{j} \circ j^r\right) \times (rj^{r-1}) = \frac{r}{j} = Dr \ln.$$

Hence, again by Theorem 14 of Chapter 5,

$$\ln \circ j^r = \mathbf{r} \ln + \mathbf{k}.$$

But

$$0 = \ln 1 = \ln j^r(1) = r \ln j(1) + \mathbf{k}(1) = r \ln 1 + k = k$$

so that $k = 0$ and

$$\ln \circ j^r = \mathbf{r} \ln$$

or

$$\ln x^r = r \ln x.$$

From the above result and property (x) we may infer:

(xii) $\operatorname{Ran} \ln = \operatorname{Dom} \ln^* =$ the set of all real numbers.

PROOF OF (xii). Since $\ln 1 = 0$ by (i), property (v) implies $\ln 2 > 0$. By property (xi), $\ln 2^r = r \ln 2$. So for any positive number M, no matter how large, we need only choose a rational number r greater than $M/\ln 2$ and we shall have

$$\ln 2^r = r \ln 2 > M.$$

Hence the function ln is not bounded from above. Combining this fact with property (x), we obtain the desired result (xii).

Finally, by the intermediate value theorem (Theorem 15 of Chapter 4) there exists a number e in $I[1, \infty)$ such that

(xiii) $$\ln e = \int_1^e \frac{1}{j} = 1.$$

Properties (i), (v)–(xii) are precisely the properties we ascribe to the logarithmic function. Consequently, in view of (xiii) we may write

$$\ln \equiv \log_e.$$

2. THE INVERSE LOGARITHMIC FUNCTION

Next we turn our attention to an investigation of the properties of ln*. From property (i), namely, $\ln 1 = 0$ we infer

(i*) $$\ln^* 0 = 1,$$

while from (xiii) we obtain

(ii*) $$\ln^* 1 = e.$$

If, in (vii) we set

$$a = \ln^* x$$
$$b = \ln^* y,$$

then,

$$\ln [(\ln^* x)(\ln^* y)] = \ln (\ln^* x) + \ln (\ln^* y) = x + y.$$

Composing the above equation with $\ln^*$ we get

$$(\ln^* x)(\ln^* y) = \ln^*\{\ln [(\ln^* x)(\ln^* y)]\} = \ln^* (x + y).$$

That is

(iii*) $$(\ln^* x)(\ln^* y) = \ln^* (x + y).$$

The following property,

(iv*) $$\ln^* r = e^r \quad \text{for any rational number } r$$

is obtained from (xi) by composing the right- and left-hand sides of

$$\ln e^r = r \ln e = r$$

with $\ln^*$. Thus

$$e^r = \ln^*(\ln e^r) = \ln^* r.$$

Now $\ln^* x$ is defined for all real numbers x, while at this point $e^x = \ln^* x$ is defined only for *rational* numbers x. We shall therefore *define*

$$e^t = a$$

(where t and a are real numbers) if and only if

$$\ln a = t. \tag{1}$$

[Note that by (iv*), equation (1) is already true for t a rational number.] Thus for all real numbers t,

$$\ln^* t = \ln^*(\ln a) = a = e^t.$$

Properties (xii) and (i*)–(iv*) include all the properties of the exponential function. We shall therefore write

$$\ln^* = \exp_e$$

or

$$\exp_e x = e^x.$$

Our next objective is to show that $D \ln^* = \ln^*$. Applying Theorem 6 of Chapter 5 to the function $\ln^*$ we have

$$D \ln^* = \frac{1}{(D \ln) \circ \ln^*} = \frac{1}{1/j \circ \ln^*} = \ln^*$$

or

$$D \exp_e x = D e^x = e^x = \exp_e x.$$

In other words, the function $\exp_e$ is its own slope function.

In Chapter 5 we found that $Dj^r = \mathbf{r}j^{r-1}$ for r a *rational* number. We are now in a position to extend this result to all *real* numbers s. First we recall that

$$e^{r \ln} = e^{\ln j^r} = j^r$$

for r rational. We extend this to all real numbers s by *defining*

$$j^s = e^{s \ln}.$$

Then for all real s and t,

$$j^s j^t = e^{s \ln} e^{t \ln} = e^{s \ln + t \ln} = j^{s+t}$$

and

$$Dj^s = D e^{s \ln} = (e^{s \ln})\mathbf{s}\,\frac{\mathbf{I}}{j} = j^s \cdot \frac{\mathbf{s}}{j} = \mathbf{s}j^{s-1}.$$

So far we have discussed the logarithmic and exponential functions with *base e* (which is called the *natural* base). Now we shall extend the meaning of these functions to include any other positive number a ($\neq 1$) as a base.

Since

$$j^s(a) = a^s = e^{s \ln a}$$

with a and s real, $(a > 0)$ we shall write

$$a^x = \exp_a x = \exp_e(x \ln a)$$

for x any real number and $a > 0$, $a \neq 1$. We see immediately that

$$\text{Dom } \exp_a$$

is the set of all real numbers and

$$\text{Ran } \exp_a = \text{Ran } \exp_e$$

is the set of all positive real numbers. Also

$$a^s a^t = a^{s \ln a} e^{t \ln a} = e^{(s+t)\ln a} = a^{s+t}$$

and

$$(a^s)^t = e^{t \ln a^s} = e^{ts \ln a} = a^{ts} = a^{st}$$

while

$$a^s b^s = e^{s \ln a} e^{s \ln b} = e^{s(\ln a + \ln b)}$$
$$= e^{s \ln ab} = (ab)^s.$$

For the derivative and antiderivative of $\exp_e$ the following rules apply:

(a) $$D \exp_a x = D e^{x \ln a} = (\ln a) e^{x \ln a} = a^x \ln a$$

and

(b) $$\int \exp_a = \frac{1}{\ln \circ \mathbf{a}} \int (\ln \circ \mathbf{a}) \exp_a = \frac{1}{\ln \circ \mathbf{a}} \exp_a + \mathbf{k}$$

or

(b')
$$\int a^x \, dx = \frac{1}{\ln a} \int (\ln a) \, \exp_a x \, dx = \frac{1}{\ln a} \exp_a x + k.$$

That $\exp_a$ is one–one follows from the fact that $\exp_e$ has this property. Therefore $\exp_a$ has an inverse (on the positive x-axis) which we shall denote by

$$\log_a \equiv \exp_a{}^*.$$

Now let

$$b = \log_a x.$$

Then

$$e^{b \ln a} = a^b = a^{\log_a x} = \exp_a \circ \exp_a{}^*(x) = x$$

and

$$b(\ln a) = \ln x$$

or

$$b = \log_a x = \frac{\ln x}{\ln a}.$$

In other words, dividing $\ln x$ by the fixed number $\ln a$ we obtain $\log_a x$. This relation also yields

$$\log_a xy = \frac{\ln xy}{\ln a} = \frac{\ln x}{\ln a} + \frac{\ln y}{\ln a}$$
$$= \log_a x + \log_a y$$

and

$$\log_a \frac{x}{y} = \log_a x - \log_a y$$

while

$$D \log_a = D \frac{1}{\ln \circ \mathbf{a}} \ln = \frac{1}{\ln \circ \mathbf{a}} \cdot \frac{\mathbf{I}}{j}.$$

3. THE NUMBER e

The number e introduced in property (xiii) of Section 1 is often defined as

$$e = \lim_{h \to 0} (1 + h)^{1/h}.$$

This is immediately obtainable as a result of property (xiii) and Theorem 11 of Chapter 4. To wit,

$$1 = \frac{\mathbf{I}}{j}(1) = D \ln (1) = \lim_{h \to 0} \frac{\ln (1 + h) - \ln 1}{h}$$
$$= \lim_{h \to 0} \frac{\ln (1 + h)}{h} = \lim_{h \to 0} \ln (1 + h)^{1/h}$$
$$= \ln \lim_{h \to 0} (1 + h)^{1/h}.$$

But ln is one–one and $1 = \ln e$. Therefore

$$\lim_{h \to 0} (1 + h)^{1/h} = e.$$

We may obtain numerical upper and lower bounds for the number e as follows. Consider the area bounded by $1/j$, the lines $\lambda(1, 0, 1)$, $\lambda(1, 0, 2.6)$ and the x-axis. Let $\pi_1 = [x_0, x_1, \cdots, x_{16}]$ be a partition of $I[1, 2.6]$ such that $x_{i+1} - x_i = 0.1$ for $i = 0, 1, 2, \cdots, 15$. (See Figure 7.1.) Then

$$\int_1^{2.6} \frac{1}{j} \leq U(\pi_1) = \sum_{m=10}^{25} \frac{1}{m} < 0.988 < 1 = \int_1^{e} \frac{1}{j}.$$

Now set $\pi_2 = [x_0, x_1, \cdots, x_{19}]$ be a partition of $I[1, 2.9]$ such that $x_{i+1} - x_i = 0.1$, $i = 0, 1, 2, \cdots, 18$. Then

$$\int_1^{e} \frac{1}{j} = 1 < 1.03 < \sum_{m=11}^{29} \frac{1}{m} = L(\pi_2) \leq \int_1^{2.9} \frac{1}{j}.$$

Since $\ln x = \int_1^{x} 1/j$ is a strictly increasing function we have

$$2.6 < e < 2.9. \qquad\qquad (1)$$

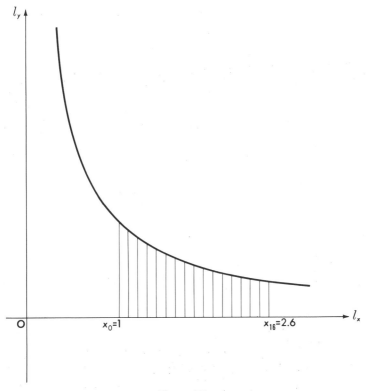

Figure 7.1

We shall now prove a very important theorem having many useful applications in both pure and applied mathematics. In particular we shall use the theorem to get a better numerical approximation for the number e.

Theorem 1 (*Taylor's Theorem with the Lagrange remainder*). *Let f and its first n derivatives exist on the closed interval $I[x_1, x_2]$. Let $I(a, b)$ be interior to $I[x_1, x_2]$. Then there exists a number c in $I(a, b)$ such that*

$$f(b) = f(a) + \frac{Df(a)}{1!}(b - a) + \frac{D^2f(a)}{2!}(b - a)^2 + \cdots$$
$$+ \frac{D^{n-1}f(a)}{(n-1)!}(b - a)^{n-1} + \frac{D^nf(c)}{n!}(b - a)^n.$$

PROOF.   Define the number β such that

$$\beta \frac{(b - a)^n}{n!} = f(b) - \sum_{k=0}^{n-1} \frac{D^kf(a)}{k!}(b - a)^k$$

and define the function g as

$$g(x) = f(b) - \sum_{k=0}^{n-1} \frac{D^kf(x)}{k!}(b - x)^k - \beta \frac{(b - x)^n}{n!}. \tag{2}$$

Now all the functions on the right-hand side of (2) are continuous and have derivatives (by assumption D^nf exists) on $I(a, b)$. Furthermore $g(b) = 0$ and from the definition of β, we also have $g(a) = 0$. Therefore Rolle's Theorem (Theorem 8 of Chapter 5) applies to g and there is a number c in $I(a, b)$ such that $Dg(c) = 0$. But

$$Dg(x) = Df(x) - \sum_{k=1}^{n-1} \frac{D^kf(x)}{(k-1)!}(b - x)^{k-1} + \sum_{k=1}^{n-1} \frac{D^{k+1}f(x)}{k!}(b - x)^k$$
$$- \beta \frac{(b - x)^{n-1}}{(n-1)!}$$

$$= [D^nf(x) - \beta] \frac{(b - x)^{n-1}}{(n-1)!},$$

and

$$0 = Dg(c) = [D^nf(c) - \beta] \frac{(b - c)^{n-1}}{(n-1)!}$$

implies

$$D^nf(c) = \beta.$$

Thus our theorem is proved.

Sometimes it is customary to set

$$R_n = \frac{\beta(b - a)^n}{n!} = \frac{D^nf(c)}{n!}(b - a)^n$$

and call R_n the *Lagrange form of the remainder*.

Let us apply Taylor's Theorem to $\exp_e$ as follows. All the derivatives of $\exp_e$ are continuous for all x. Let $I(0, x)$ play the role of $I(a, b)$ in Theorem 1. Then

$$e^x = 1 + x + \frac{x^2}{2!} + \frac{x^3}{3!} + \cdots + \frac{e^c x^n}{n!}$$

where $c \in I(0, x)$. In particular, for $x = 1$,

$$e = 1 + 1 + \frac{1}{2} + \frac{1}{3!} + \frac{1}{4!} + \cdots + \frac{1}{(n-1)!} + \frac{e^c}{n!}, \quad c \in I(0, 1).$$

Thus if we write

$$e = \sum_{k=0}^{n-1} \frac{1}{k!}$$

(recall that $0! = 1$), we introduce an error of less than $e^c/n!$ If $n = 10$, for example

$$\frac{e^c}{10!} < \frac{e^1}{10!} < \frac{2.9}{10!} < 8 \times 10^{-7}$$

[since we have shown that $e < 2.9$, cf. (1)], and

$$\sum_{k=0}^{9} \frac{1}{k!} = 2.718282 \text{ (approximately)}.$$

Thus

$$e = 2.718282$$

correct to at least six decimal places.

For our next application of Taylor's theorem we consider the function $\ln \circ (1 + j)$ for $x \in I[0, 3]$. Setting $a = 1$, $b = 1 + x$, we see that

$$b - a = x$$
$$D^k \ln (1) = (k - 1)! \, (-1)^{k-1}, \quad k = 1, 2, \cdots.$$

Thus by Theorem 1,

$$\ln (1 + x) = x - \frac{x^2}{2} + \frac{x^3}{3} - \frac{x^4}{4} + \cdots + \frac{(-1)^{n-1} x^n}{nc^n} \tag{3}$$

where $c \in I(1, 1 + x)$.

The reader may be tempted to use (3) in computing, for example, $\ln 2$, by setting $x = 1$ in (3). To wit,

$$\ln 2 = 1 - \frac{1}{2} + \frac{1}{3} - \frac{1}{4} + \cdots + \frac{(-1)^{n-1}}{nc^n}, \quad c \in I(1, 2).$$

But giving a little thought to the absolute value of the remainder term we see that

$$\left| \frac{(-1)^{n-1}}{nc^n} \right| \leqq \frac{1}{n}.$$

Hence we can be sure the error will not exceed 1×10^{-2} only for $n > 99$. This need not lead to discouragement, however. For using a little ingenuity we may still compute $\ln 2$ with an error less than 1×10^{-4} without using an inordinately large number of terms. Towards this end consider $\ln \circ (\mathbf{I} - j)$ for $x \in I[-3, 0.5]$. Then

$$\ln (1 - x) = -x - \frac{x^2}{2} - \frac{x^3}{3} - \cdots - \frac{x^n}{nd^n}, \quad d \in I(1 - x, 1). \quad (4)$$

Now from (3) and (4)

$$\ln \left(\frac{1 + x}{1 - x}\right) = \ln (1 + x) - \ln (1 - x)$$

$$= 2\left(x + \frac{x^3}{3} + \frac{x^5}{5} + \cdots + \frac{(-1)^{n-1}x^n}{nc^n} + \frac{x^n}{nd^n}\right). \quad (5)$$

Setting $x = 1/3$ in (5):

$$\ln \left(\frac{1 + \frac{1}{3}}{1 - \frac{1}{3}}\right) = \ln 2$$

and we obtain from (5) with $n = 11$:

$$\ln 2 = 2\left(\frac{1}{3} + \frac{1}{3 \cdot 3^3} + \frac{1}{5 \cdot 3^5} + \frac{1}{7 \cdot 3^7} + \frac{1}{9 \cdot 3^9} + \frac{1}{11(3c)^{11}} + \frac{1}{11(3d)^{11}}\right)$$

where $1 < c < 4/3$, $2/3 < d < 1$. Hence if we let

$$\ln 2 = 2\left(\frac{1}{3} + \frac{1}{3 \cdot 3^3} + \frac{1}{5 \cdot 3^5} + \frac{1}{7 \cdot 3^7} + \frac{1}{9 \cdot 3^9}\right) = 0.6931$$

we introduce an error of less than

$$2\left(\frac{1}{11 \cdot 3^{11}} + \frac{1}{11 \cdot 2^{11}}\right) < 1 \times 10^{-4}.$$

For a final application of Taylor's theorem, let us compute $\sqrt{146}$ correct to four decimal places. First note that if $f = j^{1/2}$ and $\alpha \neq 0$,

$$f(x) = \sqrt{\alpha} + \frac{(x - \alpha)}{2\alpha^{1/2}} - \frac{1}{4}\frac{(x - \alpha)^2}{2!\alpha^{3/2}} + \frac{3}{8}\frac{(x - \alpha)^3}{3!\alpha^{5/2}} + \cdots$$

$$+ (-1)^{n-1}\frac{1 \cdot 3 \cdot 5 \cdot \cdots (2n - 3)(x - \alpha)^n}{2^n n! c^{(n-1)/2}},$$

where $c \in I(\alpha, x)$. In the example, $x = 146$. Let $\alpha = 144$. Then $x - \alpha = 2$ and (with $n = 3$),

$$\sqrt{146} = 12 + \frac{2}{2 \cdot 12} - \frac{1}{4}\frac{2^2}{2 \cdot 12^3} + \frac{3}{8}\frac{2^3}{3! c^{5/2}}$$

where $144 < c < 146$. Thus

$$\sqrt{146} = 12 + 0.0833333 - 0.0002890 + \frac{1}{2c^{5/2}}$$

$$= 12.083044 + \frac{1}{2c^{5/2}}.$$

But

$$\frac{1}{2c^{5/2}} < \frac{1}{2 \cdot 12^5} < 1 \times 10^{-5}.$$

Thus

$$\sqrt{146} = 12.08304$$

with an error of less than 1×10^{-5}.

4. APPLICATIONS TO DECAY PROBLEMS

In many fields of science, both physical and social, problems occur which are generally classified as population growth or decay problems. More specifically they are problems where the population or amount of a given substance either increases or decreases at a rate proportional to the amount present at a given time.

For example: If a certain type of bacteria doubles in population every 12 minutes, how long will it take for an initial population P_0 to increase to $5P_0$?

The answer to this and similar problems will be found in Theorem 2 below. (Of course the range of the growth function is a set of integers, and therefore will be discontinuous. However, for large populations we may assume—with negligible loss of generality—that the growth function is continuous.)

Theorem 2. *Let $Df(t)$ exist and let $f(t) > 0$ for $t \in I[a, b]$. If $Df = \mathbf{k}f$ for $t \in I[a, b]$, then*

$$f(t) = c \exp_e (kt).$$

PROOF. Since $f \neq 0$ on $I[a, b]$, the equation $Df = \mathbf{k}f$ implies

$$\frac{Df}{f} = \mathbf{k}.$$

But $D \ln \circ f = Df/f$ (since $f > 0$), and $D\mathbf{k}j = \mathbf{k}$. Therefore, by Theorem 14 of Chapter 5,

$$\ln \circ f = \mathbf{k}j + \mathbf{c}_1.$$

Now since $\exp_e$ is one–one we have

$$f = \exp_e \circ (\ln \circ f) = \exp_e \circ (\mathbf{k}j + \mathbf{c}_1)$$

or

$$f(t) = e^{c_1} e^{kt}.$$

Setting

$$c = e^{c_1},$$

we obtain

$$f(t) = c e^{kt}.$$

Applying this result to the example stated in the second paragraph of this section, let us set the initial time at $t = 0$. Then $f(0) = ce^0 = c = P_0$. Thus for any time t, the amount of bacteria is given by

$$f(t) = P_0 e^{kt}.$$

We are also given that in 12 minutes the population is $2P_0$. Hence

$$f(12) = 2P_0 = P_0 e^{k12}$$

or

$$2 = e^{12k}$$

so that

$$k = \tfrac{1}{12} \ln 2 = 0.058.$$

Thus

$$f(t) = P_0 e^{0.058t}.$$

To obtain the time t for which $f(t) = 5P_0$ we set

$$5P_0 = P_0 e^{0.058t}$$

and obtain

$$\ln 5 = 0.058t$$

and finally

$$t = \frac{1}{0.058} \ln 5 = 27.7 \text{ min.}$$

We consider a further example.

Example 1.   *Suppose an initial mass of 2 grams of radium decomposes at time t at a rate proportional to the mass present at time t. In particular suppose that the constant of proportionality is -4.33×10^{-4} grams/year. (The negative sign indicates that the process is one of decay.) (a) How much of the initial mass of 2 grams will be left after t years? (b) How long will it take for the mass to disintegrate to half of its initial value?*

Our supposition tells us that

$$Dm(t) = -4.33 \times 10^{-4} m(t)$$

where $m(t)$ is the mass at any time t. Applying Theorem 2, we find

$$m(t) = c\,e^{-4.33 \times 10^{-4}t}.$$

Since $m(0)$ is given as 2 grams, $c = 2$, and

$$m(t) = 2\,e^{-4.33 \times 10^{-4}t} \tag{1}$$

is the amount present at any time $t \geq 0$. Equation (1) answers part (a) of our example.

To determine the number of years T such that $m(T) = \tfrac{1}{2}m(0) = 1$, we set

$$1 = 2\,e^{-4.33 \times 10^{-4}T}$$

or

$$0.5 = e^{-4.33 \times 10^{-4}T}.$$

We now solve for T by composing both sides of this last equation with the function ln. Then

$$\ln 0.5 = -4.33 \times 10^{-4} T$$

and we conclude that

$$T = 1,600 \text{ years (approx.)}$$

EXERCISES

1. Find Df if

(i) $f = \dfrac{2 - \exp_e}{2 + \exp_e}$

(ii) $f(x) = x - \ln(1 + e^x)$

(iii) $f(x) = x \ln x$

(iv) $f(x) = \dfrac{\ln x}{x}$

(v) $f = \ln \circ (\sin + \cos), \quad 0 \le x \le \frac{1}{2}\pi$

(vi) $f = \exp_e \circ \sin^3$

(vii) $f = \exp_e \circ \tan*, \quad 0 \le x < \frac{1}{2}\pi$

(viii) $f = \ln \circ | \quad | \circ \dfrac{k - \exp_e}{k + \exp_e}$

(ix) $f = \ln \circ \dfrac{k + j}{k - j}$

(x) $f(x) = 10^x \sin x$

(xi) $f(x) = \frac{1}{2}[x\sqrt{x^2 + a^2} + a^2 \ln(x + \sqrt{x^2 + a^2})]$

(xii) $f = \ln \circ \ln$.

2. Determine the following indefinite integrals:

(i) $\int \exp_e \circ 2j$

(vi) $\int \exp_e (\sin \circ \exp_e)$

(ii) $\int \dfrac{1}{a^2 - j^2}$

(vii) $\int 2^x \, dx$

(iii) $\int 2x \, e^{x^2} \, dx$

(viii) $\int^5 \dfrac{1}{x} e^{\ln x^2} \, dx$

(iv) $\int x^2 \, e^{x^3} \, dx$

(ix) $\int \exp_5 \circ 4j$

(v) $\int x \, e^{\ln x} \, dx$

(x) $\int \ln$.

3. For what values of x do the following equations hold?

(i) $\ln \circ (k + j) - \ln \circ (k - j) = 1$

(ii) $\ln \circ (k + j) + \ln \circ (k + j) = 1$

(iii) $\ln \circ (j^2 - k^2) - \ln \circ (j + k) = 0$

(iv) $\ln \circ (j + 1)^{1/2} = 2$

(v) $\log_2 \circ (j + 1) = 2$.

4.   Using Taylor's formula (Theorem 1), find ln 3, ln 5, and ln 7 correct to four decimal places. Then find ln 4, ln 6, ln 8, ln 9, and ln 10. [*Hint:* See page 186 for ln 2. Derive the formula

$$\ln (a + x) = \ln a + \frac{x}{a} - \frac{x^2}{2a^2} + \frac{x^3}{3a^3} - \cdots + R_n.]$$

5.   Use the results of the previous exercise to obtain approximations to $\log_{10} 2$, $\log_{10} 3$, $\log_{10} 5$, $\log_{10} 7$.

6.   Let $g = (1 + j)^{1/j}$. Approximate $g(1)$, $g(\frac{1}{2})$, $g(\frac{1}{4})$, $g(\frac{1}{8})$. [*Hint:* Use the results of Exercise 4 and interpolate.]

7.   Use Taylor's Theorem to approximate $\sqrt{24}$, $\sqrt{170}$, $\sqrt{258}$, to four decimal places.

8.   Find the Taylor expansion for sin and cos.

9.   Find the Taylor expansion for sin*.

10.   Determine $D \cos^*$, find Dom $\cos^*$ and derive the Taylor expansion for $\cos^*$.

11.   Find the volume generated by rotating the graph of $j^{-1/2} \ln$ from 1 to e^2 about the x-axis.

12.   Find

(i) $\displaystyle\int_0^2 \frac{dx}{e^x - 16\, e^{-x}}$

(ii) $\displaystyle\int_0^{\sqrt{5}} \sqrt{x^2 + 4}\, dx$

(iii) $\displaystyle\int_0^1 \frac{e^{2x} - e^{-2x}}{e^x - e^{-x}}\, dx$

(iv) $\displaystyle\int_1^e 2\frac{\ln}{j}$

(v) $\displaystyle\int_0^1 \frac{e^{2x} + e^{-2x} + 2}{e^x + e^{-x}}\, dx$

(vi) $\displaystyle\int_e^{e^2} \frac{1}{j(\ln)^2}$

(vii) $\displaystyle\int_1^2 \ln \circ \exp_e$

(viii) $\displaystyle\int_1^2 \exp_e \circ \ln$

(ix) $\displaystyle\int_0^1 \frac{1}{\sqrt{1 - j^2}}$

(x) $\displaystyle\int_0^\pi \cos (\exp_e \circ \sin)$.

13.   (i) Define e as the number such that the function $\exp_e$ is tangent to the line $\lambda(1, -1, -1)$ at $x = 0$. Use this fact to prove that $D \exp_e (0) = 1$.

(ii) From part (i) prove that $D\, e^x = e^x$.

14.   Where does $(-2j)\, \exp_e \circ (-j^2)$ have a maximum?

15.   Find the equation of the line tangent to $f = \exp_e + 2$ at $(0, 3)$.

16.   Mesothorium disintegrates according to the law $Dm = -km$, where k is a constant and $m(t)$ is the mass at any time $t \geq 0$. The half-life is approximately 6.7 years.

(i) Find k.

(ii) How much mesothorium will be left at the end of T years if initially (at time $t = 0$), 2 grams were present?

17.   An isotope of polonium disintegrates according to the law $Dm = -5 \times 10^{-3}\, m$. (Initially $m(0) = m_0$.)

(i) How much will be left after 100 days.

(ii) What is the half-life? the quarter-life?

18. Suppose a radio-active substance disintegrates according to the law $Dm = -\mathbf{k}m$. Let $m(0) = m_0$, $m(t_1) = m_1$. Find the expression for k. What is k if $m_0 = 8$ and $m(2) = 6$.

19. If the resistance of a medium to a moving particle (for example, a ball rolling on a horizontal plane) is proportional to the velocity of the particle,

(i) Find the expression for the velocity of the particle. [*Hint:* Resistance = force = mass × acceleration.]

(ii) If the velocity v at $t = 0$ is $v(0) = 10$ cm./sec., and $v(3) = 5$ cm./sec., find k/m where k is the constant of proportionality and m is the mass.

20. Newton's law of cooling states: A body loses heat to its surrounding medium at a rate proportional to the difference of its temperature and that of the surrounding medium. If the temperature of the air is 30° F and at the end of the first hour the temperature of the body drops from 120° F to 80° F, when will the temperature of the body be 50° F?

21. An initial amount of \$10,000 is invested. The interest is compounded continuously. The rate at which this principal is increasing at time t is always proportional to the amount of principal present at time t.

(i) If the rate of interest is 5 percent, when will the original amount double?

(ii) How long will it take for the original amount to quadruple?

(iii) How long will it take for the \$10,000 to double if it is compounded semi-annually at 5 percent?

22. The sale of a certain commodity decreases at a rate (with respect to price) that is directly proportional to the amount of sales, $s(p)$, say, at a given price p and inversely proportional to the price p plus a constant. Thus

$$Ds(p) = -\frac{ks(p)}{p + a} \quad (a, k \text{ are positive constants}).$$

Show that

$$s(p) = \frac{c}{(p + a)^k}$$

where c is a constant.

23. The population of a country is 200,000,000. If the rate of growth of the population at time t is proportional to the population at time t,

(i) What will be the population 10 years hence if each year births outnumber deaths by 5 per every 1000 population?

(ii) When will the population double?

24. A man puts \$80,000 into a fund paying interest at the rate of 4 percent per year compounded continuously. He withdraws money

continuously at a rate of $4,800 per year. When will the fund be exhausted?

25. When a certain food product is packaged, the number of bacteria of a certain type contained in the package is B_0. Sixty days later the number of bacteria is estimated to be $1,000B_0$. The maximum number permitted by the local Board of Health is $2,000B_0$. When should the package be taken off the market?

26. Let Δv be the velocity increment which a rocket in free flight (see page 177) can achieve by discharging some portion of its propellant of mass Δm. Let m_0 be the total mass of the rocket at the start of the acceleration. Show that

$$\Delta v = v_e \ln \left(\frac{m_0}{m_0 - \Delta m} \right).$$

8

TECHNIQUES FOR FINDING ANTIDERIVATIVES

We have seen (Theorem 14 of Chapter 5) that an antiderivative of a given function f is unique up to an additive constant. That is, if $DF = f$, then each function of the set $\{F + \mathbf{k}\}$ has derivative equal to f. We denote this set by $\int f$, and call it the *indefinite integral* of f. Thus if $DF = f$, we write

$$\int f = \{F + \mathbf{k}\}.$$

However, in conformity with long standing usage we shall omit the braces and write simply

$$\int f = F + \mathbf{k}.$$

The examples and exercises of Chapters 5, 6, and 7 give us the following indefinite integral formulas:

$$\int \mathbf{a}j^n = \frac{\mathbf{a}}{\mathbf{n+1}} j^{n+1} + \mathbf{k}, \quad (n \neq -1) \tag{1}$$

$$\int \frac{\mathbf{1}}{j} = \ln \circ |\ \ | + \mathbf{k}, \quad x \neq 0 \tag{2}$$

$$\int \cos = \sin + \mathbf{k} \tag{3}$$

$$\int \sin = -\cos + \mathbf{k} \tag{4}$$

$$\int \sec^2 = \tan + \mathbf{k} \tag{5}$$

$$\int \csc^2 = -\cot + \mathbf{k} \tag{6}$$

$$\int f^n Df = \frac{1}{n+1} f^{n+1} + \mathbf{k}, \quad (n \neq -1) \tag{7}$$

$$\int \frac{Df}{f} = \ln \circ | \quad | \circ f + \mathbf{k}, \quad f \neq 0 \text{ for any } x \tag{8}$$

$$\int \exp_e = \exp_e + \mathbf{k}. \tag{9}$$

The validity of these formulas may be checked simply by taking the derivative of the right-hand side of each formula.

Also, from our definition of antiderivative, we immediately obtain the following general formulas:

$$\int (f + g) = \int f + \int g \tag{10}$$

$$\int \mathbf{a} f = \mathbf{a} \int f, \tag{11}$$

(cf. Exercise 24 at the end of Chapter 5).

Using these basic formulas one can readily find the antiderivative of polynomials and certain types of composite functions involving the sums of trigonometric and exponential functions, or the powers of functions multiplied by their derivatives. For example, by (1), (4), and (10) we obtain

$$\int (3j^2 + 2 + \sin) = j^3 + 2j - \cos + \mathbf{k}$$

and by (7),

$$\int (2j^3 - 3j)^5 (6j - 3) = \tfrac{1}{6}(2j^3 - 3j)^6 + \mathbf{k}.$$

Also, (7) and (10) yield

$$\int \left(\frac{\ln^2}{j} + j \exp_e \circ j^2 \right) = \tfrac{1}{3} \ln^3 + \tfrac{1}{2} \exp_e \circ j^2 + \mathbf{k}$$

(for $x > 0$), and (8) yields

$$\int \frac{2j - 1}{j^2 - j} = \ln \circ (j^2 - j) + \mathbf{k},$$

for $x > 1$. In the above four examples the function was such that it was relatively easy to guess at the form of an antiderivative by relating it to one or more of the preceding formulas [(1)–(11)]. Moreover, the results may be checked by differentiation.

There are, however, many more antiderivative problems where the form of the answer is not readily recognizable. Consider, for example,

$$\int j \cos.$$

Even though j cos is an elementary function, formulas (1) to (11) do not give us a clue about the form of the indefinite integral. This situation may seem a bit disconcerting to the beginner—especially when definite rules for finding derivatives of elementary functions are available. Unfortunately we can offer little comfort because there are no definite rules for finding indefinite integrals and covering all cases, even for elementary functions. (Elementary functions include polynomials, rational functions, trigonometric and exponential functions, their inverses; and those functions which can be formed from them by the three elementary operations pertaining to the algebra of functions.) Indeed, there are elementary functions, for example $\exp_e \circ (-j^2)$, which do not even have elementary antiderivatives. In the sequel we shall give some techniques that have proven useful in finding antiderivatives for certain classes of elementary functions.

I. ANTIDERIVATIVES BY PARTS

The first technique we shall consider is that for finding $\int F$ when $F = f\,Dg$. Sometimes it will be easier to find $\int g\,Df$ than $\int f\,Dg$. When this is the case we recall the rule $Dfg = f\,Dg + g\,Df$ (Theorem 3 of Chapter 5). By Theorem 14 of Chapter 5 this implies

$$\int Dfg = fg + \mathbf{c} = \int f\,Dg + \int g\,Df$$

or

$$\int f\,Dg = fg - \int g\,Df + \mathbf{c}. \tag{1}$$

Equation (1) is known as the formula for "integration by parts."

For example, suppose we wished to find $\int j$ cos. We recognize that $D \sin = \cos$ and $Dj = \mathbf{1}$. Thus, applying (1) with $f = j$ and $g = \sin$, we obtain

$$\int j \cos = \int jD \sin = j \sin - \int \sin + \mathbf{c}$$

or

$$\int j \cos = j \sin + \cos + \mathbf{c}. \tag{2}$$

Why did we let $\cos = Dg$ and $f = j$? For the simple reason that if we had set $j = Dg$ and $f = \cos$, the situation would have become more complicated. For applying (1) we would have obtained

$$\int j \cos = \tfrac{1}{2}j^2 \sin - \int \tfrac{1}{2}j^2 \sin + \mathbf{c}$$

and $\tfrac{1}{2}\int j^2 \sin$ is more difficult to evaluate than $\int j$ cos. Ultimately, then, even with (1) as a guiding technique we must make the proper choice as to which of the factors of F that we set equal to f and those that we set equal to Dg.

Often (1) must be applied several times before we arrive at the desired result. Let us take for an example the problem of finding

$$\int j^2 \cos.$$

Here we let $g = \sin$ and $f = j^2$. Then (1) yields

$$\int j^2 \cos = j^2 \sin - 2 \int j \sin + \mathbf{c}_1$$

and applying (1) to $\int j \sin$ (with $g = -\cos$ and $f = j$) we obtain

$$\int j \sin = -j \cos + \int \cos = -j \cos + \sin + \mathbf{c}_2$$

and finally

$$\int j^2 \cos = j^2 \sin + 2j \cos - 2 \sin + \mathbf{c} \tag{3}$$

(where $c = c_1 + c_2$).

Sometimes when we apply (1), $\int f \, Dg$ may re-appear on the right-hand side of the equation. If the coefficient of $\int f \, Dg$ is a and $a \neq 1$, then we may add $-\mathbf{a} \int f \, Dg$ to both sides of the equality and solve for $\int f \, Dg$. Thus attempting to evaluate

$$\int \cos \exp_e,$$

for example, we let $f = \cos$ and $Dg = \exp_e$. Then by (1)

$$\int \cos \exp_e = \cos \exp_e + \int \exp_e \sin + \mathbf{c}_1. \tag{4}$$

Also (with $f = \sin$ and $Dg = \exp_e$) equation (1) yields

$$\int \sin \exp_e = \sin \exp_e - \int \exp_e \cos + \mathbf{c}_2. \tag{5}$$

Substituting (5) in the right-hand side of (4) we find

$$\int \cos \exp_e = \cos \exp_e + \sin \exp_e - \int \exp_e \cos + \mathbf{c}_1 + \mathbf{c}_2, \tag{6}$$

or

$$2 \int \cos \exp_e = \cos \exp_e + \sin \exp_e + \mathbf{c}_1 + \mathbf{c}_2,$$

and finally

$$\int \cos \exp_e = \tfrac{1}{2}(\cos + \sin) \exp_e + \mathbf{c} \tag{7}$$

[where $c = \tfrac{1}{2}(c_1 + c_2)$].

2. ANTIDERIVATIVES BY SUBSTITUTION

Suppose we were to apply (1) of the preceding section to

$$\int (1 + j^3)^{1/2} 3j^2.$$

After several attempts at choosing f and Dg, we would come to the conclusion that $\int g\,Df$ is no easier to find that $\int f\,Dg$. So we abandon (1) of Section 1. The alert reader would not have even applied integration by parts, since he would have recognized in $(1 + j^3)^{1/2}3j^2$ the form $f^n\,Df$ and hence would have used formula (7) of the introduction to obtain

$$\int (1 + j^3)^{1/2}3j^2 = \tfrac{2}{3}(1 + j^3)^{3/2} + \mathbf{k}.$$

However, analyzing the problem further, he would also recognize in the integrand the form $[(Df) \circ g]Dg$ where $Df = j^{1/2}$, $g = (1 + j^3)$ and $Dg = 3j^2$. So he could also use the chain rule to obtain the same answer. For from Theorem 4 of Chapter 5,

$$\int D(f \circ g) = f \circ g = \int [(Df) \circ g]Dg. \tag{1}$$

There are, however, many antiderivative problems where the form $[(Df) \circ g]Dg$ does not appear in the integrand, but which may be turned into such a form by composing the integrand with a suitable function. That is, if we are given $\int Df$, we look for a function g such that $\int [(Df) \circ g]Dg = f \circ g$ is easier to find than $f = \int Df$. For example, to find

$$\int (4 - j^2)^{1/2}$$

we have $Df = (4 - j^2)^{1/2}$, and choose $g = 2\sin$. Then $[(Df) \circ g]Dg = (4 - 4\sin^2)^{1/2}(2\cos)$ and

$$\int [(Df) \circ g]Dg = \int (2\cos)(2\cos) = 4\int \cos^2. \tag{2}$$

Now $\cos^2 x = \tfrac{1}{2}(1 + \cos 2x)$, so that (2) becomes

$$2\int (1 + \cos \circ 2j) = 2j + \sin \circ 2j + \mathbf{c}$$
$$= 2j + 2\sin\cos + \mathbf{c}.$$

Thus we have demonstrated that

$$\int [(4 - j^2)^{1/2} \circ (2\sin)](2\cos) = \int [(Df) \circ g]Dg$$
$$= f \circ g = 2j + 2\sin\cos + \mathbf{c}. \tag{3}$$

At this stage of the problem, this last result does not appear to be germane. After all we are looking for f and in (3) we have found $f \circ g$. But recall—and this is the crux of the matter—that $g \circ g^* = j$ and $(f \circ g) \circ g^* = f \circ j = f$. Hence, if we compose $f \circ g$ with $g^* = \sin^* \circ \tfrac{1}{2}j$ we obtain f. Explicitly,

$$f = (f \circ g) \circ g^* = (2j + 2\sin\cos + \mathbf{c}) \circ (\sin^* \circ \tfrac{1}{2}j)$$
$$= 2\sin^* \circ \tfrac{1}{2}j + 2(\sin \circ \sin^* \circ \tfrac{1}{2}j)(\cos \circ \sin^* \circ \tfrac{1}{2}j)$$
$$+ \mathbf{c} \circ (\sin^* \circ \tfrac{1}{2}j)$$
$$= 2\sin^* \circ \tfrac{1}{2}j + j(1 - \sin^2)^{1/2} \circ (\sin^* \circ \tfrac{1}{2}j) + \mathbf{c}$$
$$= 2\sin^* \circ \tfrac{1}{2}j + j(1 - \tfrac{1}{4}j^2)^{1/2} + \mathbf{c}$$

or

$$\int (4 - j^2)^{1/2} = \mathbf{2} \sin^* \circ \tfrac{1}{2}j + \tfrac{1}{2}j(4 - j^2)^{1/2} + \mathbf{c}. \qquad (4)$$

This technique may be expressed by the succinct formula:

$$f = \int Df = (f \circ g) \circ g^* = \{\int [(Df) \circ g]Dg\} \circ g^*. \qquad (5)$$

It is important to realize that since the last step in this technique involves composition with g^*, the function g we choose must be one–one. Also it is necessary that Ran $g \subset$ Dom Df. Beyond this we can only list a few helpful suggestions that will sometimes prove useful in dealing with some commonly encountered functions:

(i)   If Df contains the form $(\mathbf{a}^2 - j^2)^{1/2}$, let $g = \mathbf{a} \sin$. Then $Dg = \mathbf{a} \cos$ and $g^* = \sin^* \circ (\mathbf{1}/\mathbf{a})j$.

(ii) If Df contains the form $(j^2 - \mathbf{a}^2)^{1/2}$, let $g = \mathbf{a} \sec$. Then $Dg = \mathbf{a} \sec \tan$ and $g^* = \sec^* \circ (\mathbf{1}/\mathbf{a})j$.

(iii) If Df contains the form $(j^2 + \mathbf{a}^2)^{1/2}$, let $g = \mathbf{a} \tan$. Then $Dg = \mathbf{a} \sec^2$ and $g^* = \tan^* \circ (\mathbf{1}/\mathbf{a})j$.

(iv) If Df contains the form $\exp_e$, let $g = \ln$. Then $Dg = \mathbf{1}/j$ and $g^* = \exp_e$.

(v)   If Df contains the form $\ln$, let $g = \exp_e$. Then $Dg = \exp_e$ and $g^* = \ln$.

(vi) If Df contains a trigonometric function (trig), let $g = $ trig*. Then $Dg = D$ trig* and $g^* = $ trig.

The following examples will serve to illustrate some of the above suggestions.

Example 1.   *Find*

$$\int \frac{\exp_e}{4 + \exp_e \circ \mathbf{2}j}.$$

We use (iv) and let $g = \ln$. Then

$$\int [(Df) \circ g]Dg = \int \left(\frac{j}{4 + j^2}\right)\frac{\mathbf{1}}{j} = \int \frac{\mathbf{1}}{4 + j^2} = \tan^* \circ \tfrac{1}{2}j + \mathbf{k}$$

since $\exp_e \circ \ln = j$ and $(\exp_e \circ \mathbf{2}j) \circ \ln = j^2$. Thus

$$f = \{\tan^* \circ \tfrac{1}{2}j + \mathbf{k}\} \circ g^* = \tan^* \circ \tfrac{1}{2}\exp_e + \mathbf{k}$$

since $g^* = \exp_e$. (If the reader experiences any difficulty in showing that

$$\int \frac{\mathbf{1}}{4 + j^2} = \tan^* \circ \tfrac{1}{2}j + \mathbf{k}$$

he may apply (iii). Then

$$\int \left[\left(\frac{\mathbf{1}}{4 + j^2}\right) \circ (\mathbf{2} \tan)\right](\mathbf{2} \sec^2) = \int \mathbf{1} = j + \mathbf{k}$$

and we get our desired result by composing with $g^* = \tan^* \circ \tfrac{1}{2}j$.)

Example 2. *Find*

$$\int \frac{1}{j \ln \circ j^2}.$$

Using (v) with $g = \exp_e$, we find

$$\int [(Df) \circ g] Dg = \int \left[\left(\frac{1}{j \ln \circ j^2} \right) \circ \exp_e \right] \exp_e = \int \left[\frac{1}{(\exp_e)(2j)} \right] \exp_e$$

$$= \frac{1}{2} \int \frac{1}{j} = \frac{1}{2} \ln \circ | \quad | + \mathbf{k}.$$

Thus

$$f = (\tfrac{1}{2} \ln \circ | \quad | + \mathbf{k}) \circ g^* = (\tfrac{1}{2} \ln \circ | \quad | + \mathbf{k}) \circ \ln$$
$$= \tfrac{1}{2} \ln \circ | \quad | \circ \ln + \mathbf{k}.$$

Example 3. *Find*

$$\int \frac{j}{(1 + 2j)^{1/2}}.$$

There are of course other substitutions than those listed in (i)–(vi) above that may be used in special problems. Let us write

$$g = \frac{j^2 - 1}{2}.$$

Then, with $Df = j/(1 + 2j)^{1/2}$ as usual,

$$f = \left\{ \int [(Df) \circ g] Dg \right\} \circ g^* = \left(\int \left\{ \left[\frac{j}{(1 + 2j)^{1/2}} \right] \circ \left(\frac{j^2 - 1}{2} \right) \right\} j \right) \circ g^*$$

$$= \left(\int \frac{j^2 - 1}{2} \right) \circ g^* = (\tfrac{1}{6} j^3 - \tfrac{1}{2} j + \mathbf{k}) \circ (1 + 2j)^{1/2}$$

since $g^* = (1 + 2j)^{1/2}$. Hence

$$\int \frac{j}{(1 + 2j)^{1/2}} = \frac{1}{6} (1 + 2j)^{3/2} - \frac{1}{2} (1 + 2j)^{1/2} + \mathbf{k}.$$

Up to this point we have been concerned with changing the form of the integrand Df to $[(Df) \circ g] Dg$—because we hoped that the indefinite integral of this latter expression would be easier to find than that of the original form. Sometimes, the integrand will be of the form $[(Df) \circ g](Dg)h$, and because of the factor h, the form of the indefinite integral may not be readily recognizable. In such a case we may of course try using integration by parts again. In this case we would get

$$\int [(Df) \circ g](Dg)h = (f \circ g)h - \int (f \circ g) Dh. \tag{6}$$

Now suppose $Dh = Dg$. Then

$$\int (f \circ g) Dg = (\int f) \circ g + \mathbf{k}. \tag{7}$$

Combining (7) and (6)

$$\int [(Df) \circ g](Dg)h = (f \circ g)h - (\int f) \circ g - \mathbf{k}, \quad (Dg = Dh). \tag{8}$$

For example, consider

$$\int 3j^5(\mathbf{I} + j^3)^{1/2}. \tag{9}$$

Then we may write the integrand of (9) as

$$(\mathbf{I} + j^3)^{1/2}(3j^2)j^3.$$

With $Df = j^{1/2}$, $g = \mathbf{I} + j^3$, $h = j^3$,

$$
\begin{aligned}
\int 3j^5(\mathbf{I} + j^3)^{1/2} &= \int [(Df) \circ g](Dg)h \\
&= (f \circ g)h - (\int f) \circ g - \mathbf{k} \\
&= [\tfrac{2}{3}j^{3/2} \circ (\mathbf{I} + j^3)]j^3 - \tfrac{4}{15}j^{5/2} \circ (\mathbf{I} + j^3) - \mathbf{k} \\
&= \tfrac{2}{3}j^3(\mathbf{I} + j^3)^{3/2} - \tfrac{4}{15}(\mathbf{I} + j^3)^{5/2} - \mathbf{k}. \tag{10}
\end{aligned}
$$

But there is another way of looking at this same problem. We recall from Theorem 6 of Chapter 5 that

$$(Dg) \circ g^* = \frac{1}{Dg^*}.$$

Hence

$$
\begin{aligned}
(\{[(Df) \circ g](Dg)h\} \circ g^*)Dg^* &= [(Df) \circ g \circ g^*][(Dg) \circ g^*][h \circ g^*]Dg^* \\
&= [(Df) \circ j]\left[\frac{1}{Dg^*}\right][h \circ g^*]Dg^* \\
&= (Df)(h \circ g^*). \tag{11}
\end{aligned}
$$

Consider now the expression in braces in the first term of (11). Call it DF:

$$DF = [(Df) \circ g](Dg)h. \tag{12}$$

Then using (5)

$$F = \int DF = (F \circ g) \circ g^* = \left[\int (\{[(Df) \circ g](Dg)h\} \circ g^*)Dg^*\right] \circ g. \tag{13}$$

But from (11), this reduces to

$$F = \left[\int (Df)(h \circ g^*)\right] \circ g. \tag{14}$$

Hence [cf. (12)] we have established the formula

$$\int [(Df) \circ g](Dg)h = \left[\int (Df)(h \circ g^*)\right] \circ g. \tag{15}$$

Let us apply (15) to the example of (9) with $Df = j^{1/2}$, $g = 1 + j^3$, $h = j^3$. Then since $g* = (j - 1)^{1/3}$,

$$\int 3j^5(1 + j^3)^{1/2} = \left\{ \left[\int j^{1/2}[j^3 \circ (j - 1)^{1/3}] \right\} \circ (1 + j^3) \right.$$
$$= \left[\int j^{1/2}(j - 1) \right] \circ (1 + j^3)$$
$$= (\tfrac{2}{5}j^{5/2} - \tfrac{2}{3}j^{3/2} + k) \circ (1 + j^3)$$
$$= \tfrac{2}{5}(1 + j^3)^{5/2} - \tfrac{2}{3}(1 + j^3)^{3/2} + k. \qquad (16)$$

The reader should verify that the results expressed in (10) and (16) are both antiderivatives of $3j^5(1 + j^3)^{1/2}$, that is, that the right-hand sides of (10) and (16) differ only by a constant, and that the derivative of either is $3j^5(1 + j^3)^{1/2}$.

Another example illustrating the use of (15) is not out of place.

Example 4. *Find*

$$\int \frac{j}{(1 + 2j)^{1/2}}.$$

Let $Df = \tfrac{1}{2}j^{-1/2}$, $g = 1 + 2j$, $h = j$. Then $g* = \tfrac{1}{2}(j - 1)$. Hence

$$\int \frac{j}{(1 + 2j)^{1/2}} = \int [(Df) \circ g](Dg)h = \left[\int (Df)(h \circ g*) \right] \circ g$$
$$= \left\{ \int \tfrac{1}{2}j^{-1/2}[j \circ \tfrac{1}{2}(j - 1)] \right\} \circ (1 + 2j)$$
$$= \left[\tfrac{1}{4} \int j^{-1/2}(j - 1) \right] \circ (1 + 2j)$$
$$= (\tfrac{1}{6}j^{3/2} - \tfrac{1}{2}j^{1/2} + k) \circ (1 + 2j)$$
$$= \tfrac{1}{6}(1 + 2j)^{3/2} - \tfrac{1}{2}(1 + 2j)^{1/2} + k. \qquad (17)$$

We conclude this section with a few, more theoretical remarks. Combining (1) with the fundamental theorem of the integral calculus we obtain the following useful result:

$$f(b) - f(a) = \int_a^b Df = (f \circ g) \circ g*(b) - (f \circ g) \circ g*(a)$$
$$= \int_{g*(a)}^{g*(b)} [(Df) \circ g]Dg. \qquad (18)$$

More precisely: If Df is continuous on an interval containing $I[a, b]$, and if Dg is also continuous on an interval I' so that Ran $g \subset I[a, b]$ for all $x \in I'$, and if g has an inverse $g*$ on I' with $g*(a) = \alpha$ and $g*(b) = \beta$, then

$$\int_a^b Df = \int_\alpha^\beta [(Df) \circ g]Dg. \qquad (19)$$

For an application of (19) we evaluate

$$\int_0^a (a^2 - j^2)^{1/2}, \quad a > 0.$$

Here we let $Df = (a^2 - j^2)^{1/2}$ and $g = a \sin$. Then $g* = \sin* \circ \dfrac{1}{a}j$

and $\sin* \dfrac{1}{a}j(0) = \sin* (0) = 0$ while $\sin* \dfrac{1}{a}j(a) = \sin* (1) = \tfrac{1}{2}\pi$.

Hence

$$\int_0^a (\mathbf{a}^2 - j^2)^{1/2} = a \int_0^{\pi/2} (\mathbf{a}^2 - \mathbf{a}^2 \sin^2)^{1/2} \cos = \mathbf{a}^2 \int_0^{\pi/2} \cos^2$$

$$= \tfrac{1}{2}a^2(j + \tfrac{1}{2}\sin \circ 2j)]_{0_1}^{\pi/2} = \frac{\pi a^2}{4}.$$

3. PARTIAL FRACTIONS

For our final technique for finding the indefinite integral, we discuss the method of *partial fractions*.

Consider the rational function

$$r = \frac{n}{d}$$

where n and d are polynomials. We assume without loss of generality that n and d have no common factors, that is, that they are relatively prime. The method of partial fractions consists in expressing r in the form

$$r = \sum_{i=1}^{s_1} \frac{\alpha_{1i}}{(j - \mathbf{a}_1)^i} + \sum_{i=1}^{s_2} \frac{\alpha_{2i}}{(j - \mathbf{a}_2)^i} + \cdots + \sum_{i=1}^{s_v} \frac{\alpha_{vi}}{(j - \mathbf{a}_v)^i}$$

$$+ \sum_{i=1}^{t_1} \frac{\beta_{1i}j + \gamma_{1i}}{(j^2 + \mathbf{b}_1 j + \mathbf{c}_1)^i} + \cdots + \sum_{i=1}^{t_\mu} \frac{\beta_{\mu i}j + \gamma_{\mu i}}{(j^2 + \mathbf{b}_\mu j + \mathbf{c}_\mu)^i}$$

and then finding—by the techniques already discussed—the indefinite integral of the sum of these *partial* fractions.

For example, the reader may easily verify that

$$\frac{3j^3 + 2j^2 + j - 1}{j^4 + j^3 + j + 1} = \frac{1}{j + 1} - \frac{1}{(j + 1)^2} + \frac{2j - 1}{j^2 - j + 1}.$$

Thus

$$\int \frac{3j^3 + 2j^2 + j - 1}{j^4 + j^3 + j + 1} = \ln \circ |j + 1| + \frac{1}{j + 1} + \ln \circ |j^2 - j + 1| + \mathbf{k}.$$

[For notational convenience we write $\ln \circ |j + 1|$ rather than the more precise $\ln \circ | \ | \circ (j + 1)$.]

Let us assume that for the rational function $r = n/d$ the degree of the numerator, n, is less than the degree of the denominator, d. Otherwise, we can divide the right-hand side to obtain

$$r = \frac{n}{d} = p + \frac{q}{d}$$

where p and q are polynomials and the degree of q is less than the degree of d, (see, for example, Miller [6, 7]). Of course $\int p$ is trivial to compute.

Now if we accept the fact that every polynomial of degree m has exactly m zeros (counting the multiplicity of repeated zeros), and that complex zeros appear in conjugate pairs, then the polynomial

$$d = j^m + e_1 j^{m-1} + \cdots + e_{m-1} j + e_m$$

may be factored as follows:

$$d = (j - a_1)^{s_1}(j - a_2)^{s_2} \cdots (j - a_v)^{s_v}(j^2 + b_1 j + c_1)^{t_1} \cdots$$
$$(j^2 + b_\mu j + c_\mu)^{t_\mu}. \quad (1)$$

In (1),

$$m = \sum_{i=1}^{v} s_i + 2 \sum_{i=1}^{\mu} t_i,$$

and $b_i^2 - 4c_i < 0$ for $i = 1, 2, \cdots, \mu$. (This last statement, of course, implies that the roots of $j^2 + b_i j + c_i = 0$ are complex.) Having done this, we next form the partial fraction

$$\sum_{i=1}^{s_1} \frac{\alpha_{1i}}{(j - a_1)^i} + \cdots + \sum_{i=1}^{s_v} \frac{\alpha_{vi}}{(j - a_v)^i} + \sum_{i=1}^{t_1} \frac{\beta_{1i} j + \gamma_{1i}}{(j^2 + b_1 j + c_1)^i}$$
$$+ \sum_{i=1}^{t_\mu} \frac{\beta_{\mu i} j + \gamma_{\mu i}}{(j^2 + b_\mu j + c_\mu)^i}. \quad (2)$$

Our next objective is to solve for the α's, β's, and γ's so that the sum of the partial fractions (2) is identically equal to n/d. (We are assuming that the degree of d exceeds the degree of n.) This is accomplished as follows: First we add the partial fractions of (2) and get a common denominator identically equal to d. The numerator, n', will be a polynomial whose coefficients are combinations of the α's, β's, and γ's. Now if we are to have an identity, the α's, β's, and γ's must be chosen so that $n' \equiv n$. By setting up equalities among the coefficients of terms of like degree in j in n and n' we obtain m equations in the unknown α's, β's, and γ's. Solving these equations yields the desired result.

Let us carry out these procedures in the following case:

$$n = j - 7$$
$$d = (j + 2)^2(j^2 - j + 1).$$

Then

$$\frac{j - 7}{(j + 2)^2(j^2 - j + 1)} = \frac{\alpha_{11}}{j + 2} + \frac{\alpha_{12}}{(j + 2)^2} + \frac{\beta_{11} j + \gamma_{11}}{j^2 - j + 1}$$
$$= \frac{\alpha_{11}(j^3 + j^2 - j + 2) + \alpha_{12}(j^2 - j + 1) + (\beta_{11} j + \gamma_{11})(j^2 + 4j + 4)}{(j + 2)^2(j^2 - j + 1)}.$$
$$(3)$$

The numerator of the right-hand side of (3) may be arranged as

$$j^3(\alpha_{11} + \beta_{11}) + j^2(\alpha_{11} + \alpha_{12} + 4\beta_{11} + \gamma_{11}) + j(-\alpha_{11} - \alpha_{12} + \beta_{11} + 4\gamma_{11})$$
$$+ (2\alpha_{11} + \alpha_{12} + \gamma_{11})$$

and equating this polynomial to $n = j - 7$ we obtain

$$\alpha_{11} \qquad\; + \beta_{11} \qquad\qquad = 0$$
$$\alpha_{11} + \alpha_{12} + 4\beta_{11} + \;\; \gamma_{11} = 0$$
$$-\alpha_{11} - \alpha_{12} + 4\beta_{11} + 4\gamma_{11} = 1$$
$$2\alpha_{11} + \alpha_{12} \qquad\;\; + 4\gamma_{11} = -7.$$

Solving these four linear algebraic equations for the four unknowns $\alpha_{11}, \alpha_{12}, \beta_{11}, \gamma_{11}$ we obtain

$$\alpha_{11} = -\tfrac{38}{49}$$
$$\alpha_{12} = -\tfrac{9}{7}$$
$$\beta_{11} = \tfrac{38}{49}$$
$$\gamma_{11} = -\tfrac{51}{49}.$$

Finally,

$$\frac{j - 7}{(j + 2)^2(j^2 - j + 1)} = -\frac{38}{49}\frac{1}{j + 2} - \frac{9}{7}\frac{1}{(j + 2)^2} + \frac{1}{49}\frac{38j - 51}{j^2 - j + 1}. \quad (4)$$

Once we have obtained the decomposition of r into partial fractions, we find the indefinite integral of r by taking the sum of the indefinite integrals of the partial fractions. Continuing with the above example we get

$$\int \frac{j - 7}{(j + 2)^2(j^2 - j + 1)}$$

$$= -\frac{38}{49} \int \frac{1}{j + 2} - \frac{9}{7} \int \frac{1}{(j + 2)^2} + \frac{1}{49} \int \frac{38j - 51}{j^2 - j + 1}. \quad (5)$$

Now

$$\int \frac{1}{j + 2} = \ln \circ |j + 2| \quad (6)$$

and

$$\int \frac{1}{(j + 2)^2} = -\frac{1}{j + 1} \quad (7)$$

are antiderivatives that may be used to evaluate the first two indefinite integrals on the right-hand side of (5). The last integral on the right-hand side of (5) may be written

$$\int \frac{38j - 51}{j^2 - j + 1} = 19 \int \frac{2j - 1}{j^2 - j + 1} - 32 \int \frac{1}{j^2 - j + 1}$$

$$= 19 \ln \circ |j^2 - j + 1| - 32 \int \frac{1}{(j - \tfrac{1}{2})^2 + \tfrac{3}{4}}. \quad (8)$$

To evaluate the second integral on the right-hand side of (8) we recall from (1) of Section 2 that

$$f \circ g = \int [(Df) \circ g]Dg.$$

Hence, with $Df = 1/(j^2 + \frac{3}{4})$ and $g = j - \frac{1}{2}$,

$$\frac{2}{\sqrt{3}} \tan^* \circ \frac{2}{\sqrt{3}} j \circ \left(j - \frac{1}{2}\right) = \int \frac{1}{(j - \frac{1}{2})^2 + \frac{3}{4}}$$

or

$$\int \frac{1}{(j - \frac{1}{2})^2 + \frac{3}{4}} = \frac{2}{\sqrt{3}} \tan^* \circ \frac{1}{\sqrt{3}} (2j - 1). \tag{9}$$

Combining (6), (7), (8), and (9) in (5) we have our ultimate result:

$$\int \frac{j - 7}{(j + 2)^2(j^2 - j + 1)} = -\frac{38}{49} \ln \circ |j + 2| + \frac{9}{7} \frac{1}{j + 1} + \frac{19}{49} \ln \circ |j^2 - j + 1|$$

$$- \frac{64}{49\sqrt{3}} \tan^* \circ \frac{1}{\sqrt{3}} (2j - 1) + \mathbf{k}. \tag{10}$$

We conclude this discussion by pointing out that the method of partial fractions will always yield the indefinite integral of a rational function. For

$$\int \frac{1}{j + \mathbf{a}} = \ln \circ |j + \mathbf{a}| + \mathbf{k}$$

and

$$\int \frac{1}{(j + \mathbf{a})^n} = -\frac{1}{n - 1} \frac{1}{(j + \mathbf{a})^{n-1}} + \mathbf{k} \quad (n \neq 1)$$

while

$$\int \frac{\beta j + \gamma}{j^2 + \mathbf{b}j + \mathbf{c}} = \frac{\beta}{2} \int \frac{2j + \mathbf{b}}{j^2 + \mathbf{b}j + \mathbf{c}} + \left(\gamma - \frac{\mathbf{b}\beta}{2}\right) \int \frac{1}{j^2 + \mathbf{b}j + \mathbf{c}}$$

$$= \frac{\beta}{2} \ln \circ |j^2 + \mathbf{b}j + \mathbf{c}| + \frac{(2\gamma - \mathbf{b}\beta)}{\sqrt{4\mathbf{c} - \mathbf{b}^2}} \tan^* \circ \frac{2j + \mathbf{b}}{\sqrt{4\mathbf{c} - \mathbf{b}^2}} + \mathbf{k}.$$

(Of course we are assuming that the zeros of $j^2 + \mathbf{b}j + \mathbf{c}$ are complex, and hence $4\mathbf{c} - b^2 > 0$.) The indefinite integral

$$\int \frac{1}{j^2 + \mathbf{b}j + \mathbf{c}}$$

is evaluated as in the above example, viz.: complete the square,

$$j^2 + \mathbf{b}j + \mathbf{c} = \left(j + \frac{\mathbf{b}}{2}\right)^2 + \left(\mathbf{c} - \frac{\mathbf{b}^2}{4}\right)$$

and let $Df = 1/[j^2 + (\mathbf{c} - \mathbf{b}^2/4)]$, $g = j + \mathbf{b}/2$ in (1) of Section 2.
Indefinite integrals of the form

$$\int \frac{\beta j + \gamma}{(j^2 + \mathbf{b}j + \mathbf{c})^{i+1}}, \qquad (4\mathbf{c} - b^2 > 0),$$

may be evaluated with the aid of the reduction formula

$$\int \frac{1}{(j^2 + bj + c)^{i+1}} = \frac{2j + b}{i(4c - b^2)(j^2 + bj + c)^i}$$

$$+ \frac{2(2i - 1)}{i(4c - b^2)} \int \frac{1}{(j^2 + bj + c)^i} + k, \quad (i \neq 0).$$

4. CONCLUDING REMARKS

The techniques we have explored for finding indefinite integrals cover a large class of integrable functions. There are, however, many more integrable functions for which none of these techniques is applicable. That is, none of our methods will reduce the integrand to an elementary function whose indefinite integral is easy to obtain. In fact, many simple functions do not possess an indefinite integral that is elementary! For example, $\exp_e \circ j^2$, $\sin/j$, $(1 - j^4)^{-1/2}$ are such functions. It may be *proved* that there are no elementary functions that are antiderivatives for the above functions. Yet the value of the *definite* integral (over various intervals) can be and often is of paramount importance not only to the applied mathematician, physicist, and engineer, but also to the theoretician who seeks an understanding of the relations among natural phenomena. Accordingly, in cases where $\int_a^b f$ cannot be obtained in closed form, it is often highly desirable to have at least a good approximation to $\int_a^b f$. By a good approximation we mean one for which we can establish a reasonably small bound for the difference between the actual value of $\int_a^b f$ and the approximating value.

We shall consider here two methods for getting approximations for $\int_a^b f$. Both are relatively easy to use. The first method is known as the *Trapezoidal Rule*, the second as *Simpson's Rule*. The latter is a bit more sophisticated, but generally gives a better approximation. That is, the margin of error will generally be smaller.

A. The Trapezoidal Rule

If f is continuous on $I[a, b]$, then we can take a partition $\pi = [x_0, x_1, \cdots, x_n]$ of $I[a, b]$ in such a way that $x_i - x_{i-1} \equiv h = (1/n) \times (b - a)$ for $i = 1, 2, \cdots, n$. Then the area of the trapezoid T_i (see Figure 8.1) is given by

$$T_f\big]_{x_{i-1}}^{x_i} = \frac{(x_i - x_{i-1})}{2} [f(x_i) + f(x_{i-1})] = \tfrac{1}{2}h[f(x_i) + f(x_{i-1})]$$

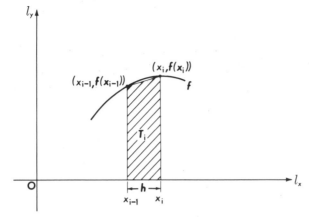

Figure 8.1

and if we write

$$T_f\big]_a^b = \sum_{i=1}^{n} T_f\big]_{x_{i-1}}^{x_i}$$

we have

$$T_f\big]_a^b = h[f(x_1) + f(x_2) + \cdots + f(x_{n-1})] + \frac{h}{2}[f(a) + f(b)] \quad (1)$$

since all terms but the first and last appear twice.

Let us apply (1) to the integral

$$\frac{1}{\sqrt{2\pi}} \int_a^b e^{-x^2/2}\, dx. \quad (2)$$

(This is a very famous integral arising in the theory of probability and statistics.) For the sake of illustration we shall let $a = 1$, $b = 2$ and take $n = 10$. If we partition $I[1, 2]$ into ten subintervals, we must determine

$$f(x) = \frac{1}{\sqrt{2\pi}}\, e^{-x^2/2}$$

for $x = 1, 1.1, 1.2 \cdots, 1.9, 2.0$. From Abramowitz [1] (many other tables could be used) we find

$$\begin{aligned}
f(1.0) &= 0.2419707\\
f(1.1) &= 0.2178522\\
f(1.2) &= 0.1941861\\
f(1.3) &= 0.1713686\\
f(1.4) &= 0.1497275\\
f(1.5) &= 0.1295176\\
f(1.6) &= 0.1109208\\
f(1.7) &= 0.0940491\\
f(1.8) &= 0.0789502\\
f(1.9) &= 0.0656158\\
f(2.0) &= 0.0539910.
\end{aligned} \quad (3)$$

Thus $h = 0.1$, and

$$h[f(1.1) + f(1.2) + \cdots + f(1.9)] = 0.1212188$$

$$\frac{h}{2}[f(1.0) + f(2.0)] \qquad\qquad = 0.0147981.$$

Therefore, from (1)

$$T_f]_1^2 = 0.1360169. \qquad\qquad (4)$$

The result (4) is meaningless unless we can relate it to $\int_a^b f$ in a quantitative fashion. We shall establish a bound for

$$\left| \int_a^b f - T_f]_a^b \right|$$

in the general case (and then apply it to the above example). Obtaining a bound on the "error" is reminiscent of Taylor's Theorem.

Let m_i be the mid-point of the interval $I[x_{i-1}, x_i]$. Then $m_i - \frac{1}{2}h = x_{i-1}$ and $m_i + \frac{1}{2}h = x_i$. Consider now the function

$$\eta(x) = \int_{m_i - x/2}^{m_i + x/2} f - \frac{x}{2}[f(m_i + \tfrac{1}{2}x) + f(m_i - \tfrac{1}{2}x)]$$

for $0 \leq x \leq h$. If we can get a bound on $|\eta(x)|$ in terms of x, we can obtain a bound on $|\eta(h)|$. This in turn will give us an estimate of the error involved in replacing $\int_{x_{i-1}}^{x_i} f$ by $T_f]_{x_{i-1}}^{x_i}$. To this end let $DF = f$. Then

$$\eta(x) = F(m_i + \tfrac{1}{2}x) - F(m_i - \tfrac{1}{2}x) - \frac{x}{2}[f(m_i + \tfrac{1}{2}x) + f(m_i - \tfrac{1}{2}x)]$$

and

$$D\eta(x) = -\frac{x}{4}[Df(m_i + \tfrac{1}{2}x) - Df(m_i - \tfrac{1}{2}x)]. \qquad (5)$$

Hence if D^2f is defined on $I(a, b)$, then the mean value theorem (cf. Theorem 9 of Chapter 5) applied to the right-hand side of (5) yields

$$D\eta(x) = -\frac{x^2}{4} D^2f(c), \quad x_{i-1} < c < x_i,$$

and

$$\eta(x) = -\frac{x^3}{12} D^2f(c)$$

since $\eta(0) = 0$. Therefore if D^2f is bounded (say by M) on $I(a, b)$, then

$$|\eta(x)| \leq \frac{x^3}{12} M$$

and

$$|\eta(h)| \leq \frac{h^3}{12} M. \qquad\qquad (6)$$

But

$$\left| \int_a^b f - T_f \right]_a^b \bigg| = \left| \sum_{i=1}^n \left\{ \int_{x_{i-1}}^{x_i} f - T_f \right]_{x_{i-1}}^{x_i} \right\} \right|$$

$$\leqq \sum_{i=1}^n \left| \int_{x_{i-1}}^{x_i} f - T_f \right]_{x_{i-1}}^{x_i} \bigg| \leqq n |\eta(h)| = \frac{nh^3}{12} M.$$

The foregoing may be summarized in the following theorem.

Theorem 1. *Let f be continuous on I[a, b] and let D²f be defined and bounded by M on I(a, b). Let*

$$T_f\right]_a^b = \frac{h}{2} [f(a) + 2f(x_1) + 2f(x_2) + \cdots + 2f(x_{n-1}) + f(b)].$$

Then

$$\left| \int_a^b f - T_f \right]_a^b \bigg| \leqq \frac{nh^3}{12} M = \frac{(b-a)^3}{12n^2} M$$

where $h = \dfrac{1}{n} (b - a)$.

In the example

$$f(x) = \frac{1}{\sqrt{2\pi}} e^{-x^2/2}$$

we have

$$D^2 f(x) = \frac{1}{\sqrt{2\pi}} (x^2 - 1) e^{-x^2/2}$$

and in the interval $I[1, 2]$,

$$|D^2 f(x)| \leqq \frac{1}{\sqrt{2\pi}} (4 - 1) e^{-1/2} = \frac{3}{\sqrt{2\pi e}} < \frac{3}{4} = M.$$

Therefore, by Theorem 1,

$$\left| \frac{1}{\sqrt{2\pi}} \int_1^2 e^{-x^2/2} \, dx - T_f \right]_1^2 \bigg| \leqq \frac{1}{12(10)^2} \left(\frac{3}{4} \right) < \frac{2}{3} \times 10^{-3}. \qquad (7)$$

Hence the value $T_f\right]_1^2$ given by (4) for the integral

$$\frac{1}{\sqrt{2\pi}} \int_1^2 e^{-x^2/2} \, dx$$

differs from the true value by less than $\frac{2}{3} \times 10^{-3}$. (Actually,

$$\frac{1}{\sqrt{2\pi}} \int_1^2 e^{-x^2/2} \, dx = 0.135905122 \qquad (8)$$

correct to nine decimal places.)

B. Simpson's Rule

For Simpson's Rule we again partition $I[a, b]$ but with the minor restriction that the number of subintervals in the partition be *even*. That is,

$$\pi = [x_0, x_1, \cdots, x_n]$$

is a partition of the interval $I[a, b]$ where $h = \dfrac{1}{n}(b - a) = x_i - x_{i-1}$, $i = 1, 2, \cdots, n$, and where n is an even integer.

We now consider

$$\int_{x_{i-1}}^{x_i} p$$

where

$$p = \alpha(j - x_i)^2 + \beta(j - x_i) + \gamma$$

is a parabola passing through the three consecutive points

$$(x_{i-1}, f(x_{i-1})), \quad (x_i, f(x_i)), \quad (x_{i+1}, f(x_{i+1}))$$

(see Figure 8.2). Recalling that $x_{i-1} = x_i - h$ and $x_{i+1} = x_i + h$, we see that the condition that the parabola pass through the given points implies

$$p(x_{i-1}) = \alpha h^2 - \beta h + \gamma = f(x_{i-1}) \tag{9.1}$$

$$p(x_i) = \gamma = f(x_i) \tag{9.2}$$

$$p(x_{i+1}) = \alpha h^2 + \beta h + \gamma = f(x_{i+1}). \tag{9.3}$$

Multiplying (9.2) by 4 and adding the result to the sum of (9.1) and (9.3) we get

$$f(x_{i-1}) + 4f(x_i) + f(x_{i+1}) = 2\alpha h^2 + 6\gamma$$

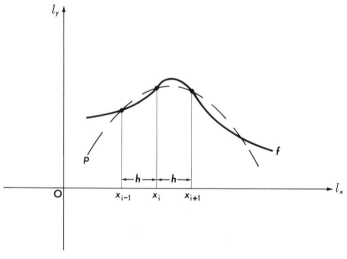

Figure 8.2

or

$$\frac{h}{3} [f(x_{i-1}) + 4f(x_i) + f(x_{i+1})] = \frac{2\alpha h^3}{3} + 2\gamma h. \qquad (10)$$

But

$$\int_{x_{i-1}}^{x_{i+1}} p = \frac{1}{3}\alpha(j - x_i)^3 + \frac{1}{2}\beta(j - x_i)^2 + \gamma(j - x_i)\Big]_{x_{i-1}}^{x_{i+1}}$$

$$= \frac{2}{3}\alpha h^3 + 2\gamma h.$$

Comparing (10) with this last result we observe that $\int_{x_{i-1}}^{x_{i+1}} p$ may be evaluated simply from the values of f at x_{i-1}, x_i, and x_{i+1}. Indeed,

$$\int_{x_{i-1}}^{x_{i+1}} p = \frac{h}{3} [f(x_{i-1}) + 4f(x_i) + f(x_{i+1})]. \qquad (11)$$

Thus

$$P_f\Big]_a^b = \sum_{j=1}^{n/2} \int_{x_{2j-2}}^{x_{2j}} p \qquad (12)$$

appears to be a good approximation to $\int_a^b f$, just as $\sum_{i=1}^{n} T_f\Big]_{x_{i-1}}^{x_i}$ appeared to be a good approximation to $\int_a^b f$.

Now let us establish a bound for

$$\left| \int_a^b f - P_f\Big]_a^b \right|$$

to see just how good this approximation is. That is let us compute a bound for the error committed if we replace $\int_a^b f$ by $P_f\Big]_a^b$. Towards this end we define

$$\varepsilon(x) = \int_{x_i-x}^{x_i+x} f - \frac{x}{3} [f(x_i - x) + 4f(x_i) + f(x_i + x)]$$

for $0 \leq x \leq h$. Some simple calculations establish

$$D^3\varepsilon(x) = -\frac{x}{3} [D^3f(x_i + x) - D^3f(x_i - x)]. \qquad (13)$$

Hence if D^4f is defined on $I(a, b)$, we may apply the mean value theorem to the right-hand side of (13) to obtain

$$D^3\varepsilon(x) = -\frac{2x^2}{3} D^4f(c), \quad x_i - x < c < x_i + x.$$

Observing that $\varepsilon(0) = D\varepsilon(0) = D^2\varepsilon(0) = 0$, we obtain, after taking three successive antiderivatives of $D^3\varepsilon$:

$$\varepsilon(x) = -\frac{2x^5}{180} D^4f(c) = -\frac{x^5}{90} D^4f(c),$$

and finally if D^4f is bounded by M on $I(a, b)$,

$$|\varepsilon(h)| \leq \frac{h^5}{90} M = \frac{(b-a)^5}{90n^5} M.$$

We formulate the following theorem, which summarizes our results:

Theorem 2.   *Let f be continuous on $I[a, b]$ and let D^4f be defined and bounded by M on $I(a, b)$. Let*

$$P]_a^b = \frac{h}{3} [f(a) + 4f(x_1) + 2f(x_2) + 4f(x_3) + 2f(x_4) + 4f(x_5) + \cdots$$

$$+ 4f(x_{n-3}) + 2f(x_{n-2}) + 4f(x_{n-1}) + f(b)].$$

Then

$$\left| \int_a^b f - P_f]_a^b \right| \leq \frac{n}{2} \frac{h^5}{90} M = \frac{(b-a)^5}{180n^4} M$$

where $h = \dfrac{1}{n} (b - a)$ and n is even.

Let us apply Theorem 2 to the same example used in the Trapezoidal Rule, namely, $a = 1$, $b = 2$ and

$$f(x) = \frac{1}{\sqrt{2\pi}} e^{-x^2/2}. \tag{14}$$

From the table of values (3):

$$P_f]_1^2 = \frac{h}{3} [f(1.0) + 4f(1.1) + 2f(1.2) + 4f(1.3) + 2f(1.4) + 4f(1.5)$$

$$+ 2f(1.6) + 4f(1.7) + 2f(1.8) + 4f(1.9) + f(2.0)]$$

$$= \frac{0.1}{3} (4.0771441) = 0.1359048. \tag{15}$$

The difference between the true value of $\int_1^2 f$ and (15) is less than

$$\frac{(b-a)^5}{180n^4} M = \frac{M}{(180)(10)^4}.$$

So we must obtain a bound for $|D^4f|$ (namely M) on $I(1, 2)$. Now

$$D^4f = \frac{1}{\sqrt{2\pi}} [x^4 - 6x^2 + 3] e^{-x^2/2}$$

and

$$|D^4f| \leq \frac{6}{\sqrt{2\pi e}} < \frac{6}{4} = \frac{3}{2} = M.$$

Hence

$$\frac{(b-a)^5}{180n^4} M < \frac{3}{2(180)(10)^4} = \frac{1}{12 \times 10^5} < 10^{-6}.$$

Thus (15) differs from the true value of $\int_1^2 f$ by less than one part in a million—a much better estimate than that furnished by the Trapezoidal Rule.

For another application let us evaluate

$$\int_0^6 j^3$$

using Simpson's Rule. If we let $n = 6$, then $h = \dfrac{1}{n}(b - a) = \frac{1}{6}(6 - 0)$
$= 1$ and

$$
\begin{aligned}
f(0) &= 0 \\
f(1) &= 1 \\
f(2) &= 8 \\
f(3) &= 27 \\
f(4) &= 64 \\
f(5) &= 125 \\
f(6) &= 216.
\end{aligned}
$$

Thus

$$
\begin{aligned}
P_{j^3}\Big]_0^6 &= \frac{h}{3}[f(0) + 4f(1) + 2f(2) + 4f(3) + 2f(4) + 4f(5) + f(6)] \\
&= \tfrac{1}{3}[4 + 16 + 108 + 128 + 500 + 216] \\
&= \tfrac{1}{3}(972) = 324.
\end{aligned}
$$

But trivially, the exact value is

$$\int_0^6 j^3 = \tfrac{1}{4}j^4\Big]_0^6 = \tfrac{1}{4}(1296) = 324.$$

So in this case the result obtained by Simpson's Rule is exact! (See Exercise 12.)

EXERCISES

1. Verify the formulas (1)–(9) on pages 193-194.

2. Find the following indefinite integrals using the formula for "integration by parts":

(i) $\int j \cos^2$

(ii) $\int j \exp_e$

(iii) $\int j^2 \exp_e$

(iv) $\int \sin \exp_e$

(v) $\int j^2 \sin^2$

(vi) $\int [\sqrt{} \circ (\exp_e - 4)] \exp_e$

(vii) $\int \ln$

(viii) $\int j \ln$

(ix) $\int (\ln)^2$

(x) $\int j^3 \exp_e \circ j^2.$

3. Find the following indefinite integrals by the method of substitution:

(i) $\int \dfrac{j}{(1 + j)^{1/2}}$

(ii) $\int j(2 + j)^{1/2}$

(iii) $\int \dfrac{2j^2}{(1 + 2j)^{1/2}}$

(xii) $\int \dfrac{1}{j^2(j^2 - 8)^{1/2}}$

(iv) $\int \dfrac{1}{(4 - j^2)^{3/2}}$

(xiii) $\int \dfrac{1}{j^2 + j + 1}$

(v) $\int \dfrac{1}{j^3(j^2 - 4)^{1/2}}$

(xiv) $\int \dfrac{1}{j^2 + 2j + 5}$

(vi) $\int \dfrac{1}{j(j^2 + 9j - 9)^{1/2}}$

(xv) $\int \dfrac{1}{2j^2 + 4j + 5}$

(vii) $\int \dfrac{2}{\exp_e + \exp_e \circ (-j)}$

(xvi) $\int \dfrac{1}{2 + \sin}$

(viii) $\int \dfrac{(1 + j)^{1/2}}{(1 - j)}$

(xvii) $\int \dfrac{1}{2 + \cos}$

(ix) $\int \dfrac{1}{j(25 + 16j^2)^{1/2}}$

(xviii) $\int \dfrac{1}{1 - \cos}$

(x) $\int \dfrac{j^2}{(16 - j^2)^{1/2}}$

(xix) $\int \dfrac{\sin}{2 - \cos}$

(xi) $\int \dfrac{j^2}{(25 - j^2)^{3/2}}$

(xx) $\int (1 - j^2)^{1/2}$.

4. Find the following indefinite integrals using partial fractions:

(i) $\int \dfrac{j^2 - 1}{j + j^2}$

(vi) $\int \dfrac{2}{(j^2 - 1)(j + 1)}$

(ii) $\int \dfrac{j + 2}{j(j + 4)}$

(vii) $\int \dfrac{1 + j}{(1 - j)^2}$

(iii) $\int \dfrac{2}{(j^2 + 1)(j - 1)}$

(viii) $\int \dfrac{1}{j^2 + 2j - 8}$

(iv) $\int \dfrac{3j + 4}{j(j - 4)^2}$

(ix) $\int \dfrac{2 - j}{(j - 1)^2(j + 2)^2}$

(v) $\int \dfrac{j + 1}{(j^2 - 1)(j + 1)^2}$

(x) $\int \dfrac{1}{(j^2 + j + 1)^2}$.

5. Evaluate the following definite integrals:

(i) $\int_0^3 \dfrac{j^3}{(j^2 + 16)^{3/2}}$

(iv) $\int_0^{\pi/2} e^x \cos 2x \, dx$

(ii) $\int_0^1 \dfrac{x^3}{\sqrt{1 + 4x^2}} \, dx$

(v) $\int_2^4 \dfrac{1 + j^4}{j(j^2 - 1)}$

(iii) $\int_0^2 \dfrac{x^2}{(4 + x^2)^2} \, dx$

(vi) $\int_0^{3\pi/4} \dfrac{1}{1 - \sin}$

(vii) $\int_0^1 \dfrac{j^2}{(4 - j^2)^{3/2}}$

(x) $\int_2^5 \dfrac{1}{(j^2 - 1)^{3/2}}$

(viii) $\int_0^1 \dfrac{x^3}{(5 - x^2)^{5/2}} \, dx$

(xi) $\int_1^3 \dfrac{1}{j^2(1 + j^4)^{3/4}}$

(ix) $\int_0^\pi e^{2x} \sin x \, dx$

(xii) $\int_0^{\pi/2} \dfrac{1}{3 + \cos}.$

6. Evaluate $\int_1^2 1/j$

(i) Using the Trapezoidal Rule (with $n = 6$)
(ii) Using Simpson's Rule (with $n = 6$)
(iii) What is an upper bound for the error in each case?
(iv) Compare the answers found with the true value obtained by integrating.

7. Evaluate $\int_0^1 [x/(x + 1)] \, dx$ by the Trapezoidal Rule and Simpson's Rule using:

(i) $n = 4$ (ii) $n = 6$.

Find an upper bound for the error in each case. Find the precise value.

8. Find an upper bound for the error in computing $\int_0^1 \sin/j$ by Simpson's Rule if ten subintervals are used. Compute $\int_0^1 \sin/j$ accurate to four decimal places.

9. Let f be continuous on $I[a, b]$ and let $D^5 f$ exist on $I(a, b)$. Let $I[c, d] \subset I(a, b)$. Using the first four terms of the Taylor series expansion for f, show that

(i) $\int_c^d f$ is approximately equal to

$$\frac{d - c}{6} \left[f(c) + 4f\left(\frac{c + d}{2}\right) + f(d) \right].$$

That is, if $D^4 f$ is identically zero,

$$\int_c^d f \equiv \frac{d - c}{6} \left[f(c) + 4f\left(\frac{c + d}{2}\right) + f(d) \right].$$

(ii) Find an upper bound for the error if

$$\frac{d - c}{6} \left[f(c) + 4f\left(\frac{c + d}{2}\right) + f(d) \right].$$

is used as an approximation for $\int_c^d f$?

(iii) Why is it sufficient to postulate the existence of $D^5 f$?

10. Do Exercise 8 using the formula derived in Exercise 9. Compare this result with that obtained by both the Trapezoidal Rule and Simpson's Rule (for $n = 4$).

11.   Evaluate $\int_0^3 [x/(x + 1)^2]\, dx$ using all three methods of approximation. For the Trapezoidal Rule and Simpson's Rule use $n = 6$. Find the precise value.

12.   Explain why the result obtained by Simpson's Rule for $\int_0^6 j^3$ was exact. (See the end of Section 4.) Would you also get an exact result for $\int_0^1 j^2$? What if we applied Simpson's Rule to $\int_a^b f$ where f is a polynomial of degree less than or equal to three?

13.   If $p(x)$ is a polynomial of at most the third degree, prove that

$$\int_c^d p(x)\, dx = \frac{d - c}{6} [p(c) + 4p(m) + p(d)]$$

where $m = \frac{1}{2}(c + d)$. (Cf. Exercises 9 and 12.) [*Hint:* Write $p(x)$ in the form $p(x) = \alpha + \beta(x - c) + \gamma(x - c)^2 + \delta(x - c)^3$ and compute $\int_c^d p$, $p(c)$, $p(m)$, and $p(d)$ from this form of $p(x)$.]

REFERENCES

[1]   Abramowitz, M., and Stegun, I. A. *Handbook of mathematical functions with formulas, graphs, and mathematical tables,* National Bureau of Standards, Applied Mathematics Series, No. 55. Washington, D.C., U.S. Government Printing Office, June 1964.

[2]   Birkhoff, G. D., and Beatley, D. *Basic geometry,* 3rd edition. New York, Chelsea Publishing Company, 1959.

[3]   MacLane, S. *Metric postulates for plane geometry,* American Mathematical Monthly, **66**, No. 7, 543–555, 1959.

[4]   Menger, K. *Algebra of analysis,* Notre Dame Mathematical Lectures Number 3. Notre Dame, Indiana, 1944.

[5]   Menger, K. *Calculus—A modern approach,* Boston, Ginn and Company, 1955.

[6]   Miller, K. S. *Elements of modern abstract algebra.* New York, Harper and Brothers, 1958.

[7]   Miller, K. S. *Engineering mathematics.* New York, Dover Publications, Inc., 1963.

SOME HINTS AND ANSWERS

Chapter I

2. See Theorem 6.
3. Let $e = a + b$ (Axiom $\mathbf{F}_1$) and use Axiom $\mathbf{F}_{11}$.
4. Axiom $\mathbf{F}_5$.
5. Assume $a \neq 0 \neq b$.
9. Axiom $\mathbf{F}_{10}$.
11.   (i) ± 3
     (iii) $2, -3$
     (v) $-3, -4$
     (vii) $1, 1, -1$
13. No. One cannot choose a unique multiplicative inverse.
15. 6
17.   (i) $x > 3/5$
     (iii) $x < -5/2$
     (v) $\frac{1}{2} < x < 1$
20.   (i) All x such that $0 < x < 1$.
     (ii) All x such that $0 \leq x \leq 1$.
     (iii) All x such that $0 \leq x < 1$.
21. Assume the contrary and use the Trichotomy law.
27. (v) $2^2 + 4^2 + \cdots + (2p)^2 = 4[1^2 + 2^2 + \cdots + p^2]$
28. $[5^{2(p+1)} - 1] = 24 \cdot 5^{2p} + (5^{2p} - 1)$
29. Since $2 < p + 1$, we infer $2(2^p) < (p + 1)p!$
32. Suppose $\varepsilon > 0$ had this property. Consider $\varepsilon/2$.
34. $2n \leftrightarrow n$
37.   (i) $-6 < x < 6$
     (iii) $x > 4$
     (v) $0 < x < 6$

Chapter 2

5. $\sqrt{3}/2$

14. (i) Vertical line $x = -2$
    (iii) Slope $= 3$ $y = 3x - 10$
    (v) Slope $= -1/12$ $\lambda(1, 12, 19)$

15. (i) 9
    (iii) $\sqrt{10}$
    (v) $\sqrt{145}$

16. (i) $\lambda(1, -3, -9)$
    (iii) $\lambda(2, -1, 6)$
    (v) $x + y = 4$

17. (i) $\lambda(3, 1, 13)$
    (iii) $\lambda(1, 2, 23)$
    (v) $\lambda(1, 1, 4)$

18. (i) $(-1, 2)$
    (iii) $\left(\frac{22}{27}, \frac{47}{27}\right)$
    (v) Do not intersect.

19. Yes. (i) 20

23. (i) $h = 2, k = 2$
    (iii) $h = -1, k = -2$
    (v) $h = 1, k = 0$

26. $(x + 2)^2 + (y - 2)^2 = 4$. (There is another circle.)

27. (i) $y^2 = 4a(a \pm x)$

28. $(x - 2)^2 = 8(y - 3)$

30. (ii) 3

Chapter 3

1. (i) Is a function. Dom $= \{2, 3, 6, 7, 8\}$
                          Ran $= \{2, 3, 8, 9, 10\}$
    (ii) Is not a function.

2. (i) Dom $=$ set of all x
           Ran $=$ set of all x.
    (iii) Dom $=$ set of all x such that $|x| \geq 1$
             Ran $=$ set of all nonnegative x.
    (v) Dom $=$ set of all x
            Ran $=$ approximately all x between -0.70 and $+5.7$.

4. (i) See Figure A.1
    (iii) See Figure A.2
    (v) See Figure A.3
    (vii) See Figure A.4
    (ix) See Figure A.5

6. $a = \pm\sqrt{3}$

8. (i) Set of all x.
    (ii) $(f + g)(x) = 3x - 1$, $(fg)(x) = x(x^2 - 1)(3 - x)$

12. (i) 81
    (iii) 4

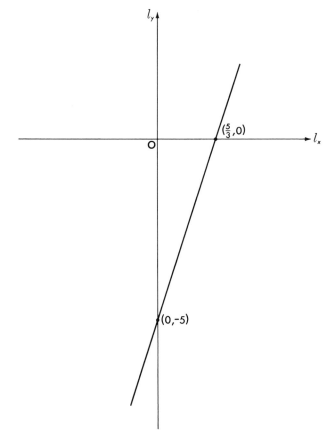

Figure A.1

     (v) 6
   (vii) 3
   (ix) 3

14.   (i) Set of all nonnegative x
   (iii) Set of all x
    (v) Set of all nonnegative x
   (vii) Set of all x

   (ix) Set of all x except $x = \dfrac{3\pi}{2} + 2n\pi,\ n \in I.$

16.   (i) $f^* = \dfrac{j + 3}{2}$

   (iii) $f^* = \dfrac{1 + j}{1 - j}$

    (v) $f^* = \sqrt{} \circ \dfrac{j - 1}{j + 1}$ Dom $f^* =$ set of all $x \geq 1$ and $< -1.$

   (vii) $f^* = \sqrt{} \circ (j^2 - 1)$

   (ix) $f^* = 2 + \sqrt{}$ Dom $f^* =$ set of all $x \geq 2$

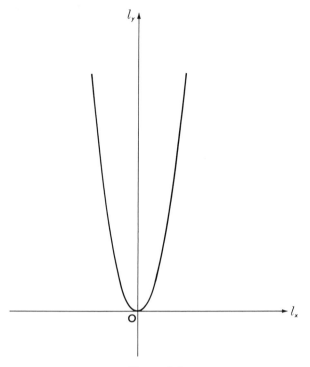

Figure A.2

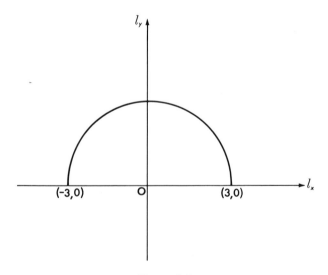

Figure A.3

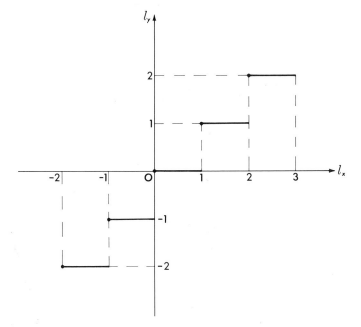

Figure A.4

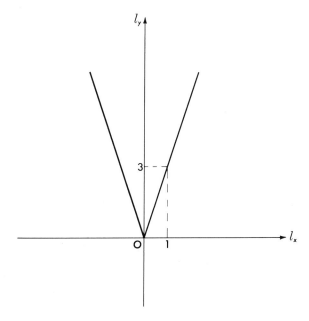

Figure A.5

Chapter 4

4. (i) $\delta < 0.0002$
   (ii) $\delta < 0.0002$
   (iii) $\delta < 0.000125$
6. (i) 0
   (ii) Does not exist
   (iii) 0
   (iv) 0
7. (ii) $-1/4$
   (iii) $-1/2\sqrt{5}$
   (iv) $\sqrt{3}/6$
   (v) 0
   (vi) k
10. (i) $f(x) = x, \; x \neq 0$
       $f(x) = 2, \; x = 0$
   (ii) $f(x) = \dfrac{1}{x-a}, \; x \neq a$
14. (ii) No.
15. Assume $f(x_0) \neq 0$ for some $x_0 \in I[0, 1]$ and use Theorem 12.
16. Show that for any $\varepsilon > 0$ there is a $\delta > 0$ such that

$$-\varepsilon|h| < \sin(a+h) - \sin a - hb < |h|\varepsilon$$

whenever $0 < |h| < \delta$, and use Theorem 9.
   19. Recall that $\cos h = 1 - 2\sin^2 \frac{1}{2}h$.
   20. The limits of (i), (iv), (v), (vi), and (vii) do not exist.

Chapter 5

1. (i) -4
   (ii) $y = -4x - 9$
   (iii) $4y = x - 19$
3. (i) $Df = (j^2 + 5)(3j^2 - 2) + 2j(j^3 - 2j + 5)$
   (iii) $Df = \dfrac{(j^2 - 1)\cos - 2j\sin}{(j^2 - 1)^2}$
   (v) $Df = \dfrac{(2j + 1)\sin + (2 - j)\cos - 2}{(\sin - j)^2}$
4. (i) $x = 1$
   (ii) $x = -1$
   (iii) $x = 3$
   (iv) $x = \frac{1}{3}(2 \pm \sqrt{13})$
6. (i) $D^2f = 20j^3 + 18j + 10$
       $D^3f = 60j^2 + 18$
   (iv) $D^2f = -3\sin + 4$
        $D^3f = -3\cos$
   8. Assume f has a maximum, say M on $I(0, 1)$. Find an $x_0 > 0$ such that $f(x_0) > M$.

10. (i) $Df = 3(j + 2)^2$

   (iii) $Df = 4 \sin^3 \cos$

   (v) $Df = 2 \sin \cos$

11. (i) $D \tan = \sec^2$

   (ii) $D \tan^* = \dfrac{1}{1 + j^2}$ on $I(-\tfrac{1}{2}\pi, \tfrac{1}{2}\pi)$

12. $f^* = \tfrac{1}{4} + \tfrac{1}{4}\sqrt{} \circ (1 + 8j)$

   $Df^* = \dfrac{1}{(1 + 8j)^{1/2}}, \quad Df^*(6) = \tfrac{1}{7}$

17. (i) $f = j + 2$ for $0 \leqq x \leqq 2$

       $f = j - 2$ for $2 < x \leqq 3$

   (ii) Use Theorems 14 and 15 of Chapter 4.

20. (i) $Df = \dfrac{2}{j}$

   (ii) $Df = \cot - 1$

   (iii) $Df = 1$

   (iv) $Df = 0$

   (v) $Df = \dfrac{3(\ln)^2}{j}$

21. (i) $Df = (2j - 2)f$

   (iii) $Df = \sec^2 f$

   (v) $Df = 0$

22. (i) $Df = \dfrac{j \ln \cos - \sin}{j \, (\ln)^2}$

   (iii) $Df = \dfrac{2j}{j^2 - 2}$

   (v) $Df = \dfrac{\cos \circ \ln}{j}$

23. (iii) $Df = j^j(1 + \ln)$

25. (i) $j^3 + j^2 - j + k$

   (iii) $\tfrac{3}{4}j^4 - \tfrac{1}{5}j^5 + \tfrac{2}{7}j^7 + k$

   (v) $\ln (x + 1) + k$

   (vii) $-\tfrac{1}{2} \cos 2x + k$

   (ix) $\tfrac{1}{2}x - \tfrac{1}{4} \sin 2x + k$

   (xi) $\ln (x^2 + 1) + k$

   (xiii) $-\dfrac{1}{j + 1} + k$

   (xv) $\tfrac{1}{2}(\ln)^2 + k$

27. (i) Does not exist.

   (iii) $\dfrac{2}{\pi + 2}$

   (v) 0

   (vii) -1

   (ix) $-\tfrac{1}{2}$

28. A square: each side equal to $\tfrac{1}{4}\ell$.

29. Base $= 10$,   Altitude $= 10$.

31. (i) 400 ft.

   (ii) $200\sqrt{2}$ ft.

33. Radius $= \sqrt[3]{\dfrac{50}{\pi}}$ inches,   Height $= \sqrt[3]{\dfrac{50}{\pi}}$ inches

35. (i) $v(2) = 256$ ft./sec.
        $v(5) = 160$ ft./sec.
    (ii) $t = 10$ sec.
    (iii) Zero
    (iv) $t = 20$ sec.
    (v) $v(20) = -320$ ft./sec.

36. $P = R - C = 8x - C(x)$
    Maximum profits for $x = 1,350$ units.

Chapter 6

1. $L(\pi_1) = 0.555$
   $U(\pi_1) = 0.805$
   $L(\pi_2) = 0.667$
   $U(\pi_2) = 0.792$
   $$\int_0^1 (1 - j^2)^{1/2} = \frac{\pi}{4} = 0.785$$

2. For j^2
   $L(\pi_1) = \frac{7}{32} = 0.219$
   $U(\pi_1) = \frac{15}{32} = 0.456$
   $L(\pi_2) = \frac{65}{256} = 0.254$
   $U(\pi_2) = \frac{97}{256} = 0.379$
   $$\int_0^1 j^2 = \tfrac{1}{3}$$

6. 20

8. (i) $1/40$
    (iii) $41/5$
    (v) $1/2$
    (vii) $\sqrt{2}$
    (ix) $\pi/2$

9. (i) 0
    (iii) $17/4$
    (v) $1/6$

10. (iii), (iv), (v), (vi)

11. (i) $8/3$
    (iii) 8

12. $x = \sqrt[3]{-4/3} - 1$

13. Areas of the two regions are $1/(n + 1)$ and $n/(n + 1)$.

15. (i) 224
    (iii) $37/3$

16. (i) $\pi/20$
    (ii) $\pi^2/4$
    (iii) $3\pi/4$

17. (ii) $9\pi/8$
    (iv) $9\pi/2$

21. (i) 2
    (iii) 113
    (v) 3/2

23. $W = 62.5\pi \int_0^6 [36 - (y - 6)^2]dy + \frac{1}{2}(\frac{4}{3}\pi 6^3)(5)(62.5)$
    $= (62.5\pi)(864)$ ft.-lbs.

24. $(62.5\pi)(960)$ ft.-lbs.

26. $W = \int_0^5 12j$ ft.-lbs.

Chapter 7

1. (i) $Df = \dfrac{-4\,\mathrm{exp}_e}{(2 + \mathrm{exp}_e)^2}$

   (iii) $Df(x) = \ln x + 1$

   (v) $Df = \dfrac{\cos - \sin}{\cos + \sin}$

   (vii) $Df = \dfrac{\mathrm{exp}_e \circ \tan^*}{1 + j^2}$

   (ix) $Df = \dfrac{2k}{k^2 - j^2}$ (What about $x = k$?)

   (xi) $Df(x) = \sqrt{a^2 + x^2}$

2. (i) $\frac{1}{2}(\mathrm{exp}_e \circ 2j) + k$

   (iii) e^{x^2}

   (v) $\frac{1}{3}x^3 + k$

   (vii) $\dfrac{1}{\ln 2}2^x + k$

   (ix) $\dfrac{\mathrm{exp}_5 \circ 4j}{4\ln 5} + k$

3. (i) $x = k\dfrac{e - 1}{e + 1}$

   (iii) $x = k + 1$

   (v) $x = 3$

3. $\ln 3 = 1.0986$
   $\ln 5 = 1.6094$
   $\ln 7 = 1.9459$

5. $\log_{10} 2 = 0.301$
   $\log_{10} 3 = 0.477$
   $\log_{10} 5 = 0.699$
   $\log_{10} 7 = 0.845$

6. $g(\frac{1}{8}) = 2.56$ (approx.)

7. $\sqrt{24} = 4.8990$
   $\sqrt{170} = 13.0384$
   $\sqrt{258} = 16.0624$

8. $\sin x = x - \dfrac{x^3}{3!} + \dfrac{x^5}{5!} - \cdots + (-1)^{n-1}\dfrac{x^{2n-1}}{(2n-1)!} + \cdots$

   $\cos x = 1 - \dfrac{x^2}{2!} + \dfrac{x^4}{4!} - \cdots + (-1)^{n+1}\dfrac{x^{2n-2}}{(2n-2)!} + \cdots$

11. $\dfrac{8\pi}{3}$

12.   (i) Multiply numerator and denominator by e^x and then factor the denominator.

    (iii) $e^{-1}(e^2 - 1)$

    (v) $e + e^{-1} - 2$

    (vii) $3/2$

    (ix) $\pi/2$

14. $x = -1/\sqrt{2}$

16.   (i) $k = 0.10$

    (ii) $m = 2\,e^{-kT}$

17.   (i) $m(100) = m_0\,e^{-0.5}$

    (ii) Half-life $= 138.6$ days

19.   (i) $m\dfrac{dv}{dt} = kv$

    where $m =$ mass, $v =$ velocity, $k =$ constant of proportionality

    (ii) $\dfrac{k}{m} = -0.23$

20. $DT_b = -\mathbf{k}(T_b - \mathbf{30})$

23. $DP = \mathbf{k}P$

25. The growth of bacteria follows the exponential law, that is, $DB = \mathbf{k}B$.

Chapter 8

2.   (i) $\frac{1}{4}j^2 + \frac{1}{4}j\sin \circ 2j + \frac{1}{8}\cos \circ 2j + \mathbf{k}$

    (iii) $\exp_e(j^2 - 2j + 2) + \mathbf{k}$

    (v) $\frac{1}{6}j^3 - (\frac{1}{4}j^2 - \frac{1}{8})\sin \circ 2j - \frac{1}{4}j\cos \circ 2j + \mathbf{k}$

    (vii) $j\ln - j + \mathbf{k}$

    (ix) $j(\ln)^2 - 2j\ln + 2j + \mathbf{k}$

3.   (i) $2\sqrt{1 + j} + \mathbf{k}$

    (iii) $\frac{1}{15}(3j^2 - 2j + 2)\sqrt{1 + 2j} + \mathbf{k}$

    (v) $\dfrac{\sqrt{j^2 - 4}}{8j^2} + \dfrac{1}{16}\cos^* \circ \dfrac{2}{j} + \mathbf{k}$

    (vii) $2\tan^* \circ \exp_e + \mathbf{k}$

    (ix) $\dfrac{1}{5}\ln \circ \left(\dfrac{\sqrt{16j^2 + 25} - 5}{j}\right) + \mathbf{k}$

    (xi) $\dfrac{j}{(25 - j^2)^{1/2}} - \sin^* \circ \frac{1}{5}j + \mathbf{k}$

    (xiii) $\dfrac{2}{\sqrt{3}}\tan^* \circ \dfrac{2j + 1}{\sqrt{3}} + \mathbf{k}$

    (xv) $\dfrac{1}{\sqrt{6}}\tan^* \circ \dfrac{2}{\sqrt{6}}(j + 1) + \mathbf{k}$

    (xvii) $\dfrac{2}{\sqrt{3}}\tan^* \circ \left(\dfrac{\sqrt{3}}{3}\tan\right) \circ \frac{1}{2}j + \mathbf{k}$

(xix) $\ln \circ (2 - \cos) + \mathbf{k}$

(xx) $\frac{1}{2}[j(\mathbf{1} - j^2)^{1/2} + \sin^*] + \mathbf{k}$

4. (i) $j - \ln + \mathbf{k}$

(iii) $-\frac{1}{2} \ln \circ (j^2 + \mathbf{1}) + \tan^* - \ln \circ |j - \mathbf{1}| + \mathbf{k}$

(v) $\frac{1}{2} \frac{1}{j + 1} - \frac{1}{4} \ln \circ \left| \frac{j + \mathbf{1}}{j - \mathbf{1}} \right| + \mathbf{k}$

(vii) $\frac{2}{1 - j} + \ln \circ |\mathbf{1} - j| + \mathbf{k}$

(x) $\frac{2j + \mathbf{1}}{3(j^2 + j + \mathbf{1})} + \frac{4}{3\sqrt{3}} \tan^* \circ \frac{2j + \mathbf{1}}{\sqrt{3}} + \mathbf{k}$

5. (i) $1/5$

(iii) $\frac{\pi}{16} - \frac{1}{8}$

(v) $\ln \frac{5}{2} - \frac{3}{8}$

(vii) $\frac{1}{\sqrt{3}} - \frac{\pi}{6}$

(ix) $\frac{1}{5}(e^{2\pi} - 1)$

(xi) $\sqrt[4]{2} - \frac{1}{3}\sqrt[4]{10}$

7. (i) For $n = 4$, $\left. T_f \right]_0^1 = \frac{509}{1,680} = 0.3030$

$M \leq 2$, Upper bound is $\frac{1}{96} = 0.0104$

$\int_0^1 \frac{x}{x + 1} \, dx = 1 - \ln 2 = 0.30685$

Index

Absolute value, 16
Absolute value function, 66
Accumulation point, 84
Additive inverse, 75
Algebra of functions, 71
Analytic geometry, 22
  fundamental theorem of, 36
Angle, 28, 29
  improper, 30
  measure of, 28, 29
  proper, 30
  right, 30
  straight, 30
  supplement of, 30
Antiderivative, 134
  by parts, 195
  by substitution, 196
Area, 153
  curve, 116
  of nonpositive function, 168
  of triangle, 46
Arc, 28
Archimedean property, 11
Axioms, angle, 29
  area, 153
  completeness, 10
  continuity, 30
  distance, 23
  field, 2
  incidence, 23
  on, 24
  order relation, 5
  ray, 25

Axioms (*contd.*)
  similarity, 30
  volume, 171

Base, 181
  natural, 181
Between, 22, 24
  relation, 23
Bolyai-Lobachefskian geometry, 22
Bound, 9
  greatest lower, 9
  least upper, 9
  lower, 9
  upper, 9
Bounded function, 103
  set, 9

Calculus, differential, 117
  fundamental theorem, 165
Chain rule, 123
Circle, 59
Circular arc, 28, 53
  length of, 53
Closed interval, 83
Completeness, 10
Composition, 75
Congruent, 22, 30
  angles, 22
Conic, 63

Constant function, vi, 67
Contained in, v
Continuity, 30
  of composite function, 102
  of compound function, 102
  on interval, 103
Continuous function, 101
  integrability of, 160, 168
Coordinates, 25
  translation of, 61
Correspondence, one–one, 13
Cosecant, 71
Cosine, 70
Cost function, 140
Cotangent, 71
Curvature, 117

Decay problems, 187
Decreasing function, 108
Definite integral, 156
Degree, 28
Derivative, 116
  applications of, 137
  chain rule, 123
  of inverse function, 126
  maxima, 129
  minima, 129
  of power function, 118
  of sine function, 120
  of special functions, 117
Determinant, 47
Differential calculus, 117
Differentiation, general rules of, 121
Directrix, 59
Disc, 170
Distance, 23
  formula, 42
  relation, 23
Domain, 65

e, 181, 183, 185
Eccentricity, 63
Element of, v
Ellipse, 60
Empty set, v
Equation of a line, 40
Error, in Simpson's rule, 212
  in Taylor's expansion, 184
  in trapezoidal rule, 209
Euclidean geometry, 22
  parallel postulate, 22
Even function, 174
Exponential function, 144, 180

Falling bodies, 138
Fields, 2
  finite, 5
  order relation, 5
  ordered, 5
Finite fields, 5
  geometry, 24
Fixed point theorem, 106
Foci, 59
Fractions, 1
  partial, 202
Function, 65
  absolute value, 66
  addition of, 73
  additive inverse, 75
  algebra of, 71
  bounded, 103
  composition of, 75
  constant, vi, 67
  continuous, 101
  cosecant, 71
  cosine, 70
  cost, 140
  cotangent, 71
  decreasing, 108
  derivative, 116
  domain of, 65
  equality of, 72
  even, 174
  exponential, 155, 180
  of a function rule, 123
  graph of, 68
  greatest integer, 66
  identity, 67
  image of, 65
  increasing, 108
  inverse, 80
    logarithmic, 179
  limit of, 85
  logarithmic, 144, 177
  marginal, 140
  maximum of, 127
  minimum of, 127
  monotone, 131
    decreasing, 131
    increasing, 131
  multiplication of, 73
  multiplicative inverse, 75
  neutral, 79
  odd, 174
  one–one, 79
  power, 67
  profit, 141
  range of, 65
  revenue, 141
  secant, 71
  signum, 67
  sine, 70
  square root, 66
  strictly decreasing, 131

Function (*contd.*)
strictly increasing, 131
tangent, 71
trigonometric, 69
unity, 74
zero, 74
Fundamental theorem, of analytic geometry, 36
of calculus, 165

Geometry, analytic, 22
Euclidean, 22
finite, 24
hyperbolic, 22
Lobachefskian, 22
synthetic, 22
Graph of function, 68
Greatest integer function, 66
Greatest lower bound, 9

Hyperbola, 60
Hyperbolic geometry, 22

Identity function, 67
Image, 65
Improper angle, 30
Incidence, 23
Incompleteness, 8
Increasing function, 108
Indefinite integral, 145, 193
Induction, 19
Inductive set, 10
Inequalities, 16
triangle, 16
Inscribed polygon, 54
Integers, 1
positive, 1, 10
Integrability of continuous function, 160, 168
Integrable, 156
Integral, definite, 156
indefinite, 145
lower, 156
of nonpositive function, 168
upper, 156
Integration. *See* Antiderivative.
Intermediate value theorem, 105
Intersection, v
of lines, 49
Interval, 24
closed, 83
open, 83
Inverse, 2, 80
logarithmic function, 179
Irrational numbers, 10
Isomorphic, 13

j, 67

L'Hospital's rule, 136
Lagrange remainder, 184
Law of the mean, 135
Least upper bound, 9
Length of circular arc, 53
Limit, 85
of composite functions, 97
of compound functions, 93
of continuous functions, 102
point, 84
of special functions, 98
uniqueness of, 92
Line, 37
distance from point to, 45
intersection of, 49
slope of, 38
Lobachefskian geometry, 22
Logarithmic function, 144, 177
inverse, 179
Lower bound, 9
greatest, 9
Lower integral, 156
Lower sum, 155

Mapping, 65
one–one, 26
Marginal function, 140
Mathematical induction, 19
Maxima and minima, 137
Maximum, 127
relative, 133
Mean value theorem, 131
Measure of angle, 28, 29
Minimum, 127
relative, 133
Minus, 2
Modulo, 18, 29
Monotone decreasing, 131
Monotone functions, 131
Monotone increasing, 131
Multiplicative inverse, 75

Natural numbers, 1
Neutral function, 79
Numbers, fractional, 1
irrational, 10
natural, 1
rational, 1, 7, 10
real, 10

Odd function, 174
On, 22, 24
One–one, 79
  correspondence, 13
Open inscribed polygon, 53
Open interval, 83
Order relation, 5
Ordered fields, 5
  pair, 36
  sequence, 53
Origin, 36

Pair, ordered, 36
Parabola, 59
  axis of, 63
Parallel postulate, 22
Partial fractions, 202
Partition, 154
  refinement of, 154
Perpendicular, 30
Polygon, 53
Population growth, 187
Positive integers, 1, 10
Postulates. *See* Axioms.
Power function, 67
Profit function, 141
Proper angle, 30
Pythagorean theorem, 34
  converse of, 35

Radian, 28
Range, 65
Rational complex numbers, 7
Rational numbers, 1, 7, 10
Ray, 25
Real numbers, 10
Refinement, 154
Region, 148
Relative maximum, 133
Relative minimum, 133
Revenue function, 141
Right angle, 30
Right triangle, 34
Rolle's theorem, 129

Secant, 71
Set, v
  bounded, 9
  empty, v
  inductive, 10

Signum function, 67
Similarity, 30
Simpson's rule, 211
  error in, 212
Sine, 70
Slope, 38
  of curve, 116
Solids, 170
Square root function, 66
Straight angle, 30
Strictly decreasing, 131
Strictly increasing, 131
Sum, lower, 155
  upper, 155
Supplement, 30
Synthetic geometry, 22

Tangent, 71, 110
  line, 114
Taylor's expansion, error in, 184
Taylor's theorem, 184
Translation, 61
Trapezoidal rule, 207
  error in, 209
Triangle, 30
  area of, 46
  inequality, 16
  right, 34
Trichotomy law, 5
Trigonometric functions, 69
Tri-operational algebra, 71

Union, v
Unity function, 74
Upper bound, 9
  least, 9
Upper integral, 156
Upper sum, 155

Volume, 169

Work, 175

Zero, 2
  function, 74